Health Science Fundamentals

Exploring Career Pathways

Lab Activity Manual

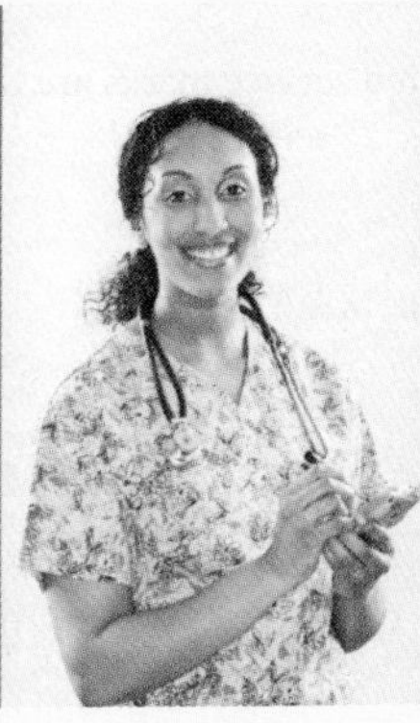

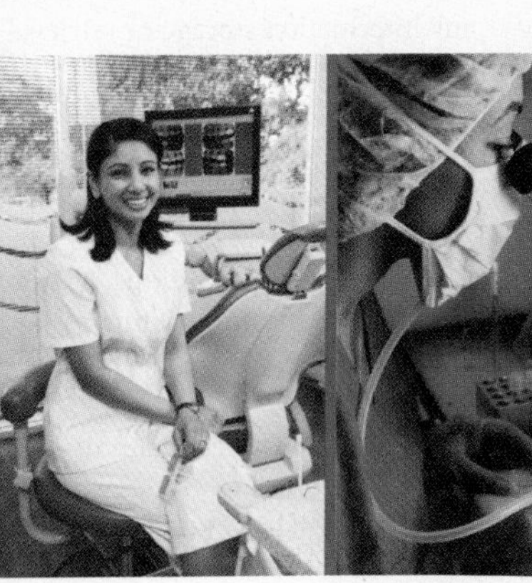

Revised First Edition

Shirley A. Badasch, M.Ed, RN

Doreen S. Chesebro, B.Ed, LVN

Upper Saddle River, New Jersey 07458

Cover Art courtesy of Shutterstock.

Taken from:

Health Science Fundamentals: Exploring Career Pathways, Lab Activity Manual
by Shirley A. Badasch, M.Ed, RN and Doreen S. Chesebro, B.Ed, LVN

Published by Prentice Hall
Upper Saddle River, New Jersey 07458

Pearson Learning Solutions, 501 Boylston Street, Suite 900, Boston, MA 02116
A Pearson Education Company
www.pearsoned.com

Printed in the United States of America

1 2 3 4 5 6 7 8 9 10 V011 16 15 14 13 12 11

000200010270606242

MH/CO

ISBN 10: 0-558-78161-6
ISBN 13: 978-0-558-78161-3

Contents

Index of Procedures and Scenarios

Chapter 18 ■ Measuring Vital Signs and Other Clinical Skills

Chapter 19 ■ Therapeutic Techniques and Sports Medicine

Chapter 20 ■ Medical Assisting and Laboratory Skills

Scenarios

SCENARIO

1 Do You Have Time for Me?

You are a health information technician in a busy family practice office. You are in charge of scheduling all office visits. Some of your appointments are by phone, and some are return visits for patients that are already at the office.

Your job is very important because scheduling keeps the day running smooth and patients happy. As busy as people are today, they do not like to be kept waiting. You have to determine the approximate time allotments for each procedure and be sure that you remember when the doctor does special procedures.

Procedure Category	*Schedule Time Needed*
New patient	45 minutes
Routine check-ups	30 minutes
Disease complaints	30 minutes
Office surgical procedure	60 minutes
Office diagnostic test (labs, EKG)	15 minutes

Client's Name	*Reason for visiting doctor*	*Time needed?*
Lori Lieberman	Sore throat	
Misty Buffum	Bloody diarrhea (new patient)	
Doug Pettitti	Excise a skin lesion	
Abdul Halabi	Check-up	
Mollie O'Connell	Upper respiratory infection (new patient)	
Shantiqua Badawi	Pregnancy test	
Karen Winters	Biopsy growth on face	
Theresa Davis	EKG	
Kiku Tamaki	School physical (speaks very little English)	
Manuel Hernandez	Chest pain and trouble breathing	

Things to keep in mind when scheduling patients:

- Your doctor only works until 1230 on Fridays.
- Next Monday is a holiday.
- Next Thursday, from 1400–1500, there is a staff meeting.
- Lunch is from 1230–1400 every day.
- Your doctor only does office surgeries on Wednesdays from 0800–1100.

QUESTIONS TO ANSWER:

- What do you need to be sure to tell each client after you schedule their appointment?
- What is the purpose of tickler cards?
- How would you handle a rude patient that insists he/she see the physician immediately?
- How would you handle patients that were upset because the doctor is running behind due to an emergency and they have been waiting for over an hour?

Appointment Book

Time	Monday	Tuesday	Wednesday	Thursday	Friday
0800					
0815					
0830					
0845					
0900					
0915					
0930					
0945					
1000					
1015					
1030					
1045					
1100					
1115					
1130					
1145					
1200					
1215					
1230					

Appointment Book *(continued)*

Time	Monday	Tuesday	Wednesday	Thursday	Friday
1245					
1300					
1315					
1330					
1345					
1400					
1415					
1430					
1445					
1500					
1515					
1530					
1545					
1600					
1615					
1630					
1645					
1700					

Address the below appointment reminder card. On the back of the card, it states "This is a reminder that you have an appointment with Dr. Hopkins on__________ at __________. Please call (000)888-0000 if you need to reschedule."

Hopkins Family Medicine

SCENARIO

2 To Test or Not to Test

You currently are employed by a great group of surgeons. They have several medical office assistants on staff, and since each of you are multi-talented, you take turns rotating through the various office positions. This week it is your turn to work in outpatient scheduling.

It is your task to schedule the diagnostic tests that will provide valuable information so that the physicians can treat the patients correctly. Besides needing to be very organized, this job requires strong communication skills.

The patients are often nervous about the tests and what the results may show. You must get them to understand not only when the test will be done, but also any prep that is needed prior to the tests that could affect the results if not done correctly. This task can be challenging.

The first patient to stop by your desk is Charles Conrad. The note from the doctor says you are to schedule Charles for a colonoscopy. Charles is 65 years old and is quite frightened that this test might show he has colon cancer. He has heard some awful things from his friends about how bad the prep can be. He would like to get the colonoscopy done before he leaves on a trip to see his new grandson in two weeks. Please schedule this procedure for Mr. Conrad.

Once you finish with Mr. Conrad, Rosalia Gonzales says she needs your help in scheduling a mammogram. Rosalia is 34 years old and speaks very little English. Her sister died recently from breast cancer, and the doctor has recommended she have this test. She has never had one before. Please schedule this procedure for Mrs. Gonzales.

QUESTIONS TO ANSWER:

- What could happen if a patient arrived for a procedure and had not carried out the test preparation because you had not given him correct instructions?
- Keeping in mind that many of the patients you are scheduling tests for are frightened about what the outcome might show, how can you make sure they understand your instructions?
- What communication techniques would you use if the patient you were scheduling was deaf?
- What is the function of the tickler cards in this situation?

Reminder to check on test results

Patient Name: ______________________________

Diagnostic Test: ____________________________

Date of Test: _______________________________

Phone Number of Lab or Testing Site:

____

Date Checked on Test Results: ______________

Reminder to check on test results

Patient Name: ______________________________

Diagnostic Test: ____________________________

Date of Test: _______________________________

Phone Number of Lab or Testing Site:

____

Date Checked on Test Results: ______________

SCENARIO

3 The Aftermath

There is blood everywhere! Blood is pooled in the bed, all over the floor, and there is some even dried on the ceiling. The adrenaline is still flowing and your heart is pumping rapidly. You know you will never be able to sleep tonight. You have just witnessed your first code, and thank goodness the patient survived!

The patient has just been taken to the operating room, and you have been given the task of cleaning up this mess. To make things even more complicated, the charge nurse has just informed you that the patient is HIV positive. There are soiled linens on the bed and multiple contaminated needles on the procedure trays. You are afraid to touch anything.

Once you remove the linens and clean up the equipment, the housekeeping staff will wash down the room. After you finally get the unit cleaned up, you take the dirty procedure trays down to Central Supply. This is the last task you must do before heading home for the night.

Wanda, the Central Supply department chair, is a good friend of your mother and she even gave you a job working in Central Supply last summer. She is so excited to see you. She explains that two of her employees called in sick, and she is really short-handed. There have been three codes tonight and she is running out of clean equipment. She asks if you have a few minutes to clean those dirty instruments and wrap them for autoclave so the hospital will be prepared in case any more emergencies occur during the night. You are exhausted, but you agree to help her.

QUESTIONS TO ANSWER:

- What skills will you need to use to complete these tasks?
- How do you protect yourself from being exposed to the HIV virus when cleaning up the soiled linens and equipment?
- What types of equipment that might have been used in the code would you need to autoclave? Which equipment would you not autoclave?

SCENARIO

4 Protect Your Cranium!

Dakarai, a 20-year-old male, was pumped for the concert. He hopped on his motorcycle and hit the road. The plan was that he would meet all of his buddies at the amphitheater. Because of the high cost of gas he thought driving there on his bike would be a good way to save money.

His mother continued to "be mom" even though he had moved out, and she nagged him about wearing a helmet. Dakarai did not think the helmet looked cool and was glad he lived in a state that did not require head protection. On his way to the concert he accelerated too quickly, lost control, and crashed.

Dakarai suffered severe head trauma, multiple lacerations, and abrasions. When he woke up with a splitting headache, he found himself in a neurological unit and learned that he might not be able to walk again. Just as Dakarai was dealing with learning he may be a paraplegic the rest of his life, you come in to change his sterile dressing on his right shoulder.

Dakarai is abrupt and rude with you, but you know he is on an emotional roller coaster. You also know that you have to remain focused on your task and cannot be rushed so you do not risk contaminating the sterile field. He definitely does not need any more complications.

After you are done changing his dressing you need to get him up in the chair for the afternoon. Dakarai does not want to get up but you encourage him, telling him a change of scenery might make him feel better. Dakarai finally agrees, and you get the Hoyer (mechanical) lift to help you accomplish the task.

QUESTIONS TO ANSWER:

- What do you need to do if you are not sure if you contaminated the sterile field or not?
- What do you need to do if you notice greenish drainage that has an odor when you are changing the dressing?
- What do you need to do if the mechanical lift you go to get is different than the kind you trained on?
- What hospital resources might be available to help Dakarai cope with his diagnosis and make lifestyle adjustments?

SCENARIO 5

School Provides Free Sports Physicals

The athletic trainer has recruited your health sciences class to help with the sport physicals for the upcoming football season. You and a few other students have been recruited due to your interest in sports medicine.

During the physical exam, the students will be responsible for gathering the following information: vital signs, height, weight, and vision. They will be doing the physicals in the school gym.

The coaches have a scale, but you will need to bring the rest of the equipment you need from the classroom. You will need to complete the form on the following page for each athlete before they see the physician.

QUESTIONS TO ANSWER:

- What equipment do you need to bring to the gym?
- How can you ensure privacy for your patients in a school gym?
- You take an athlete's blood pressure and it is very high. He is very nervous. What do you do?
- The team's star athlete has an irregular pulse and very high blood pressure. If you write this on the form, he might not get to play and could lose his chance for scholarships. What do you do?

Sports Physical Form

Name: ______________________ Date: __________ Sport: __________________

Address: ____

Birthday: ____________________ Allergies: _______________________________

Medications: ____

Vital Signs:

Oral Temperature: _____________________ °C

Radial Pulse: ________________________

Apical Pulse: ________________________

Respirations: ________________________

Blood Pressure: ______________________

Height and Weight:

Height: _______ feet/inches

Weight: _______ pounds

Vision Test:

Right eye: _________________________ Left eye: __________________________

Corrective Lenses: ____________________

SCENARIO

6

Does Baby Benjamin Measure Up?

You have been looking forward to this clinical experience for a long time. You love working with children, and you have dreams of working in pediatrics after graduation. Today you are going to be working in a free pediatric clinic at a local community hospital.

Your first patient is a 6-month-old baby boy, named Benjamin. His mother has brought him in for his check-up. Benjamin is not a happy boy. He is scared of you and starts to scream. You note on his chart that the doctor wants you to get vital signs, height and weight, and measure his head circumference.

Benjamin also needs a urine specimen to be collected and tested this visit. You tell his mother to remove his clothes so you can get his height and weight, and you leave the room to gather your equipment. When you return, Benjamin is still fully clothed and still crying. Once again you ask his mother to remove his clothes so you can get an accurate weight. Benjamin's mother continues to cuddle her son, but does not begin to remove his clothes.

You notice that she is talking to him in Spanish. You suddenly realize that she does not speak English. How will you handle this challenging situation?

QUESTIONS TO ANSWER:

- How will you communicate with the mother that does not speak English about the exam?
- If you do not have an infant scale, how can you weigh the patient?
- What alternative modes of measuring body temperature could you use if your clinic did not have an aural thermometer?
- Why are apical pulses taken on infants?
- Why should an infant not be crying when you count respirations?

SCENARIO

7

Good Morning Roger

You have been assigned to work on the rehabilitation unit today. Your first patient is an 82-year-old gentleman named Roger. Roger had a stroke two weeks ago that left him very weak on the right side. He is right-handed, so he gets frustrated very easily.

He also has very poor vision and has been declared "legally blind." He lost his vision due to his diabetes. Roger wears dentures on the top, but has been able to keep his own teeth on the bottom. It is policy that all patients on the rehabilitation unit must be dressed in loose clothing and out of bed, sitting in their wheelchairs for breakfast. You do not need to worry about Roger's bath, as this has been done by the 3–11 shift.

Your assignment is to assist Roger with the above tasks, as well as with his breakfast, so he will not be late for his morning therapy session. Roger is very independent and wants to feed himself, he just needs some assistance. Roger also asks you for a special favor. He knows you are busy, but he has not had a shave in two days, and his whiskers are getting pretty scratchy.

QUESTIONS TO ANSWER:

- What skills do you need to perform and in what order should they be done?
- Since Roger is visually impaired but wants to feed himself, how can you help him remember where the food is located on his tray?
- Which side of the body will you undress first and why? Which side of the body will you dress first?

SCENARIO 8

Lights Out

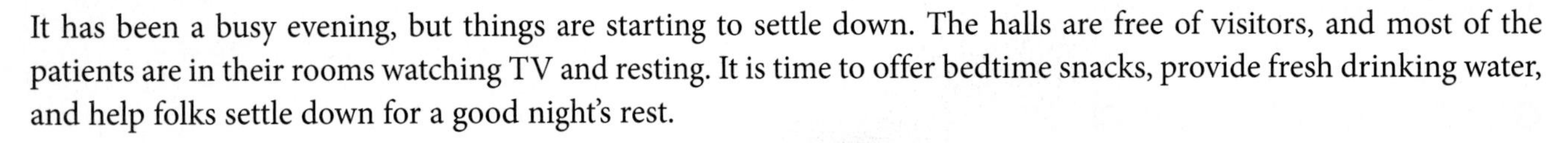

It has been a busy evening, but things are starting to settle down. The halls are free of visitors, and most of the patients are in their rooms watching TV and resting. It is time to offer bedtime snacks, provide fresh drinking water, and help folks settle down for a good night's rest.

Your first task is to serve nourishments. You have several diabetics on the floor, and they need some crackers and milk before bed. Once snacks are served, you begin your rounds to tuck your patients in for the night.

Your first patient is Lucy Long. Lucy slipped on a banana in the grocery store and broke her left hip four days ago. She is 75 years old and her skin is paper thin. She is the perfect candidate to develop a decubitus ulcer, and she refuses to move off her back.

You offer Lucy a back rub if she will allow you to position her on her side for a couple of hours. She agrees and you examine her skin while performing the back rub. So far, so good and no skin breakdown or redness is noted. You position Lucy on her side and hope she will fall asleep before she rolls back on her back again.

Finally you stop in to see Tim McDonald. Tim recently lost his right leg in an accident at work. Tim is sitting in the wheelchair and needs assistance in getting back to bed. He needs to be lifted into bed, so you call another nurse to help you.

You also need to place the bed cradle back on the bed, as Tim cannot stand the weight of the sheets on his fresh stump. After getting Tim in bed and chatting with Tim for about 10 minutes, you make sure all the patients have fresh water for the night. You dim the lights in the hall and wish them all sweet dreams.

QUESTIONS TO ANSWER:

- What skills do you need to be able to perform to settle these folks in for the night?
- Why can laying on your back for prolonged periods of time lead to the formation of decubitus ulcers?
- What type of nourishments would be appropriate for a diabetic patient? A heart patient? A patient on a clear liquid diet?

SCENARIO

9 I Can Still Hear You

Three days ago, a very sad event occurred. Juan and Julie had just gotten engaged. They were so happy that they were practically floating. As they were walking out of Wal-Mart and crossing the parking lot to their car, a teenager driving while talking on his cell phone struck Juan with his car.

As Juan lay on the ground bleeding and unconscious, Julie screamed and covered him with her body as if to shield him from any further danger. This could not be happening. Juan was airlifted to the hospital and remains in the Neuro ICU with massive head trauma. He is still unconscious. Julie has not left the hospital since he was admitted. Juan is your patient today.

You have been assigned to bathe Juan, give him mouth care, and make his bed. You ask Julie if she would wait outside in the waiting room while you complete AM care on Juan. Julie asks if you could please wash his hair and change his gown. He still has dried blood in his hair, and she knows he would not want everyone staring at his dirty hair.

Juan is also on nasal oxygen and has been breathing through his mouth. He has IV fluids running into his right arm. He has a Foley catheter, and your instructor reminds you to be very careful when doing his catheter care.

QUESTIONS TO ANSWER:

- In what order would you complete these skills to be the most efficient with your time?
- Why do you turn the patient's head to the side when doing oral care?
- Why would you need to explain what you were doing to an unconscious patient who does not respond to your voice?
- What complication could occur if the catheter was left kinked?

SCENARIO

10 Granny Doesn't Know Me Anymore

One of the sad things about Alzheimer's disease is that individuals eventually forget basic skills such as hygiene, how to feed themselves, and toilet training. Often as the disease progresses, these patients will need to be placed in an extended care facility.

That is where you have been assigned to work today—the Alzheimer's unit in a local nursing home. You will be taking care of Frieda, a 78-year-old female who is in the late stages of Alzheimer's disease. She does not talk much and does not remember how to walk. It is almost like taking care of a large infant.

This is Thursday, and it is Frieda's day to get a shower, nail care, and shampoo. Due to her inactivity and poor eating habits, she has a terrible constipation problem. Frieda has not had a bowel movement in the past five days, so the doctor has also ordered a soap suds enema for her today.

All of these tasks need to be completed between breakfast and her art therapy at 10:30. While she is in art therapy, you can get her bed made. The shower room is down the hall and to the right. Make sure you have all your supplies as you cannot leave Frieda alone in the shower room. What supplies will you need? In what order will you accomplish these tasks?

QUESTIONS TO ANSWER:

- What communication techniques would you use if Frieda becomes agitated and will not cooperate with you during her care?
- How can you maintain Frieda's privacy when she is naked in the shower?
- What will you do if the patient experiences cramping during the enema?
- If Frieda cannot use the bedpan, how will you handle the outcome of the enema?

The Flip-Flop Trip Up

Going out the door to get a pedicure done, Marie realized she forgot her book to read. Turning to get her book, Marie's flip-flops got tangled and she fell, hitting the bed and landing on a wooden floor. Marie broke her sacrum in two places and her pelvis in two places.

She has recently returned home from the hospital, but has physical therapy coming to her house three times a week. You have been assigned to work with Marie today. When you read her chart, you see they have been working with Marie on getting out of bed and walking with a walker.

Today you are also going to help her learn how to walk with a cane. She is to put most of her weight on the right side. She is very frightened of falling and weak after several weeks of bed rest. When you finish ambulating the patient, you are to apply ice to her sacrum for 15 minutes to decrease edema and pain.

QUESTIONS TO ANSWER:

- What equipment will you need to bring to Marie's home to carry out these tasks?
- How will you deal with Marie's fright about falling again and encourage her to learn a new procedure?
- Marie argues she needs to hold the cane in her left hand since that is the weaker side. Why does she need to hold the cane in her right hand?
- Why do you need to assess a patient's skin after ice has been applied to it?

SCENARIO

12 Home Sweet Home

Today you are working as a nursing assistant on a medical-surgical unit. As you return to the med-surg unit after lunch, Diane, the unit secretary, tells you that the physician has been in and discharged Mr. Binkie.

His wife is on the way to pick him up, and she will be here in about 20 minutes. Mr. Binkie is a 28-year-old male who has been in the hospital for 5 days with a staph infection. He had been snorkeling in the Caribbean and rubbed against some coral. When he returned home, his arm had become red, swollen, and sore. He was admitted to the hospital and put on IV antibiotics.

You know he will be excited to be going home, as he has missed his children and complains he cannot get any rest at the hospital due to people checking on him every hour. Mr. Binkie is in a semi-private room, and to make things worse, his roommate snores very loudly.

When you go in to see how close he is to being ready to go home, you note that he still has his IV connected, and he says the nurse has not been in to go over his prescriptions yet. He asks you, "How can I get my valuables back that were sent to the cashier's office?" You assure him that you will get those things for him.

Mr. Binkie insists he can walk to the car, but you explain it is hospital policy that all patients must be escorted out in a wheelchair. Your task is to discharge Mr. Binkie and then return to the unit.

The housekeeping staff has finished cleaning his bed when you return, and you need to make a closed bed so the room will be ready for the next patient that needs it.

QUESTIONS TO ANSWER:

- Which tasks are within your scope of practice as a nursing assistant and which are not?
- What do you need to do if some of the patient's valuables are missing?
- What will you do if Mr. Binkie tries to give you a cash tip when you take him to the car?
- Why do you make a closed bed when you return versus an open bed?

SCENARIO

13 I Can't Get Up

Abby Sullivan is a 73-year-old female who is recovering from the heart bypass surgery she had yesterday. She is still in the ICU, and she is on a ventilator. She also has an external pacemaker, chest tubes, central line, and multiple IVs.

Abby's surgery went well, but she is having an adverse reaction to some of the medications. Abby is very agitated and confused. She has tried to get out of bed, and she has tried to pull out several of her tubes. She has actually pulled her IV out twice.

Her family has gone home for the night to get some much needed rest, so there is no one out in the waiting room who can stay with her. You contact her surgeon who gives you an order to use restraints if needed. You decide they are definitely needed, as you are afraid for her safety.

You have two major goals to accomplish with these restraints. One is to keep her in bed so she does not fall and fracture any bones, and the other one is to keep her from pulling out all of her tubes.

QUESTIONS TO ANSWER:

- Which type(s) of restraints do you need to apply?
- What extra care will the patient need when you use them?
- What alternatives could you use in place of restraints?

SCENARIO

14 Midday Meal Time

Lunch has just arrived on the unit and, as a nursing assistant, one of your assigned tasks is to help pass out meal trays and assist with feeding patients when needed. All of your patients can feed themselves except for Abdul Smith.

Mr. Smith, an 82-year-old male, has had a right BKA (below the knee amputation) due to diabetes and also has some upper extremity weakness.

After you help the rest of your patients get started with their lunch, you go to Mr. Smith's room to prepare him for his meal. Before eating, Mr. Smith tells you he "needs to micturate." When you go to remove the urinal, you notice he has slipped down in the bed and his left foot is hanging off the end of the bed.

You assist Mr. Smith with repositioning and then with eating his meal. When he is through with lunch, he asks if you could please clean his dentures as his family is coming to visit in an hour, and he does not want food stuck in his teeth.

QUESTIONS TO ANSWER:

- What procedures do you need to do and in what order?
- Why is it important to reposition Mr. Smith before assisting with feeding?
- What complications could occur if Mr. Smith gets a tray that does not have a diabetic diet on it?

SCENARIO

15 To Do or Not to Do—That Is the Question

Matt, a physical therapy assistant student, is training with you in the physical therapy department today. You introduce Matt to the first patient on the schedule today, Kathy Pearson. Ms. Pearson, a new resident at Shady Brook Estates, is struggling with limited movement.

To help prevent contractures and to help increase her mobility, Ms. Pearson's physician has written the following order: ROM qod by PT. You ask Matt if he would like to perform Ms. Pearson's range of motion exercises today.

You also mention to Matt that Mr. Pearson is very hard of hearing. Matt, still in training, has not learned how to perform these exercises yet, but is afraid to admit that to you.

QUESTIONS TO ANSWER:

- What should Matt do?
- How do ROM exercises help prevent contractures?
- How do you respond when asked to do things beyond your scope of practice?
- How can you communicate with patients that are hard of hearing?

SCENARIO

16 Victory Comes Crashing Down

As Bobby waited in the exam room, he thought back to the track meet yesterday. He kept replaying the moment in his head. He pictured himself reaching for the baton being passed to him. The handoff was done with absolute precision.

He knew his team was in the lead and their time had to be the fastest they had posted all season. As Bobby rounded the last turn and the finish line was in his sight, he felt his ankle turn and twist. Bobby crashed to the ground and the team's hopes of a victory crashed with him.

In slow motion, he could see the baton flying off the track and landing with a thud in the grass. How could this have happened! All of the team's hours of practice in the heat was for naught, and there was only one more meet this season.

His ankle was sprained, and he was not sure if his teammates would ever forgive him. Instead of participating in a victory celebration, he was here waiting to have his ankle wrapped and get crutches. Your job is to provide Bobby with care for his sprained ankle and instruction for walking with crutches.

QUESTIONS TO ANSWER:

- What complications can occur if crutches are not fitted properly to the patient?
- Why is wrapping the ankle the treatment of choice? What other treatment is used?
- What other situations might require a joint to be wrapped or taped?

The Perfect Host/Hostess

As a medical assistant, you are responsible for patient admissions. You are often the first person with whom the patient comes in contact with and you need to help the patient feel comfortable.

Today you welcome a new patient, Mr. Wong. Mr. Wong is a 44-year-old male admitted to the unit with acute gastroenteritis. There are no family members with him. His wife has gone to the beach for a weekend with her girlfriends, and she is driving back but will not be here for about 3 more hours.

Mr. Wong is wearing shorts, a football T-shirt, and sandals. Mr. Wong has brought his medicine from home: Synthroid 137 mcg, Actos 30 mg, and Diovan HCT tab 80/12.5. Mr. Wong is allergic to shellfish. It makes his mouth and tongue swell. He wears bifocals and is proud to report he still has all of his teeth. He has a gold necklace, a watch, and a gold wedding band. His wallet has $55 in cash and 3 credit cards.

He was in the hospital twice before. When he was 24, he got hit in the jaw with a baseball and had to have his jaw wired. When he was 32, he had a little problem with kidney stones and had to have lithotripsy.

His main concern is how to turn on the television because there is a football game starting in 15 minutes that he cannot miss.

You know you must make careful observations and notify the nurse immediately if there are any acute problems. As you develop your rapport with Mr. Wong, you fill out the admission checklist form, orient him to the room, and gather baseline information on the patient.

QUESTIONS TO ANSWER:

- How can you make the patient feel at ease?
- What acute problems might you encounter during admission?
- What are your legal responsibilities related to Mr. Wong's belongings?
- When his wife arrives, what information can your share with her and what information is protected by the HIPAA Law?

SCENARIO

18 Dip to Diagnose

As a Medical Assistant, you love your job because no two days are the same and the job never gets boring. You get to do various tasks that help the physician in determining a diagnosis for the patient. A diagnosis is the first step in making the patient feel better.

You call your first patient of the day, Mabeline O'Malley, to come back to the exam room. Mabeline is a 33-year-old female who is eight months pregnant with triplets. She is in a wheelchair because she tripped over her toddler's toys and broke her right tibia.

As she comes back to the exam room, you ask how she has been feeling. Since she is having multiple babies, the doctor is watching her closely for gestational diabetes and toxemia.

The first thing you do is get her weight; a large increase in pounds and swelling could be a sign of toxemia. Since she can't stand, you will have to weigh her in the wheelchair.

Next you instruct her on how to obtain a midstream clean-catch urine. You offer to assist her, but Mrs. O'Malley says she can handle it. When Mrs. O'Malley brings you the urine specimen, you test the urine using a reagent strip, looking for signs of glucose and protein.

You continue to be fascinated by the information you can obtain with the urine test dipstick. You document the results of the test on her progress notes. As the doctor comes in, you wish Mrs. O'Malley good luck in case the babies come before you see her again. You consult the schedule and go to call your next patient.

QUESTIONS TO ANSWER:

- What would you do if you did not note the time you started the dipstick test? (Would it make a difference?)
- How would you get the patient's weight if you did not have a chair scale in your office?

SCENARIO

19 Assume the Position

Though it is early in the morning, the sun is shining, and it is already quite warm outside as you unlock the office door. It would be a great day to play golf or lie by the pool, but the general practitioner you work for has a full schedule today.

The first thing you do is turn on the computer and print out the patient appointments for the day. As a medical assistant, it is your responsibility to greet the patients and prepare them for the doctor's exam or procedure. This involves placing them in the right position.

Below is a copy of the day's schedule, which includes the patient's name and procedure being done. Position each patient as they arrive, so the doctor can be efficient in carrying out the treatments and procedures she must do today and not get behind schedule.

Time	*Name*	*Procedure*
9:00–9:30	Ed Bath	Drainage of Abscess on Left Buttock
9:31–10:00	Myrtle Gomaz	Pap Smear
10:01–10:45	Peter Cheng	Proctoscope Exam
10:46–11:20	Pierre deMontfort	Rectal Exam and Oil Retention Enema
11:30–1:00	Lunch	
1:00–1:30	Ariella Lieberman	Breast Exam
1:31–2:15	Marcella Mancini	Severe Hypotension, (Goes into shock while in the office)
2:25–3:00	Chuck Brown	Abdominal Pain
3:01–3:45	Gretel Braun	COPD and Chest Pain
3:46–4:15	Bob Beamer	Hemorrhoids
4:16–5:00	Geevan Patel	Insert Foley Catheter

QUESTIONS TO ANSWER:

- What alternative exam position could you place a patient in if they had hemorrhoids and were pregnant?
- How would you handle an elderly patient that was very modest and did not feel comfortable removing their clothes and putting on a patient gown?
- In which exam positions should you not leave the patient unattended and why?

SCENARIO 20 Habits Can Be Deadly

Susan is waiting to see the gerontologist. She hates going to the doctor and is very anxious about this appointment. To calm her nerves, she moves into the corner of the room and sneaks a cigarette. She knows she should not smoke for various health reasons, but cannot seem to break her bad habit.

As she lights up her cigarette, her portable oxygen tank sparks a fire. Your coworker tends to Susan who has second degree burns on her face and chest. After ensuring the rest of the clients in the waiting room are safe, you focus on the rack of magazines which have caught on fire.

After putting the fire out you think the emergency is over, but suddenly Pedro, another client in the waiting room, grabs his chest and collapses from what appears to be a cardiac arrest. He does not have a pulse and is not breathing. Was the stress of the fire too much for him?

QUESTIONS TO ANSWER:

- How do you put out the fire?
- What does your coworker do to treat Susan's burns?
- How do you respond to the client that has collapsed?
- What would you need to do if the fire got out of control and you cannot extinguish it?

SCENARIO 21 Action at the Eatery

You and your friends are celebrating getting an "A" on your medical midterms at the local eatery. As you are waiting for your food, you notice a person at the next table with their hands around their throat and their lips getting cyanotic. You recognize this emergency and jump into action.

QUESTIONS TO ANSWER:

- What is the medical emergency?
- What do you do if the person refuses your assistance?
- How do you determine if the person is just "playing around?"
- How would the rescue procedure change if the victim weighed 350 pounds?
- What would you do if the patient loses consciousness?

SCENARIO

22 4th of July Gone Awry

It is a beautiful day. There is not a cloud in the sky, and you are happy to have the day off so you can enjoy the holiday. You are attending a neighborhood 4th of July party.

Everyone is enjoying "pigging out" on hotdogs and hamburgers, and playing Frisbee and volleyball. Suddenly, you hear a woman scream, "My baby, my baby! Somebody help my baby!"

You scan the crowd and see a woman picking up her baby who must have fallen face down in the baby pool when the mother was not looking. The baby's body is limp and unresponsive. The baby's lips are turning blue, and she has a bluish-grey color to her complexion. You have just been certified in infant CPR and go to render assistance while another guest calls 911.

QUESTIONS TO ANSWER:

- What do you do?
- Would you handle this situation differently if you were alone?
- What other circumstances might cause an infant to stop breathing?

SCENARIO

23 The Lost Lego Legend

You are babysitting and excited that after tonight you will have enough money to buy the used car you have been saving up for. You have just finished cleaning up from dinner when Shantiqua, the 5-year-old, runs in and cries that baby Carol has just swallowed one of her Lego pieces that she had put in to the crib for the baby to play with.

You hear the high pitched sounds of the baby's cry as she struggles to get any air exchange. Her little lips are turning blue. Your adrenaline kicks into high gear. You rush over to baby Carol's crib, swoop her up, and begin trying to release the Lego.

QUESTIONS TO ANSWER:

- What procedure do you do?
- How can you tell if a baby is choking or not since they will not use the universal sign of the hands around the throat?
- What would you do if the infant becomes unconscious?

SCENARIO

24 When Seconds Count

You are driving home from teaching first aid to a troop of Girl Scouts. You are singing with the radio and wondering if you should try out for the next *American Idol* when you pass by a car that has crashed into a tree and is in a ditch. You pull over and rush to see if everyone is all right.

As you get out of your car, you smell burnt rubber and hear cries for help. As you survey the scene, you see one passenger sitting on the side of the road moaning as a fountain of blood spurts out from her left lower arm.

A second victim is standing next to the car. She is alert and oriented, but holding her right arm, which is hanging from her elbow at a strange angle. As you take a closer look, you suspect the bone is fractured, but it has not pierced the skin.

A passerby stops and asks if there is anything he can do to help. He says he "does not have first aid training, but he is a quick study." You have the first aid supplies that you used in the class in the trunk of your car.

QUESTIONS TO ANSWER:

- Which supplies will you need?
- What do you need to do and in what order?
- What do you have the passerby do?
- How will you know if one of the victims is going into shock?

SCENARIO

25 Sticks and Stones Will Break Your Bones

Terrie Thomas, a 26-year-old male, was out riding an ATV (all terrain vehicle/ "4 wheeler") with his friends. While racing up a steep hill, his vehicle suddenly flipped over. Terrie was lucky to jump off so as to not have the vehicle land on him.

He heard, as well as felt a loud snap as his arm landed on a rock. He suffered a mild concussion and a simple fracture of his right radius, which needed a closed reduction to repair it. The orthopedist reduced the fracture, then applied a cast to immobilize the break. It was a painful procedure, as he could not sedate Terrie due to the concussion.

The doctor told him he was lucky to have survived with only a broken arm and to have avoided needing surgery. He told Terrie that he would like to admit him overnight due to his concussion.

Terrie has been admitted to your unit for observation. After getting him settled into his room, you complete his neurological checks and get ready to perform his cast care.

QUESTIONS TO ANSWER:

- What do you need to check for?
- Why is it important to elevate the extremity above the patient's heart level?
- What could malodor from the cast indicate?

SCENARIO

26 Pearly Whites

It is another busy day at the dental clinic. You have been a dental assistant here for just two weeks. Today is Thursday, which means you wear white scrubs and have a heavy refugee patient load. You enjoy meeting the patients from different cultures, but still struggle with trying to communicate and learning their cultural beliefs.

Your first patient, Jace Lim, is in for a cleaning and X-rays. When your patient sits in the dental chair, you catch a whiff of his breath and you are overcome with nausea. Your patient's halitosis is overwhelming.

Mr. Lim is a refugee from Cambodia, and he speaks limited English. When he first looks at you and your uniform, his expression suddenly changes from a smile to one of fright.

You remember from your training that you must watch your nonverbal expressions, maintain professionalism at all time and use tact. This is one of those situations your instructor warned you about—one in which maintaining professionalism might not be easy.

You have 30 minutes to brush and floss his teeth and determine how to best communicate to Mr. Lim the importance of proper oral hygiene. X-rays will be taken by the dental hygienist, and after they are developed, you need to properly mount them.

QUESTIONS TO ANSWER:

- With respect to his culture, why might Mr. Lim be frightened when he sees you?
- How do you handle this situation with respect to his culture?
- What is a tactful way to handle his halitosis?
- How do you make sure your patient understands your instructions?

SCENARIO 27 Don't Turn Your Back!

"Hey hon!" your mom calls from the den when you walk in the door from school. She introduces you to a friend of hers, Mrs. Fedak, who is visiting. Mrs. Fedak has her 2½-year-old daughter, Isabel, with her. Isabel is cute as a button and Mrs. Fedak explains that Isabel is quite a handful, and she is at the age where she likes to get into everything!

After exchanging pleasantries, you head to your room. You put your book bag down and know you have to get your chores and homework done before you can go out. It's your turn to clean the bathrooms, so you get to work. While you are cleaning, you are jamming to your iPod, drowning out the sound of the world around you.

You have had quite a day. It started with a pop quiz in physics and just went downhill from there. Thank goodness there was a substitute in history.

You are just about done with the first bathroom, and as you stand back to admire the sparkling sink and mirror, you turn around and see Isabel drinking the bottle of cleaner! What do you do?

QUESTIONS TO ANSWER:

- What could you have done to prevent this accident?
- What complications could occur from this poisoning?
- Why don't you just read the label of the cleaner to see what to do if the cleaner is ingested instead of calling poison control?
- Why might poison control ask for the age and weight of the victim?

SCENARIO 28 Black Diamond Disaster

You are on a ski retreat in the mountains with some friends. On your way up the ski lift, the cool air chills your exposed face and the snow is gently falling on the ground. It is a perfect day for skiing, and so far the beginner and intermediate slopes have been a blast.

As you and your friend, Manuel, get off the lift you wobble a little bit, but then regain your balance. You both decide to try the expert black diamond slope this time. After all, how hard can it be?

Neither of you will admit the fear you feel as you look at the incline of the slope, nor will either of you admit that this slope might be too advanced. You egg each other on, and then go for it.

Your buddy teases you that you've actually spent most of the time going down on your gluteus maximus, but you feel a rush as you consider you have successfully navigated your way halfway down the mountain. You've even worked up enough courage to try going over the moguls or bumps. As you continue down the slope, your speed becomes harder and harder to control. You fly over a mogul, go sailing in the air, and then "wham!"

You land hard on your shoulder and you continue to slide down the hill. As you come to a stop, your head hits a rock. You remain conscious, but are in agonizing pain. You know you've dislocated your shoulder and feel blood running down the back of your head. Manuel, who was not far behind, can't stop in time and swerves to avoid you and lands in the woods. During the fall, his right leg slams into a briar patch causing a large wound on his thigh. On top of that, his left foot came out of the boot and a sharp broken tree branch sliced his foot. How will ski patrol handle your injuries?

QUESTIONS TO ANSWER:

- Should ski patrol suspect a back or neck injury? If so, what should they be sure to do?
- What purpose does a dressing serve?
- Why don't you remove a dressing once it has been applied?
- What complications could possibly occur from these injuries?

SCENARIO 29 Moving Day

You are the nurse for Dino Pappas today. Dino is a pleasant 54-year-old man who is paralyzed from the waist down due to a gunshot wound five years ago. He is in the hospital due to exacerbation of his emphysema. He is glad to be moving from his current semi-private room to a private room. His roommate and his roommate's visitors have been very loud and inconsiderate. Mr. Pappas states he has not even been able to watch his favorite TV shows!

Mr. Pappas had received some Tylenol earlier as he was running a fever, and you first must see if his fever has gone down. You grab the electronic thermometer, take his temperature, and note that he is afebrile.

As you are gathering his medications and belongings, the respiratory therapist walks in and wants to assess his pulmonary function and administer his breathing treatment before he is transferred. As the RT finishes up, he connects Mr. Pappas' oxygen via nasal canula to the portable oxygen tank, so Mr. Pappas is ready for transfer. You slide him from the bed to the wheelchair, secure his oxygen tank, and wheel him and his belongings to his new room.

When Mr. Pappas arrives in his private room, he is thrilled. You make sure you put away all of his belongings and help him back in bed. You position him on his right side, using the logrolling technique as he turns on his favorite show, *The Price is Right*!

QUESTIONS TO ANSWER:

- What is your role in assisting/promoting respiratory therapy?
- What pulmonary techniques might Mr. Pappas need?
- How often should Mr. Pappas change position? Why is this important?
- How would you handle the roommate conflict, if transferring the patient was not an option?

SCENARIO

30 Spin Cycle

You have been working in the lab for just over a year now. Working here gives you great satisfaction, as you know your role is crucial in detecting and diagnosing diseases. This doctor's office keeps you on your toes and brings a variety of different tests each day.

As you wait for your first patient, you make sure all of your supplies are stocked. As you look up, Mr. Liam Curtis arrives and hands you his lab orders. You see that you will need to centrifuge his urine and look at it under a microscope as well as measure the specific gravity with a refractometer.

He states he has been having some problems with his urination, and "the doctor is checking on his kidneys." You explain to him how to obtain a midstream clean-catch urine specimen and that when he is done, he is to bring the specimen back to you. When he returns, you thank him and get to work.

QUESTIONS TO ANSWER:

- What can you learn from centrifuging urine and from looking at it under the microscope?
- What other tests might the doctor order?
- What time of day is the ideal time to obtain a urine specimen for centrifuging?

SCENARIO

31 Relief at Last!

You knock on Mrs. Jones' door before you go back in. Mrs. Jones is a pretty independent and somewhat bossy 43-year-old woman. You have already helped her with some of her AM care, but she still needs to have an enema and a moist hot soak for her knee before she showers for the day.

Mrs. Jones tells you that she is actually looking forward to the enema, though she quickly clarifies—the results of the enema, not the actual administration! She tells you the iron pills the doctor has her on for her anemia have caused her major problems with constipation. Mrs. Jones said she needs to have a bowel movement before her visitors arrive at lunch time, so she will not be passing so much flatus and feeling so uncomfortable.

You explain to Mrs. Jones that you will be administering the moist hot soak for the osteoarthritis in her right knee first. You explain this will enable her right knee to bend more easily as she will need to have it bent for the enema procedure. After you complete this task, she comments on how much better her knee feels. She says she cannot wait for her abdomen to feel as good!

You explain the oil retention enema procedure to Mrs. Jones and instruct her that she will need to stay on her side and try to retain the enema solution for about 30 minutes. After administering the enema you tell her you will be checking on her every few minutes.

Twenty-five minutes later Mrs. Jones tells you it is time—she cannot hold it any longer. You assist her to the bathroom. She also announces that she will take a shower right after having her bowel movement and please be sure her new gown and towels are in the bathroom. You know you should not get annoyed, and you try to put yourself in Mrs. Jones' place. You know that she must be scared and feel out of control; she is waiting to get her test results back and has not seen the doctor yet today.

While Mrs. Jones is out of the bed, you make her bed, make sure her water pitcher is full, and move on to your next patient.

QUESTIONS TO ANSWER:

- Why would a moist hot soak be used for osteoarthritis?
- Why is the Sims' position used for enema administration?
- What would you do if the patient could not retain the enema for the needed time?
- How can you handle dealing with a patient that is overly demanding and unreasonable?

Faded Photographs

You have been working as a recreational therapist in a long-term care facility for about three years. Today you will be working with residents in the Alzheimer's Unit, a job that can be quite trying sometimes but also quite rewarding.

Today, you hope the music therapy and art therapy sessions you have planned will help them recall multiple memories. You have planned a music therapy session from 9:00 to 10:00 this morning, followed by an art therapy session from 10:00 to 11:00.

Billy Bancroft is one of the residents who will be attending your sessions today. Billy is 84 years old, but if you ask him his age, he will swear he is 32. Billy was a drummer in a band when he was in his twenties and thirties.

Matilda Owens, 90 years old, will also be attending your session. Matilda is new to the facility. She claims to be 39 and believes she is still teaching first grade at a local elementary school. She is constantly asking when her students will be finished with their physical education class.

The final resident that will attend your sessions today is Henrietta Haywood. Henrietta believes she is 21 and a dancer for the USO that boosts morale for the American Armed forces. When you check her records, you discover that she is really 79 years old and she did dance for the USO for twelve years.

As you enter the recreation area, you see Mr. Bancroft and Ms. Haywood sitting in front of the television, which is turned to a popular game show. Ms. Owens is pacing the room trying to find her students.

QUESTIONS TO ANSWER:

- Considering your patients' ages and interests, what type of music selections will you choose for their music therapy?
- Why can Ms. Haywood not remember how to brush her teeth, but still remember all the dance steps she learned?
- How might art therapy help Alzheimer patients recall memories?
- How will you handle a resident who does not want to cooperate and participate in the therapy session?

SCENARIO

33 I Can Do It Myself!

While in anesthesia training, you are working part-time as a nurse at a small local hospital. Today you have been assigned to work on a medical unit where many of the patients have chronic medical conditions, such as cardiac or renal problems.

As you enter your first patient's room, you are greeted with a pleasant, "Good Morning!" You are pleased to make the acquaintance of Doug Munroe. Doug is a 58-year-old male who has been recently diagnosed with Parkinson's Disease. Doug has some minor tremors, but with just a small amount of assistance, he can get out of bed and ambulate around the room. He is very independent and wants to care for himself as much as possible.

The first order of business is to assist Mr. Munroe in getting ready for breakfast. You search for his toothbrush and toothpaste so he can brush his teeth when he goes into the bathroom to empty his bladder. Mr. Munroe is being evaluated for some kidney problems and is on a low-sodium diet. He has had some swelling in his lower extremities recently, so the doctors are running some diagnostic tests.

The aroma in the hall lets you know the breakfast carts have arrived. It smells like homemade cinnamon rolls today. You gather Mr. Munroe's tray and set him up for breakfast. He assures you he can feed himself, so you move on to your other patients.

While you are feeding Mrs. Patel down the hall, Mr. Munroe's doctor makes his rounds and writes the following orders:

Midstream clean-catch urine specimen today

24-hour urine test for creatinine

You gather the equipment and go in to help Mr. Munroe, who is uncircumcised, get started with his tests.

QUESTIONS TO ANSWER:

- What types of food should Mr. Munroe not be allowed to eat on a low sodium diet?
- What happens if you accidentally discard a urine specimen during the 24-hour period?
- When should you collect the midstream clean-catch urine specimen?
- Why is it important to encourage Mr. Munroe's independence? (Include both physical and psychological reasons.)

SCENARIO

34 A Wild Night in the ER

You are working the second shift in the emergency room at a small community hospital. You do not mind working there on Wednesday nights as it is usually pretty quiet. Tonight though, the waiting room is packed and they just keep coming.

You have seen 16 patients, and they all have complained of the same symptoms: severe headache, severe vomiting, diarrhea, and abdominal cramps. The patients range in age from 5 to 36 and the only things they have in common is that they all were at the same amusement park earlier today and they all state that the symptoms came on very suddenly. You are afraid you might have an epidemic on your hands.

The emergency physician notifies the health department, and they ask him if diagnostic tests for Salmonella have been done. He instructs you to obtain a routine urine specimen and stool specimen from each of the patients. Once you have obtained the stool specimens, he tells you to test them for occult blood. He tells you to take all precautions because he is not sure what disease this is and it might be contagious.

QUESTIONS TO ANSWER:

- What personal protective equipment will you need and what standard precautions will you need to take?
- How will you protect the patient's confidentiality and privacy in a crowded emergency room that may only have curtains separating the patient's exam room?
- Why would you need to notify the health department?

SCENARIO

35 Lie to Ride

Paul Pence is a 43-year-old male who has been admitted to your hospital with cancer of the liver. He has been undergoing chemotherapy and radiation treatments for the past week and has an IV and urinary catheter. Because his immune system is so weak from his treatments, he has been placed in protective isolation.

Today Paul has to go to the X-ray department for a cystoscopy with dye. He will need to be transported to radiology on a stretcher. You have been assigned this task and his procedure is scheduled for 0930.

Later in the morning, you receive word that Mr. Pence is finished with his procedure, and you need to report to radiology to pick him up. When you get to radiology, you find that he is still on a stretcher and still has an indwelling catheter. The radiologist tells you to plug the catheter when Mr. Pence returns to the room and then reconnect it in about 4 hours for 30 minutes. He wants to do this to help Mr. Pence with bladder retraining. After you disconnect the catheter, you have to measure the urine in the drainage bag and record it as Mr. Pence is on I&O.

QUESTIONS TO ANSWER:

- Are there any special precautions you need to take because Mr. Pence in on protective or reverse isolation?
- What role does body mechanics play in this scenario?
- How does plugging a catheter help with bladder retraining?

SCENARIO 36

Sweet Dreams Anita

When you report to work for the 3–11 shift at Sweet Pines Estate, you are told in report that Anita Huggins is failing fast and the doctors do not expect her to live through the night.

She had been talking to her husband, Hubert, earlier that day and he had died 10 years ago. Her kidneys are failing and she is having increased periods of Cheyne-Stokes breathing. Her blood pressure has been dropping also.

Her family had been called that morning and most were by her bedside or in the waiting area, but Anita did not seem to be aware they were there. Hospice has been working with the family for a while, so they were prepared to say good-bye. Anita's living will states she is a DNR.

Anita shares a semi-private room with her roommate Mazel Murdock. Mazel was very upset when you made rounds and did not want to be in the room alone if Anita died. They have become very close in the two years they have shared living space.

About 9:00 that night, Anita quietly passed away. Her family stayed with her for about another hour and then went home after telling you which funeral home they would be using. Once they left, you and your coworker began post-mortem care.

QUESTIONS TO ANSWER:

- How can you help Mazel during the time Anita is dying?
- Why is it important to get dentures in the mouth right after the patient passes away?
- How would this scenario have been different if the patient did not have a living will and was not a DNR?
- What is your responsibility related to the patient's belongings?

SCENARIO

37 The Final Rodeo

As a child, little Joe Carter had always watched westerns with his father and dreamed of becoming a cowboy. Years later, he was living out his fantasy by working as a cowboy on a ranch in Oklahoma and competing in rodeos. Then, tragedy struck.

Four months ago, he was involved in a rodeo accident that left him paralyzed from the neck down. Being only 27 years old, this has been a major adjustment for him. He had to give up the career he had always dreamed of, move back in with his parents, and depend on someone else for every activity of daily living. Needless to say, Joe has been very depressed.

You have been assigned to be Joe's home-health aide. Five days a week, you come to Joe's house and help him with things such as hygiene, skin care, and meals. You are about the same age as Joe, and the two of you have become good friends. He really looks forward to your visits. Mr. and Mrs. Carter have put a hospital bed in Joe's room and gotten some other medical equipment, such as a wheelchair and mechanical lift.

Today you have several tasks you need to accomplish. First you need to get a weekly weight for Joe. Since he cannot stand, you will have to do this with a mechanical lift. During the night, Joe has slipped to the bottom of the bed. You will need to move him up in bed before you can use the lift.

Next, you must complete the basic tasks such as brushing his teeth and feeding him breakfast. You bathe Joe every other day and this was done yesterday, so you do not need to worry about a bath today. When you bathed him yesterday, you noticed a reddened area on his sacrum and you are worried about his skin breaking down and a decubitus forming.

Today you are going to position him on his right and then his left side for about two hours each and try to keep him off his back as much as possible. You will have to plan some things to entertain Joe when you turn him on his right side toward you. When he lies on his left side (away from you) he can watch television. Before you position him however, you want to do foot care on Joe and put on a new external urinary catheter. His toenails look like weapons.

When you get to Joe's home you get one more surprise. Due to his immobility and lack of feeling, constipation has become a problem for Joe. He has not had a bowel movement in five days and his abdomen is distended. You will have to add a packaged enema to the day's activities. You have a full day planned, so you better get started.

QUESTIONS TO ANSWER:

- Why would skin assessment be a major component of Joe's care?
- What extra challenges would you have administering an enema to a patient that is paralyzed?
- What resources could you use or recommend to the family to help deal with the patient's psychological health?
- What fears might a patient have about being lifted with a mechanical lift?

SCENARIO

38 Irish Dancing on Hold

Patricia Quinlivan is a patient at Coastal Rehabilitation Center. Patricia had a knee replacement five days ago, and she has come to Coastal for additional physical and occupational therapy. Patricia is a widow and lives alone except for two cats, so her doctor felt a couple weeks in rehab would be the best thing for her.

Besides her knee issues, Patricia has been having some trouble with kidney stones. She had a lithotripsy procedure before leaving the hospital. The physician's discharge orders included straining her urine for renal calculi and checking each urine specimen for blood.

As you enter Mrs. Quinlivan's room, she is awake and wishes you a "top of the morning." You just love her Irish accent. She tells you that her "bladder is about to burst and could you please help her get on the bedside commode." She finds this more comfortable than the toilet because it is higher, and it is easier for her to get up and down. Once she finishes, you put down the lid on the bedside commode and help her back to bed.

Next on the agenda is getting a bath before breakfast and therapy. You prepare a bath basin for her to do a partial bath. Mrs. Quinlivan can do most of her bath, but she is just a wee bit stout. She will need some assistance cleaning her back and perineal area.

While she starts on her bath, you test her urine for blood and strain it. It is negative for blood and no evidence of kidney stones. By this time, Mrs. Quinlivan has done all of the bath she can manage. You change the water and then do her back and perineal care.

While Mrs. Quinlivan gets dressed in her favorite sweatsuit, you empty the bath basin and tidy up the room. Mrs. Quinlivan is in her wheelchair and ready for breakfast. She is anxious to get to the dining room to have her morning cup of coffee and chat with her new friends, Irma and Dorothy. You wheel her to the dining room and help her prepare for breakfast. Mrs. Quinlivan is on a regular diet, so she does not have any restrictions. After breakfast, she will be going to her physical therapy session.

Later that morning, you pick up Mrs. Quinlivan from therapy. She has worked really hard this morning and her knee is quite swollen. The therapist suggests that she return to her room and elevate it until lunch. She also tells you to apply a cold compress to her knee.

QUESTIONS TO ANSWER:

- It would be faster for you to give Mrs. Quinlivan a bedpan, rather than helping her up to the bedside commode. Why is it better for her to use the commode?
- What personal protective equipment will you need to carry out these procedures?
- How do you proceed if the HemaCombistix is positive for blood and/or you find stones or particles in the urine strainer?

SCENARIO

39 The Magic Book

You are working as a pharmacy technician at a local drugstore. Jeanette McGregor, one of your regular customers, comes in and asks if you can give her some information about a drug her mother has recently been put on.

Her mother has a mild form of dementia and had taken all of her pills out of the bottles, put them in a jewelry box, and then threw away the bottles. Now her mother cannot remember what the name of the new medication is and what it is for.

You reach for the *Physicians' Desk Reference (PDR)* and tell her you will be happy to try and help. Mrs. McGregor shows your mother's new pill. It is a small, pink, round pill with a 200 on it. On the back it says "Abbott Laboratories." You turn to Section 4 of the *PDR* to look at the medication pictures and see what the name of the medicine is. You recognize the pill to be ______________________.

Once you tell Mrs. McGregor the name of the medication, she asks you what are the indications and usage for this particular medication. She was not sure why the doctor had prescribed it, as she had not been able to go with her mother to that appointment.

You turn to the "Brand and Generic Name Index" to see what page the product information for this drug would be on. You make a note that you need to turn to page ___________, which is in the "Product Information" section.

When you turn to the "Product Information" section, you look for "Indications and Usage." You tell Mrs. McGregor that there are two reasons that this medication is given. They are:

1. ____

2. ____

You suggest that she check with her mother's physician to find out the particular reason he has prescribed this medication.

Mrs. McGregor thanks you for your help and asks if she can just take up a few more minutes of your time. As long as you have the *PDR* handy, she wonders what the usual dose is and if there are any general adverse reactions she needs to be on the lookout for with her mother. You research this for her and write down the information on a pharmacy notepad (see following page).

Pharmacy R_X Notepad

Name of Drug: ______________________________

Usual Dose: ______________________________

General Adverse Reactions:

1. ______________________________
2. ______________________________
3. ______________________________
4. ______________________________
5. ______________________________
6. ______________________________

After Mrs. McGregor leaves, you get a call from Nanette Nightingale. She is new to the state and is trying to update her emergency numbers. She asks if you could please give her the name and phone number for the Poison Control Center in this state.

Once again, you open your *PDR* and turn to Section 3 where all the state Poison Control Centers are listed. You give the phone number and address for the one in this state. She is very grateful.

Your final phone call for the morning is from a physician's assistant. He has a patient with severe diarrhea, and he wants to know what the best medications are for this problem. He is on call and does not have his *PDR* at home. He knew you would have access to one.

You tell him you will be happy to tell him what is listed in the *PDR*. You turn to the "Product Category Index" section and look under "Antidiarrheals Medications." You tell him the first three medications listed.

1. ______________________________

2. ______________________________

3. ______________________________

Before disconnecting, he asks you to do him one more favor. He needs to get some more Lanoxin samples for his office and wants to talk to the manufacturer about this. He knows they are made by GlaxoSmithKline. He asks you if you could give him their phone number and address so he can contact them. You tell him no problem, and turn to the "Manufacturers' Index" in your *PDR*.

The phone number is ______________________________ and the address is ______________________________.

You look at your watch and notice it is 11:30 and almost time for lunch. It has been a busy morning, and the time has flown. Thank goodness for your trusty *PDR*.

Procedures

PROCEDURE 9.1 Scheduling Office Visits

BACKGROUND: Careful scheduling is essential for a well-run office. Appointments must be scheduled to prevent long waits for patients while also keeping the staff working at top efficiency. Accommodating the patient as much as possible tells the patient that you are concerned about him or her.

PREPROCEDURE

1. Assemble materials.
   a. Pen or pencil
   b. Appointment book
   c. Appointment reminder cards for tickler file
   d. Appointment cards
   e. Calendar
   f. Procedure list with approximate time allotments for each procedure
   g. Written instructions for patient/client preparation prior to visit
2. Prepare provider schedules for at least three months.
   a. Mark out vacation or holiday times.
   b. Schedule monthly, weekly, or daily meetings.
   c. Mark schedule to identify hours for patient/client appointments.
3. Follow the correct procedure for the type of appointment system in your office.
4. Write clearly and neatly so that names and procedures are easy to read.

PROCEDURE

5. Schedule appointments.
   a. By phone:
      (1) Clarify reason for appointment.
      (2) Discuss most convenient time for client/patient (e.g., a.m., p.m.).
      (3) Offer various times.
      (4) Ask for proper spelling of first and last names once a time is chosen.
      (5) Ask for information, such as birthday or Social Security number, if name is common (e.g., Smith, Jones).
      (6) Write patient's/client's telephone number and where he or she can be reached during the day of appointment.

      (7) Allocate **sufficient** time for the visit when scheduling a procedure.
   b. In person:
      (1) Follow steps 1 to 5 of procedure above.
      (2) Give patient/client an appointment card with date and time of appointment.

   c. For appointments more than three months in the future:
      (1) Ask patient/client to address an appointment reminder card.
      (2) Fill in month patient is to return.
      (3) Instruct patient/client that a card will be sent as a reminder to call and make an appointment.
   d. Place appointment reminder card in tickler file so that it is sent at the correct time.

PROCEDURE 9.2 Scheduling a New Patient/Client: First-Time Visit

BACKGROUND: Gathering essential information from each new patient provides the information needed for patient care and timely billing for services rendered. The patient feels secure when everything is taken care of efficiently.

PREPROCEDURE

1. Assemble materials.
   a. Appointment book
   b. Scheduling guidelines
   c. Telephone
   d. Pencil

PROCEDURE

2. Ask patient/client for the following:
   a. First, last, and middle names
   b. Birth date
   c. Home address
   d. Telephone number
3. Ask patient/client if this is a referral. If yes:
   a. Determine information you need from the referring provider.
   b. Add this information to the medical chart. (Your provider needs to send a consultation report to the referring provider.)
4. Ask what the chief complaint is and when it started.
5. Find the first appointment that allows the appropriate amount of time.
6. Offer a choice of days and times.
7. Enter the following:
   a. Patient's/client's name NP next to name indicating new patient)
   b. Time and date of appointment
   c. Patient's/Client's day telephone number
8. Explain payment procedure (e.g., patient/client must pay for visit, your office will bill).
9. Give directions to the office.
10. Explain parking arrangements.

POSTPROCEDURE

11. Repeat day, date, and time the appointment is scheduled.

PROCEDURE 9.3 Scheduling Outpatient Diagnostic Tests

BACKGROUND: Patients are often fearful about diagnostic tests. Scheduling the diagnostic tests as soon as possible and when it is most convenient for the patients gives them confidence that they are cared for in a timely and caring way.

PREPROCEDURE

1. Assemble materials.
   a. Written order from provider
   b. Patient's chart
   c. Test preparation instructions for client/patient
   d. Name, address, and phone number of laboratory
   e. Telephone

PROCEDURE

2. Read provider's order.
3. Ask patient/client when he or she is available.
4. Call test lab.
5. Order test
   a. Set up time and date
   b. Give name, age, address, and telephone number of patient/client
   c. Ask if there are special instructions for patient/client prior to the test
6. Provide patient/client with the following:
   a. Name, address, and telephone number of laboratory
   b. Date and time
   c. Instructions (in writing) for preparation prior to test
7. Verify instructions with patient/client.

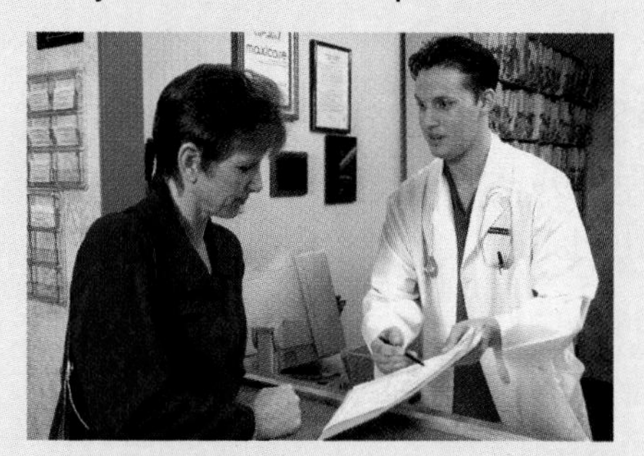

8. Record test time in patient's/client's chart.

POSTPROCEDURE

9. Put a reminder in the tickler file or on a calendar to check for results.

PROCEDURE 15.1 Activities with Alzheimer's Patients

BACKGROUND: For people who have Alzheimer's disease, activities help structure the time. Activities also improve a patient's self-esteem.

ALERT: Follow Standard Precautions (see Section 17.2).

PREPROCEDURE

1. Wash hands.
2. Identify the patient and the activity in which he or she will be participating. Pay attention to:
   a. the patient's skills and abilities
   b. what the patient enjoys
   c. physical problems
   d. the physician's recommendations
3. Gather equipment for the activity (if needed).
4. Break the activity into small, measurable steps.

PROCEDURE

5. Greet the patient, and tell him or her what you are going to do today.
6. Help the patient get started with the activity.
7. Explain each step of the activity using simple terms. It may be necessary to repeat the explanation or to clarify in terms the patient understands.
8. Help the patient through difficult steps or if he or she appears frustrated. As much as possible, let the patient do most of the activity on his or her own.
9. Do not criticize or correct the patient.

POSTPROCEDURE

10. Put away equipment.
11. Wash hands.
12. Record the patient's response to the activity.

PROCEDURE 15.2 Music Therapy

BACKGROUND: Music helps Alzheimer's patients recall memories and emotions.

ALERT: Follow Standard Precautions (see Section 17.2).

PREPROCEDURE

1. Identify the patient.
2. Identify the type of music that the patient enjoys.
3. Provide a comfortable space in which the patient can listen to the music.
4. Gather and set up equipment. Choose music, something to play it on, pictures that mean something to the patient to help them recall memories.
5. Block other sources of sound. Close windows and doors, turn off televisions and other radios, and reduce background noise as much as possible.

PROCEDURE

6. Start the music.
7. Encourage the patient to clap or sing along with the music. When appropriate, encourage the patient to dance or move with the music.
8. While playing the music, show the patient pictures to help with memories.

POSTPROCEDURE

9. Put away equipment.
10. Record the patient's response to the activity.

PROCEDURE 15.3 Art Therapy

BACKGROUND: Like music, art can help an Alzheimer's patient reconnect with the world around him or her. Art provides a way for the patient to express himself or herself.

ALERT: Follow Standard Precautions (see Section 17.2).

PREPROCEDURE

1. Identify the patient.
2. Assemble materials. Avoid potentially harmful materials, such as sharp blades and tools. Materials may include the following:
   a. nontoxic acrylic paints or watercolor paints
   b. brushes and canvases or watercolor paper
   c. clay
3. Prepare a work area for the patient. Neatly arrange materials and cover surfaces to protect them from spillage.

PROCEDURE

4. Help the patient start the project.
5. Encourage the patient to talk about what he or she is doing. Ask the patient to remember events related to the project or to tell a story about the project.
6. Help the patient through difficult steps or if he or she appears frustrated. As much as possible, let the patient do most of the project on his or her own.
7. Do not criticize or correct the patient.
8. When the patient is finished with the project, help him or her clean up.

POSTPROCEDURE

9. Put away equipment.
10. Clean work space.
11. Record the patient's response to the activity.

PROCEDURE 17.1 Hand Hygiene (Washing)

BACKGROUND: Contaminated hands are the most common cause of infection. Proper handwashing technique is the most effective way to prevent the spread of infection.

PREPROCEDURE

1. Wash your hands between patient contacts.
2. Wash your hands after removing protective gloves.
3. Wash your hands after contact with body fluids, even if gloves have been worn.

PROCEDURE

4. Stand at sink. Avoid contact of your uniform with the sink. Roll a paper towel out to have ready to use after washing your hands.
5. Turn on water and adjust water temperature.
6. Wet the hands and wrist area. Keep hands lower than elbows.
7. Using soap from dispenser lather thoroughly.

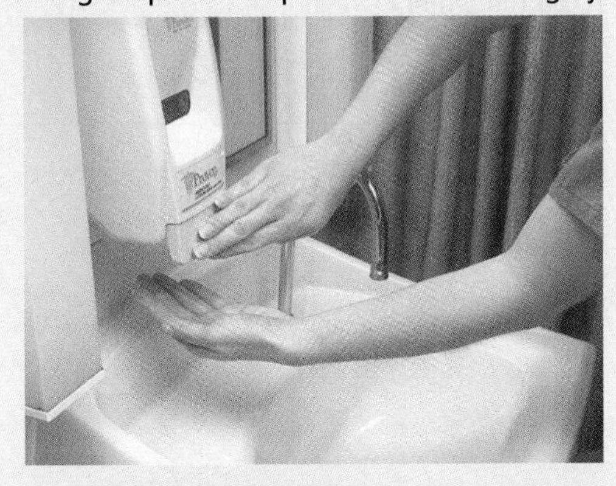

8. Using soap and friction, wash the palms, backs of the hands, fingers, between the fingers, knuckles, wrists and forearms. Clean nails. If no nail brush is available, rub nails across palms of hands.
9. Continue washing for at least 15 seconds.
10. Rinse thoroughly with fingertips downward.

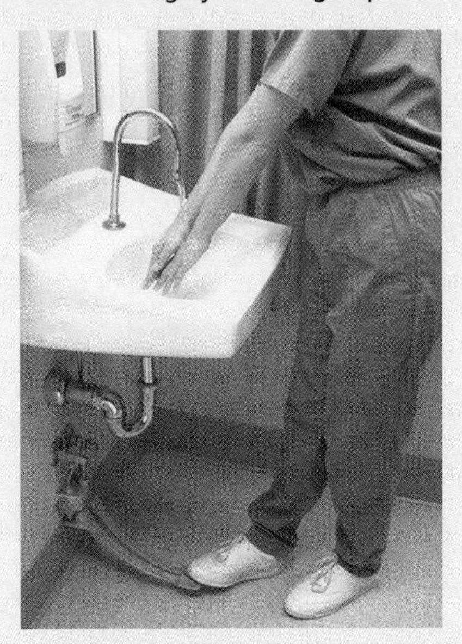

11. Dry hands.
12. Use a paper towel to turn off faucets and open door if necessary.

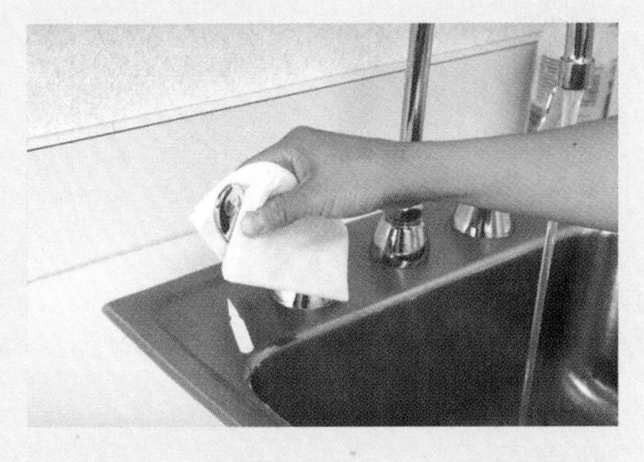

13. Use lotion on hands to prevent chapping, if needed.

PROCEDURE 17.2 Personal Protective Equipment

BACKGROUND: Personal protective equipment (PPE) are a variety of barriers and respirators used alone or in combination to protect mucous membranes, airways, skin, and clothing from contact with infectious agents.

PREPROCEDURE

1. Determine the expected level of exposure.
2. Refer to the CDC guidelines for the use of Personal Protective Equipment to determine the appropriate PPE equipment to use.
3. Always practice safe work practices, which includes:
   a. Keep hands away from face.
   b. Work from clean to dirty.
   c. Limit surfaces touched.
   d. Change when torn or heavily contaminated.
   e. Perform hand hygiene.

PROCEDURE

NOTE: When using Personal Protective Equipment, don in the order the procedures are given. Prior to donning protective equipment:

   a. Remove your watch or push it well up your arm.
   b. Wash your hands.

Gown

1. Untie the gown's waist strings; then put the gown on and wrap it around the back of your uniform.
2. Tie or snap the gown at the neck and at the waist making sure your uniform is completely covered.

Mask

Surgical type masks are used to cover the nose and mouth and provide protection from contact with large infectious droplets (over 5 mm in size). For protection from inhalation of small particles or droplet nuclei particulate respirators are recommended. The health care worker must be fitted for these masks prior to use in order to maintain appropriate seal and protection. The infection control department staff will do fit testing for the employee during the employees orientation period.

1. Determine the appropriate type of face mask to be used.
2. Place the mask snugly over your nose and mouth. Secure the mask by tying the strings behind your head or placing the loops around your ears.
3. If the mask has a metal strip, squeeze it to fit your nose firmly.
4. If you wear eyeglasses, tuck the mask under their lower edge.

Goggles/Face Shield

Goggles or face shield should be worn when there is a risk of contaminating the mucous membranes of the eyes.

Mouthpieces, Resuscitation Bags, and Other Ventilation Devices

Use a ventilation device, which provides protection for the caregiver from oral contact and secretions, as alternative to mouth to mouth resuscitation.

Gloves

Gloves should be worn when there is risk of touching blood or body fluids. Gloves are worn only once and are discarded according to agency policy. Some care activities for an individual patient may require changing gloves more than once. Hands should be thoroughly washed after gloves are removed.

1. Use clean, disposable gloves.
2. Select a glove that provides appropriate fit.
3. Place the gloves on the hands so that they extend to cover the wrist of the isolation gown.

(continued)

Removing Personal Protective Equipment

Remember that the outside surfaces of your Personal Protective Equipment are contaminated.

1. While wearing gloves, untie the gowns waist strings.
2. With your gloved left hand, remove the right glove by pulling on the cuff, turning the glove inside out as you pull.
3. Remove the left glove by placing two fingers in the glove and pulling it off, turning it inside out as you remove it. Discard. Wash your hands.
4. Untie the neck strings of your gown. Grasp the outside of the gown at the back of the shoulders and pull the gown down over your arms, turning it inside out as you remove it.
5. Holding the gown well away from your uniform, fold it inside out. Discard it in the laundry hamper.
6. Wash your hands. Turn off the faucet using a paper towel and discard the towel in trash container.
7. Remove the mask/goggles to avoid contaminating your face or hair in the process. Untie your mask and/or remove your goggles by holding only the strings/strap. Discard.
8. Wash your hands and forearms with soap or antiseptic after leaving the room.

PROCEDURE 17.3 Caring for Soiled Linens

BACKGROUND: The hospital laundry uses water temperature and cleaning products capable of destroying any pathogens that might be present in patient's bed linens.

ALERT: Follow Standard Precautions.

PREPROCEDURE

1. Wash hands.
2. Don disposable gloves.

PROCEDURE

3. Fold the soiled bed linens inward upon themselves when removing them from the bed.
4. Hold the linens away from your uniform when removing from room.
5. Place in the nearest hamper.

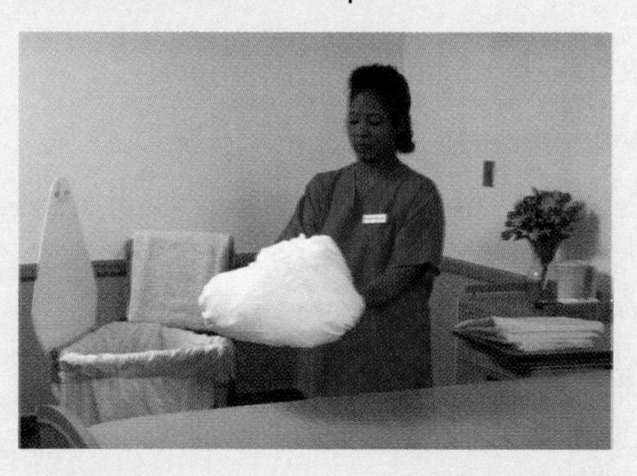

6. Should the outside surface of the linen hamper bag become soiled it should be placed in a clean outer bag prior to pickup by the laundry staff.

PROCEDURE 17.4 Disposing of Sharps

BACKGROUND: Because of the danger inherent in handling sharp objects or contaminated needles the health care industry has moved towards needleless systems whenever possible. When a needleless system cannot be provided, needles with have a protective sheath used to cover before and after use. There is no longer any need to recap used needles.

ALERT: Follow Standard Precautions.

PREPROCEDURE

1. Select the safest method of using sharps, using a needleless system whenever possible.
2. Wash hands.
3. Don disposable gloves.
4. Locate the closest sharps container to the area you will be working in.

NOTE: Gloves are not meant to protect the care giver from needle stick or sharps injuries.

PROCEDURE

5. After the use of any needle place the protective sheath before leaving the patient area.
6. If sharps are used during a procedure, carefully separate them from other items on the tray and cover them with the procedure tray cover.
7. Place any disposable sharps items in the closest sharps container.
8. For non-disposablê sharps items place them in the designated area of the closest dirty utility room.
9. Remove and discard disposable gloves.
10. Wash hands.

PROCEDURE 17.5 Wrapping Instruments for Autoclave

BACKGROUND: Reusable items used for providing patient care must be cleaned and sterilized before re-use. This requires that the item be cleaned and appropriately wrapped prior to being sterilized. This will include instruments, basins, glassware, patient care equipment, and any other items deemed necessary. The facility will provide an area, known as the Decontamination Room, for this activity.

ALERT: Follow Standard Precautions.

PREPROCEDURE

1. Retrieve/receive instruments and equipment to be decontaminated.
2. Don appropriate attire:
   a. scrub uniform
   b. head cover
   c. cover gown
   d. gloves
   e. goggles and/or face mask

PROCEDURE

3. Sort grossly soiled instruments from those less soiled.
4. Soak instruments that have gross soil in approved enzymatic hospital cleaner. If manual scrubbing is necessary, a soft bristled brush will be used below the water line to decrease the possibility of aerosol contamination.

(continued)

5. Place instruments with moving parts or hard to reach areas in Sonic Cleaner in open position for cycle. All large surface instruments, retractors and elevators will be cleaned manually.
6. Rinse all instruments, washed mechanically or manually, in standing tap water, and running tap water.
7. Immerse instruments with moving parts in instrument lubricant for 45 seconds.
8. Wash instrument trays, washbasins, and rubber items in warm water.
9. Rinse items in standing tap water and running tap water, and dry before wrapping.
10. Wash glassware, such as syringes, in warm water and appropriate cleaner. Rinse in standing, running tap water, and distilled water.
11 Air-dry syringes before preparing for sterilization.
12. After the cleaning process, move all instruments to the assembly table in the clean processing room.
13. Assemble, using the appropriate item list for each tray. Note any shortages and try to locate any missing instruments.
14. Make note of any sets with missing instruments.
15. Place tray with items onto designated wrapper. Fold each side of the wrapper in towards the middle. Secure the wrapper with autoclave tape.

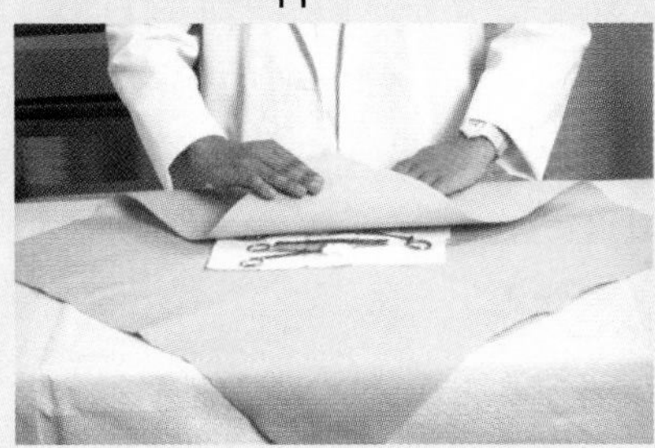

(a)

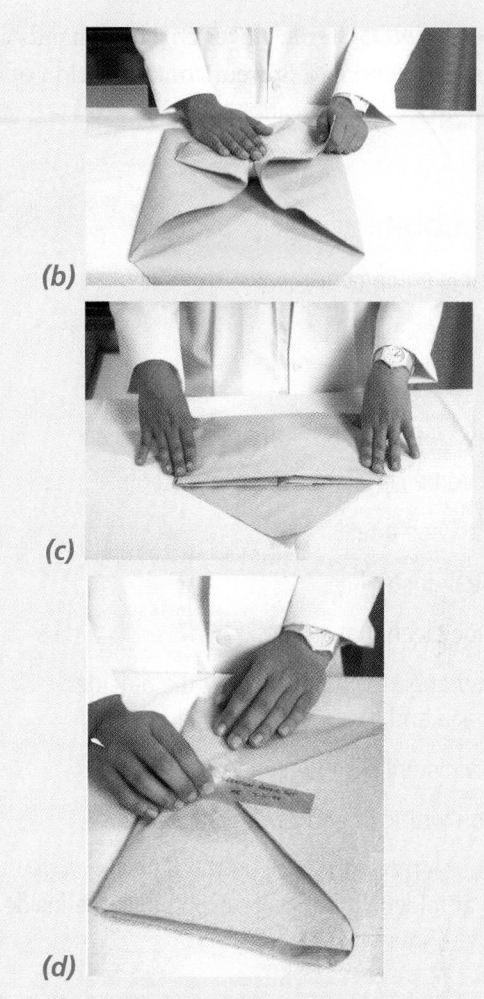

(b)

(c)

(d)

16. Notify autoclave personnel of trays, items when readied for sterilizing.

POSTPROCEDURE

17. Personnel are responsible for maintaining a clean area.
18. Hand washing is mandatory prior to leaving the area.

PROCEDURE 17.6 Putting on Sterile Gloves and Removing Gloves

BACKGROUND: Sterile gloves cover the hands and allow treatment of open skin areas. Following the procedure is essential to prevent contamination of the gloves. Contamination allows bacteria to enter the treatment area and may cause infection.

PREPROCEDURE

1. Assemble equipment.
2. Wash hands.

PROCEDURE

3. Pick up wrapped gloves.
4. Check to be certain that they are sterile.
   a. Package intact
   b. Seal of sterility
5. Place on clean, flat surface.
6. Open wrapper by handling only the outside. (Figures a and b).
7. Maintain sterility of wrap and gloves.
8. Position with cuff end toward self.
9. Use your left hand to pick up the right-handed glove at folded cuff edge, touching only the inside of glove (Figure c).

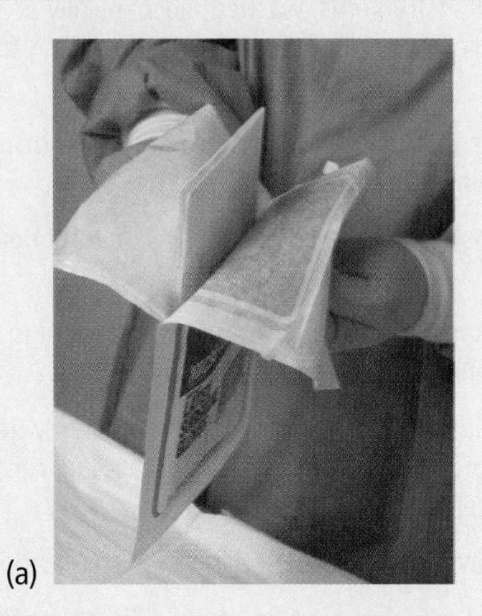

(a)

10. Grasp inside of glove with thumb and forefinger.
11. Lift glove out and insert other hand.
12. Put on glove while maintaining sterility.
13. Put glove on right hand (Figure d).

(continued)

PROCEDURE 17.6 Putting on Sterile Gloves and Removing Gloves (continued)

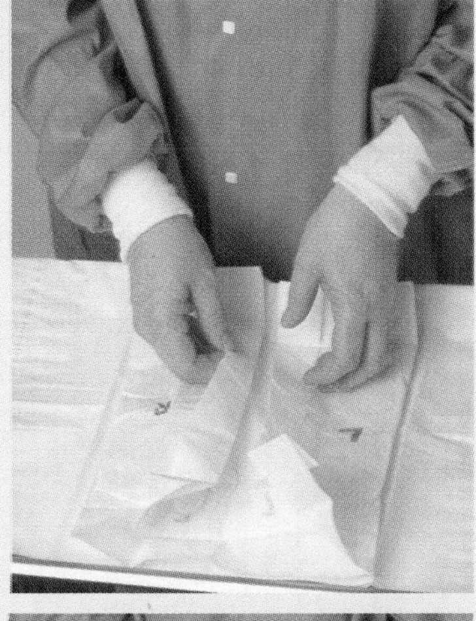

(b)

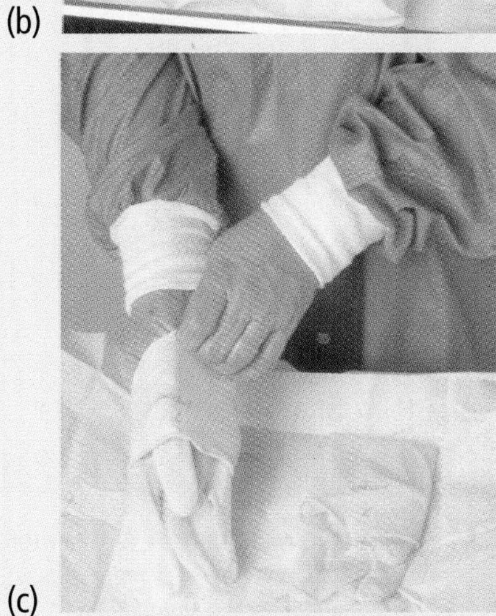

(c)

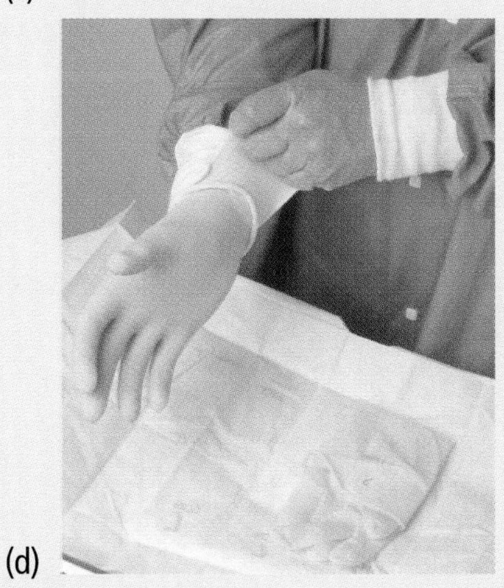

(d)

14. Use gloved right hand to pick up left-handed glove (Figures e–f).
15. Place finger of gloved right hand under cuff of left-handed glove.

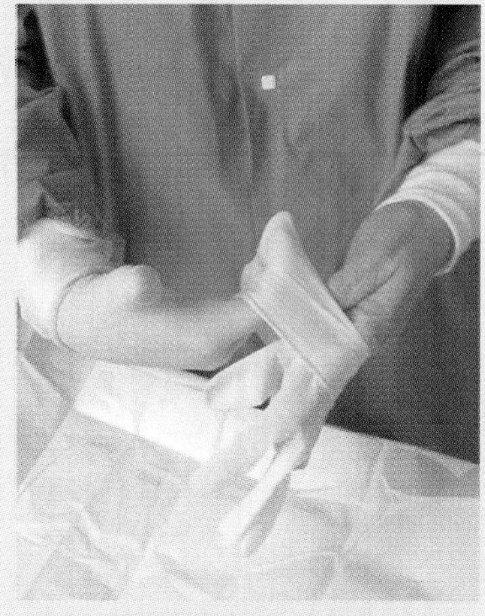

(e)

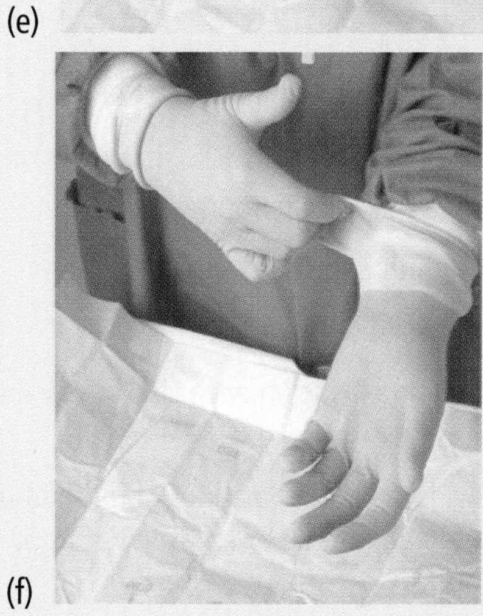

(f)

16. Lift glove up and away from wrapper to pull onto left hand.
17. Continue pulling left glove under wrist. (Be certain that gloved right thumb does not touch skin or clothing.)
18. Place fingers under cuff of right glove and pull cuff up over right wrist with gloved left hand.
19. Adjust fingers of gloves as necessary.
20. Keep hands in view and above waist one sterile gloves are on.
21. If either glove tears, remove and discard. Begin with new gloves!

POSTPROCEDURE

22. Turn gloves inside out as you remove them.

PROCEDURE 17.7 Transmission-Based Precautions: Applying Personal Protective Equipment

BACKGROUND: A primary responsibility of all health care workers is to prevent the spread of pathogenic microorganisms. Wearing appropriate protective equipment is one way health care workers can protect themselves and others from being infected by pathogenic microorganisms.

ALERT: Follow Standard Precautions

PREPROCEDURE

1. Assemble equipment.
2. Wash hands.

PROCEDURE

3. Cover all hair on head with a paper cap.
4. Put on a mask by:
    a. Unfolding mask if appropriate.
    b. Cover mouth and nose with mask.
    c. Secure mask by:
        (1) Pulling elastic on each side of mask over ear, or
        (2) Tying top string at sides of mask at back of head and tie lower string at back of neck.

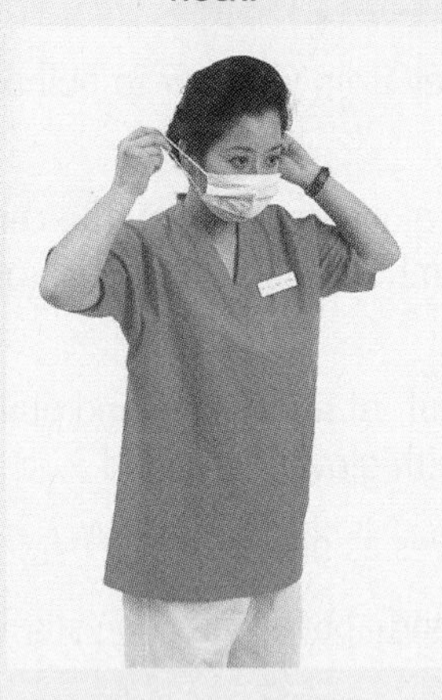

5. Put on gown with opening at back. Slip arms into sleeves of gown.

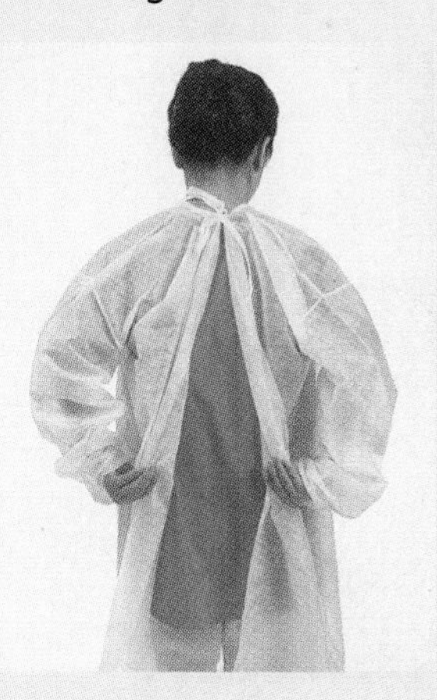

    a. Tie bow at back of neck.
    b. Overlap gown edges.
    c. Tie at waist with bow or fasten with Velcro strip.
    d. Make sure that uniform is completely covered.

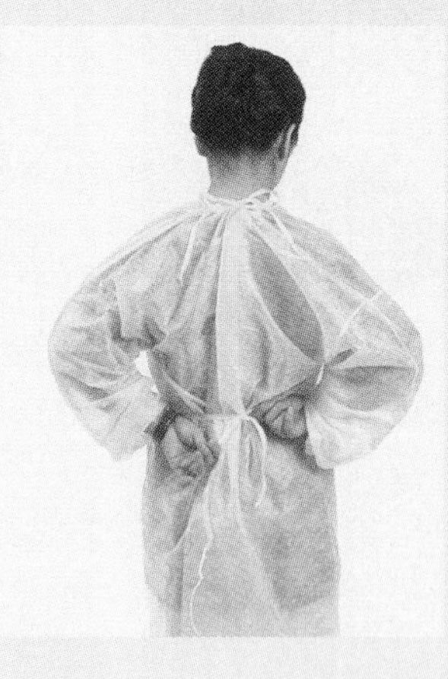

PROCEDURE 17.8

Transmission-Based Precautions: Removing Personal Protective Equipment

BACKGROUND: A primary responsibility of all health care workers is to prevent the spread of pathogenic microorganisms. Removing and disposing of protective equipment appropriately is one way health care workers prevent the spread of pathogenic microorganisms.

ALERT: Follow Standard Precautions

PREPROCEDURE

1. Untie waist tie of gown.

PROCEDURE

2. Remove gloves by:
   a. With dominant hand, remove other glove by grasping it just below wrist.
   b. Pulling the first glove inside out as you remove it from hand.
   c. With first two fingers of ungloved hand, reach inside glove without touching outside of glove —pull glove off hand covering the first glove. (The second glove removed surrounds the first and both are inside out.) Discard.
3. Wash hands.
4. Untie gown at neck.
5. Remove gown by:
   a. Crossing arms and grasping shoulder of gown with each hand.
   b. Pull gown forward causing it to fold inside out.
   c. Roll gown so that all contaminated portions are inside of roll, and place in dirty hamper marked *Toxic Waste or Hazardous Waste* inside room.
6. Wash hands.
7. Remove cap and mask, and discard.

POSTPROCEDURE

8. Use paper towel to open door.

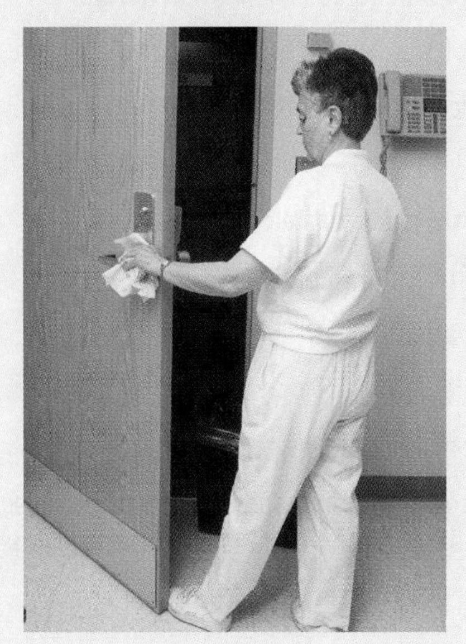

9. Discard towel inside room.
10. Wash hands immediately after leaving the room.

PROCEDURE 17.9 Changing a Sterile Dressing

BACKGROUND: Proper technique in changing a sterile dressing prevents wound infection and contamination to the health care worker.

ALERT: Follow Standard Precautions.

PREPROCEDURE

1. Wash hands.
2. Assemble supplies.
    a. Pair of nonsterile examination gloves
    b. Pair of sterile examination gloves
    c. Sterile dressing material
    d. Tape
    e. Biohazardous waste container
3. Explain procedure to patient.
4. Position patient/client.

PROCEDURE

5. Put on nonsterile gloves.
6. Remove soiled dressing and examination gloves. Note appearance of wound (size, color, drainage).
7. Discard in biohazardous waste container.
8. Wash hands.
9. Designate a site to be used as a sterile field.
    a. Place sterile drape on site.
    b. Open and place all sterile dressing supplies on sterile field.
    c. Pour wound-cleaning solution or antiseptic into sterile container.
10. Put on sterile gloves.
11. Medicate wound as directed by physician.
12. Apply a double layer of gauze to wound or incision.

NOTE: If moderate to heavy drainage is expected, reinforce dressing. If drainage seeps through to outer layer, wound will be contaminated.

POSTPROCEDURE

13. Remove gloves and place in biohazardous waste container.
14. Wash hands.
15. Secure dressing with tape.
16. Document the following:
    a. Date
    b. Time
    c. Type of dressing applied
    d. Appearance of wound
    e. Your name and certification

PROCEDURE 18.1 Using an Electronic Thermometer

BACKGROUND: There are many different kinds of thermometers. The electronic thermometer is the most commonly used in the hospital setting. If another kind of thermometer is used please refer to the procedure manual provided by the facility. This procedure explains how to use an electronic thermometer to measure body temperature. When you use an electronic thermometer, it is very important to check to see that the batteries are charged. A low battery can cause an inaccurate temperature reading.

ALERT: Follow Standard Precautions. Also, for this and all Procedures involving patient movement, see Section 21.4 for information on proper body mechanics.

PREPROCEDURE

1. Wash hand (follow hand-washing guidelines).
2. Assemble equipment:*
   a. Plastic thermometer cover/sheath
   b. Electronic thermometer with appropriate probe (blue for oral and axillary; red for rectal)
3. Identify patient. Pull privacy curtain or close the door to provide for the patient's privacy.
4. Explain procedure to patient.
5. Need to ask the patient if they have had anything to eat, drink or smoke in the last 15 minutes. If they have, you need to wait 15 minutes to take an oral temperature.

PROCEDURE

6. Place plastic thermometer cover over probe to prevent contamination.
7. Insert probe in proper position to measure body temperature (blue-tipped probe under tongue or in axilla; red-tipped probe in rectum). If taking axillary temperature, need to hold arm down.
8. Hold probe in place until thermometer indicates reading is complete.

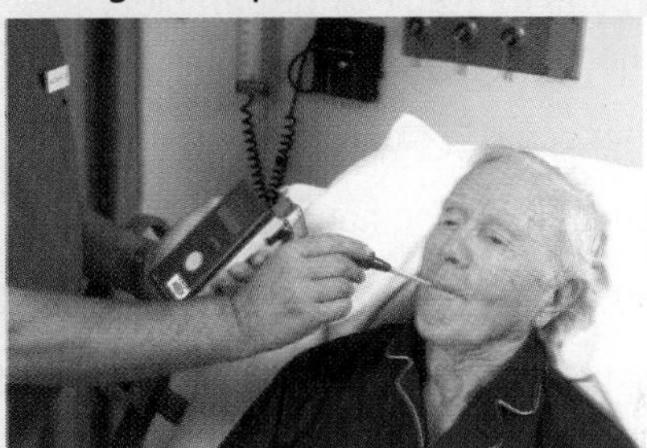

9. Remove plastic sheath and discard it into a biohazardous waste container.

POSTPROCEDURE

10. Record temperature. Health care professionals will record a patient's temperature on their chart. Report elevated temperature to a supervisor.
11. Position patient for comfort. Open curtain or door.
12. Wash hands (follow hand-washing guidelines).
13. Return electronic thermometer to its storage place.
14. Report any unusual observation immediately.

12/15/11	1900
	T– 97.4°F Ⓡ
	________ S. Jones CNA

* **Wear gloves when measuring rectal temperatures. Follow facility policy for measuring oral temperature.**

PROCEDURE 18.2 Measuring an Oral Temperature Using a Mercury or Nonmercury Thermometer

BACKGROUND: This procedure explains how to measure temperature with an oral probe.

ALERT: Follow Standard Precautions.

PREPROCEDURE

1. Wash hands (follow hand-washing guidelines).
2. Assemble equipment:*
   a. Clean oral (reusable or disposable) thermometer
   b. Alcohol wipes
   c. Watch with second hand
   d. Disposable thermometer cover
3. Identify patient and preferred route to be used. Pull privacy curtain or close door.
4. Explain procedure to patient.

PROCEDURE

5. Apply disposable probe cover.
6. Ask patient whether he or she has been smoking, eating, or drinking. If the answer is yes, wait 15 minutes before taking temperature.
7. Place thermometer under tongue and to the side of the mouth.
8. Instruct patient to hold thermometer with closed lips. You might need to help the patient hold the thermometer.
9. Leave in mouth until thermometer indicates reading is complete.
10. Remove from mouth.
11. Remove and discard disposable cover in a biohazardus waste container.
12. Note thermometer reading correctly.
13. Open curtain or door.

*** Follow facility policy for wearing gloves.**

POSTPROCEDURE

14. Wash thermometer in cool water and dry. Discard thermometer if it is disposable.
15. Wash hands (follow hand-washing guidelines).
16. Record temperature correctly on pad.
17. Report any unusual observation immediately.

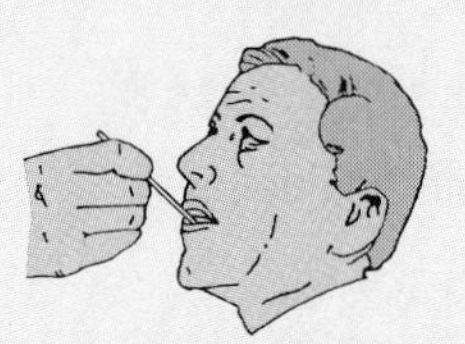
A Insert the thermometer gently into the client's mouth under the tongue.

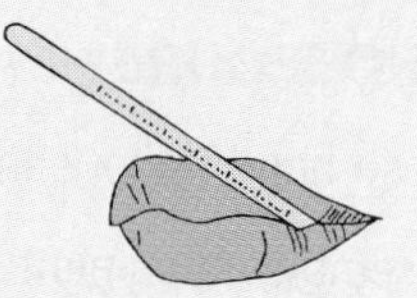
B Position the thermometer to the side of the mouth.

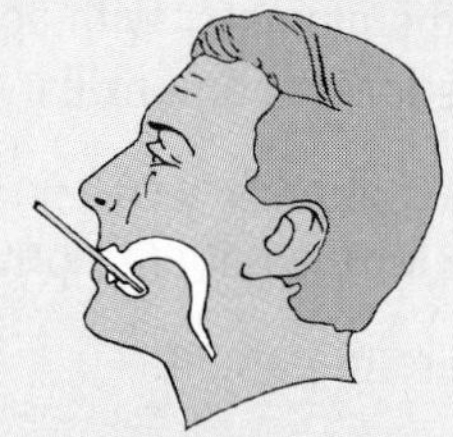
C Instruct the client to keep the thermometer under the tongue by gently closing the lips around the thermometer.

12/03/11	1600
	T– 99.6°F (R)
	________ S. Jones CNA

PROCEDURE 18.3

Measuring a Rectal Temperature

BACKGROUND: This procedure explains how to measure a temperature using a rectal thermometer probe.

CAUTION: Do not take a rectal temperature if a patient has had recent rectal surgery, rectal injury, or has had recent treatment that causes body tissues to become thin and fragile. For example, do not take a rectal temperature on a patient who has been undergoing chemotherapy or radiation or has been taking steroids. Rectal temperatures can also be dangerous for people with heart disease because the thermometer can stimulate the vagus nerve in the rectum which can slow down the heart rate.

ALERT: Follow Standard Precautions.

PREPROCEDURE

1. Wash hands (follow hand-washing guidelines).
2. Assemble equipment:
   a. Clean rectal (reusable or disposable) thermometer
   b. Alcohol wipes
   c. Watch with second hand
   d. Lubricant
   e. Disposable nonsterile gloves
   f. Disposable thermometer cover
3. Identify patient and preferred route to be used.
4. Explain procedure to patient. Pull privacy curtain or close the door.
5. Put on disposable gloves.

PROCEDURE

6. Remove thermometer from container and apply disposable cover.
7. Lower backrest on bed. Have patient lie on their left side with right leg bent at the knees.
8. Apply lubricant to probe end.
9. Separate buttocks by pulling up on upper buttock.
10. Insert thermometer 1.5 inches into rectum, or 1 to 1.2 inch for an infant. Do not force thermometer.
11. Hold in place until thermometer indicates reading is complete.
12. Remove thermometer. Wipe anal area to remove excess lubricant and any feces. Cover the patient.
13. Remove and discard disposable cover in a biohazardous waste container.
14. Read thermometer correctly. Open curtain or door.

POSTPROCEDURE

15. Clean equipment and return to appropriate storage place.
16. Remove and discard disposable gloves.
17. Wash hands.
18. Record temperature correctly. Remember to indicate that it is a rectal temperature with an R.
19. Report any unusual observation immediately.

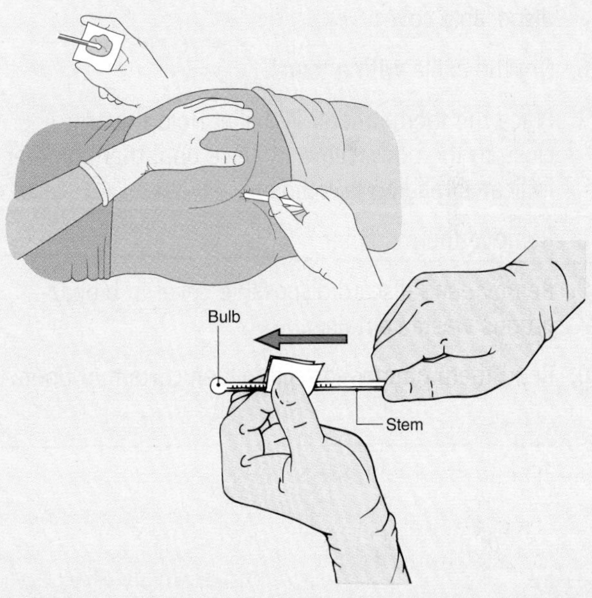

12/14/11 1500
T– 99.2°F (R)
J. Gonzalez CNA

PROCEDURE 18.4 Measuring an Axillary Temperature

BACKGROUND: This procedure explains how to measure a temperature using an axillary probe.

ALERT: Follow Standard Precautions.

PREPROCEDURE

1. Wash hands (follow hand-washing procedure).
2. Assemble equipment:
   a. Clean reusable or disposable thermometer
   b. Alcohol wipes
   c. Watch with second hand
   d. Disposable thermometer cover
3. Identify patient and preferred route to be used. Pull privacy curtain or close the door.
4. Explain procedure to patient.

PROCEDURE

5. Remove thermometer from container and apply disposable cover.
6. Dry the axilla with a towel.
7. Place the thermometer in axilla. Hold the arm close to the body. Leave in place until thermometer indicates reading is complete.
8. Remove thermometer.
9. Remove and discard disposable cover in biohazardous waste container.
10. Read thermometer correctly. Open curtain or door.

POSTPROCEDURE

11. Clean equipment and return to appropriate storage space.
12. Wash hands (follow hand-washing guidelines).
13. Record temperature correctly. You must indicate it was an axillary temperature.
14. Report any unusual observation immediately.

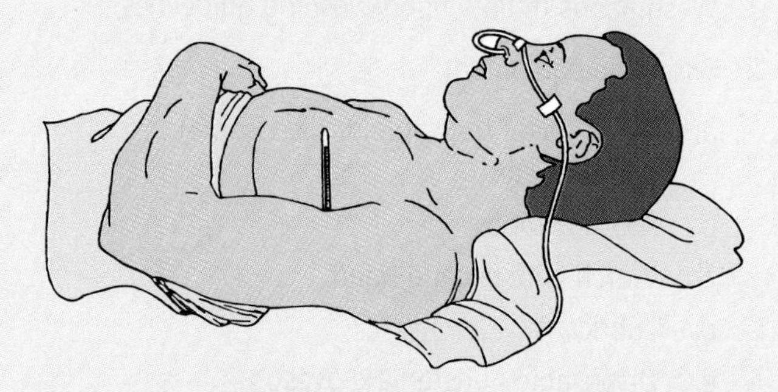

6/14/12 0400
T– 97°F AX
——— H. Ferguson RMA

PROCEDURE 18.5

Measuring an Aural (or Tympanic) Temperature

BACKGROUND: The human body has a homeostatic mechanism that regulates all systems and maintains normal function. One of the body's homeostatic mechanisms is the control of body temperature. Body temperature is the balance between heat production and heat loss.

The hypothalamus is the main regulator of body temperature. Factors such as loss of skin integrity with an extensive burn, exposure to extreme weather conditions, disease states such as tumors or strokes involving the hypothalamus can affect our ability to maintain normal body temperature. An elevated temperature, pyrexia, is a protective mechanism for the body, believed to aid the body in fighting disease.

The elderly patient may have difficulty maintaining homeostasis. For that reason an elevated temperature may not be their first sign of infection. The pediatric patient has greater variation in temperature control and may respond to a disease state with a more elevated degree of pyrexia.

ALERT: Follow Standard Precautions.

PREPROCEDURE

1. Determine the device to be used for measuring the patient's temperature. Special devices are available for use in the outer ear canal.

Note: While the use of an aural (tympanic) thermometer has proven easiest for use in the pediatric patient, research is still in progress to determine its reliability.

2. Review the patient's graphic record to determine baseline temperature and any recent alterations from baseline.

PROCEDURE

3. Wash hands.
4. Explain procedure to patient.
5. Gently pull the ear straight back for children under age 1, or up and back for age 1 or older. Insert the covered probe gently but firmly into the external ear.
6. Activate the device.
7. Note the temperature reading.
8. Remove the device and discard the probe cover in a biohazardous waste container.

POSTPROCEDURE

9. Assure that the patient is comfortable and has no further needs before leaving the area.
10. Record the reading on the designated form. Remember to indicate that this was an aural route.
11. Note if the temperature is elevated. Compare the reading with previous temperature readings.
12. If temperature is elevated, communicate that information to the nurse in charge of the patient's care.

PROCEDURE 18.6 Counting a Radial Pulse

BACKGROUND: It is important for health care workers to monitor the patient's physical status. One way to determine this status is by counting the patient's pulse rate. This procedure explains how to count a radial pulse.

ALERT: Follow Standard Precautions.

PREPROCEDURE

1. Wash hands (follow hand-washing guidelines).
2. Assemble equipment:
   a. Watch with second hand
   b. Pad and pencil
3. Identify patient. Pull privacy curtain or close the door.
4. Explain procedure to patient.

PROCEDURE

5. Place three fingers on the radial artery—do not use thumb.
6. Count pulse (number of beats or pulsations) for 1 minute.
7. Record pulse rate on pad immediately. Open curtain or door.

POSTPROCEDURE

8. Wash hands (follow hand-washing guidelines).
9. Record pulse rate on chart.
10. Immediately report any unusual observation. Examples include an irregular pulse, a bounding or weak pulse, or a pulse rate less than 60 bpm or more than 100 bpm.

NOTE: If the pulse is difficult to assess, irregular, weak, or rapid, the apical rate should be assessed.

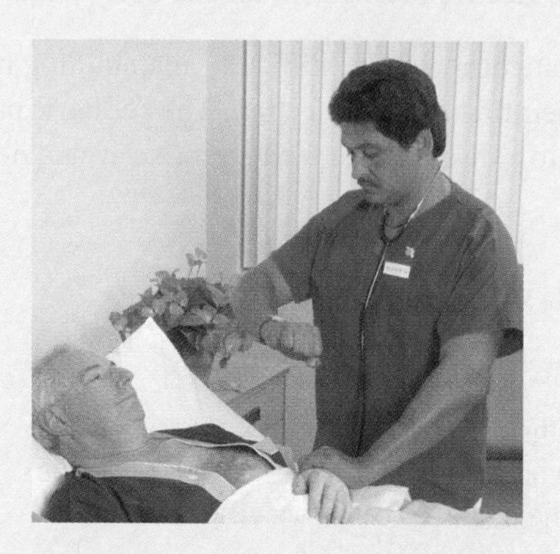

2/14/11	1300
	Pulse = 72
	Regular and strong
	________ T. Morales CNA

PROCEDURE 18.7 Counting an Apical Pulse

BACKGROUND: The apical pulse is assessed upon admission, when the peripheral pulse is difficult to assess, and also when giving medications that alter heart rate and rhythm, such as digoxin.

ALERT: Follow Standard Precautions.

PREPROCEDURE

1. Assemble equipment.
   a. Stethoscope
   b. Alcohol swabs
2. Wash hands (follow hand-washing guidelines).
3. Identify patient. Pull privacy curtain or close door.
4. Explain procedure to patient.

PROCEDURE

5. Uncover left side of patient's chest.
6. Locate the apex of the heart between the fifth and the sixth rib, about 3 inches to the left of the median line and slightly below the nipple.
7. Place stethoscope over apical region and listen for heart sounds. The apical rate of an infant is easily palpated with the fingertips.
8. Count the beats for 1 minute; note rate, rhythm, and strength of beat.
9. Cover patient. Open the curtain or door.
10. Record pulse rate on pad.

POSTPROCEDURE

11. Wash hands (follow hand-washing guidelines).
12. Record apical pulse rate on chart. Remember to indicate that it was an apical pulse.
13. Report any unusual observation immediately.

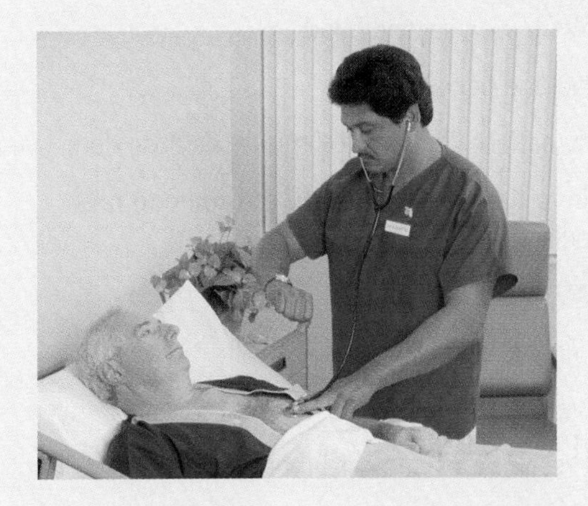

12/14/11	1000
	82 / 78 AP
	Pulse deficit = 4
	Quality of beat strong
	________ S. Padlewski RMA

PROCEDURE **18.8**

Counting Respirations

BACKGROUND: It is important for health care workers to monitor the patient's physical status. One way to determine this status is by counting the patient's respiratory rate. This procedure explains how to count the number of times a patient breathes in a minute.

ALERT: Follow Standard Precautions.

PREPROCEDURE

1. Wash hands (follow hand-washing guidelines).
2. Assemble equipment.
   a. Watch with second hand.
   b. Pad and pencil.
3. Identify patient. Pull privacy curtain or close door.
4. Explain to the patient that you are going to take their pulse.

PROCEDURE

5. Relax fingers on pulse point.
6. Observe rise and fall of chest.
7. Count respirations and calculate rate.
8. Note rate, rhythm, and quality of respirations.

POSTPROCEDURE

9. Open curtain or close door.
10. Wash hands (follow hand-washing guidelines).
11. Record the respiratory rate accurately. Make sure you take it for 30 seconds and multiply times two. If respirations are irregular, take for one full minute.
12. Report any unusual observation immediately. This could include irregular respiration, noisy breathing, and pain with or difficulty breathing.

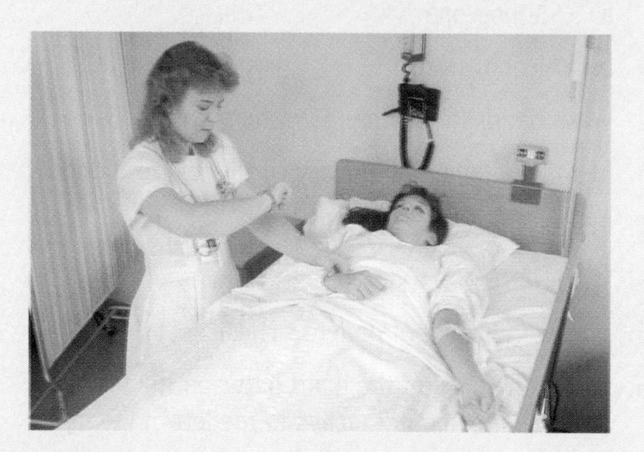

5/22/12 0930
Resp. 20 and regular
M. Taylor CNA

PROCEDURE 18.9 Palpating a Blood Pressure

BACKGROUND: As a health care worker, it is important to monitor the patient's physical status. One way to determine this status is by measuring the patient's blood pressure. This procedure explains how to palpate a blood pressure so you will know how high to inflate the blood pressure cuff.

ALERT: Follow Standard Precautions.

PREPROCEDURE

1. Wash hands (follow hand-washing guidelines).
2. Explain procedure to patient. Pull privacy curtain or close door.

PROCEDURE

3. Select the appropriate cuff for your patient. A cuff that is too small may cause a false-high reading and a cuff that is too large may cause a false-low reading.
4. Support patient's arm, palm side up, on a firm surface.
5. Roll up patient's sleeve above elbow, being careful that it is not too tight.
6. Wrap wide part of cuff around patient's arm directly over brachial artery. Most cuffs have an arrow to position over the brachial artery. The lower edge of cuff should be 1 or 2 inches above bend of elbow.
7. Find radial pulse with your fingertips.

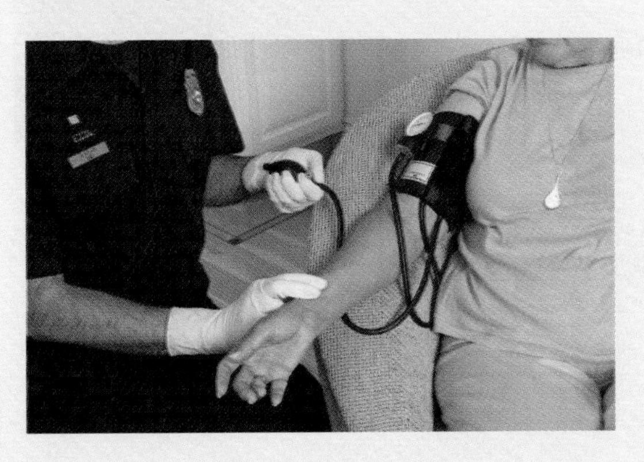

8. Inflate cuff until you can no longer feel radial pulse. Continue to inflate another 30 mm of mercury.
9. Open valve and slowly deflate cuff until you feel the first beat of radial pulse again.
10. Observe mercury or dial reading. This is the placatory systolic pressure. It is recorded, for example, as B/P 130 (P).
11. Deflate cuff rapidly and squeeze out all the air.
12. Using your first and second fingers, locate brachial artery. You will feel it pulsating. Place bell or diaphragm of stethoscope directly over artery. You will not hear the pulsation. Do not hold the stethoscope in place with your thumb.
13. Tighten thumbscrew of valve to close it. Turn to the left.
14. Hold stethoscope in place and inflate cuff until the dial points to about 30 mm above the palpated B/P.
15. Open valve counterclockwise. Let air out slowly until you hear first beat.
16. At this first sound, note reading on sphygmomanometer. This is the systolic pressure.
17. Continue to release air slowly. Note number on the indicator at which you hear last beat or the sound changes to a dull beat. This is the diastolic pressure.
18. Open valve and release all the air.
19. Remove cuff. Open curtain or door.

POSTPROCEDURE

20. Record time and blood pressure.
21. Clean stethoscope—earpieces and diaphragm.
22. Wash hands.
23. Report any unusual observation immediately.

PROCEDURE **18.10** **Measuring Blood Pressure**

BACKGROUND: As a health care worker, it is important to monitor the patient's physical status. One way to determine this status is by measuring the patient's blood pressure. This procedure explains how to determine the patient's systolic (highest pressure) and diastolic (lowest pressure) blood pressure.

ALERT: Follow Standard Precautions.

PREPROCEDURE

1. Wash hands (follow hand-washing guidelines).
2. Assemble equipment:
   a. Alcohol wipes
   b. Sphygmomanometer
   c. Stethoscope
   d. Pad and pencil
3. Identify patient. Pull privacy curtain or close the door.
4. Explain procedure to patient.

PROCEDURE

5. Delay obtaining the blood pressure if the patient is in acute pain, has just exercised, or is emotionally upset, unless there is an urgent reason to obtain a blood pressure reading.
6. Select the appropriate arm for application of the cuff. Limbs that have an intravenous infusion, breast or axillary surgery on that side, arteriovenous shunt, or are injured or diseased should not be used.
7. Apply cuff correctly. This should be about one inch above the anticubital space. (Refer to steps 4 and 5 in Procedure 18.9 "Palpating a Blood Pressure".)
8. Clean earpieces on stethoscope.
9. Place earpieces in ears.
10. Locate brachial artery. Place stethoscope over it.
11. Tighten thumbscrew on valve. (Remember the two clues: righty tighty and lefty loosey.)
12. Hold stethoscope in place. Do not use your thumb.
13. Inflate cuff to 170 mm.
14. Open valve. If systolic sound is heard immediately, reinflate cuff to 30 mm mercury above systolic sound.
15. Note systolic at first beat.
16. Note diastolic.
17. Open valve and release air.
18. Record time and blood pressure reading correctly on pad. Open curtain or door.

POSTPROCEDURE

19. Wash hands.
20. Wash earpieces on stethoscope.
21. Put away equipment.
22. Record blood pressure in chart.
23. Report any unusual observation immediately.

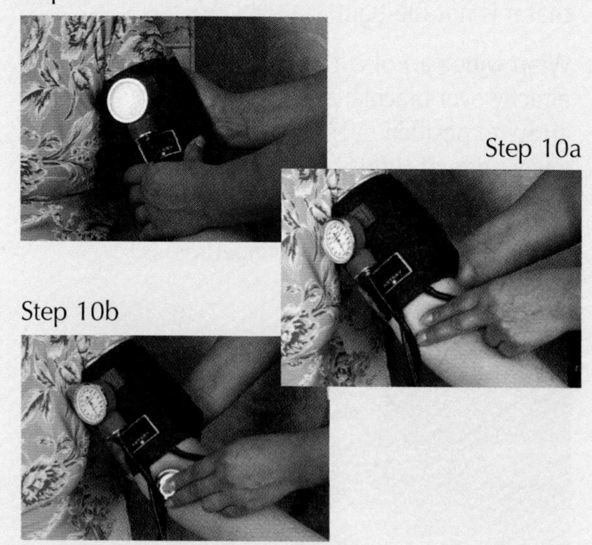

Step 7

Step 10a

Step 10b

7/29/11	0900
	B/P 134/88
	left arm, sitting
	________ R. Martin CNA

PROCEDURE 18.11 AM Care

BACKGROUND: AM care refreshes the patient. Clean teeth, clean hands, morning elimination, and other comfort measures help improve appetite and enjoyment of breakfast.

ALERT: Follow Standard Precautions.

PREPROCEDURE

1. Wash hands.
2. Gently awaken patient.
3. Assemble equipment:
   a. Washcloth and towel
   b. Toothbrush and toothpaste
   c. Emesis basin
   d. Glass of water
   e. Denture cup if needed
   f. Clean gown if necessary
   g. Clean linen if necessary
   h. Comb and brush
   i. Disposable gloves (two pair)
4. Explain what you plan to do.
5. Provide privacy by pulling privacy curtain.
6. Elevate head of the bed if allowed.
7. Put on disposable gloves.

PROCEDURE

8. Provide a bedpan or urinal if needed, or escort patient to bathroom.
9. Empty bedpan or urinal, rinse it, and dispose of gloves.
10 Put bedpan or urinal out of sight.
11. Allow patient to wash hands and face.
12. Put on disposable gloves.
13. Assist with oral hygiene.
14. Provide a clean gown if necessary.
15. Smooth sheets if patient remains in bed.
16. Transfer to a chair if patient is allowed out of bed.
17. Allow patient to comb hair; assist if necessary.
18. Prepare the overbed table.
    a. Clear tabletop.
    b. Wipe off.
19. Position overbed table and make sure call bell is within reach if patient is to remain in the room, or transport patient to dining room.

POSTPROCEDURE

20. Remove and discard gloves.
21. Wash hands.

10/06/11	*0630*
	AM care given
	Patient looking forward to breakfast
	No complaints
	________ *S. Gomez CNA*

PROCEDURE 18.12 PM Care

BACKGROUND: PM care refreshes, relaxes, and comforts a patient, providing a quiet time before sleep.

ALERT: Follow Standard Precautions.

PREPROCEDURE

1. Wash hands.
2. Tell patient what you are going to do.
3. Provide privacy.
4. Assemble equipment:
   a. Washcloth and towel
   b. Toothpaste and toothbrush
   c. Glass of water
   d. Emesis basin
   e. Denture cup, if necessary
   f. Night clothes
   g. Lotion
   h. Linen as needed
   i. Disposable gloves

PROCEDURE

5. Encourage patient to do his or her own care if capable.
6. Assist if unable to do his or her own care.
7. Put on disposable gloves.
8. Provide bedpan or urinal if necessary, or escort to bathroom.

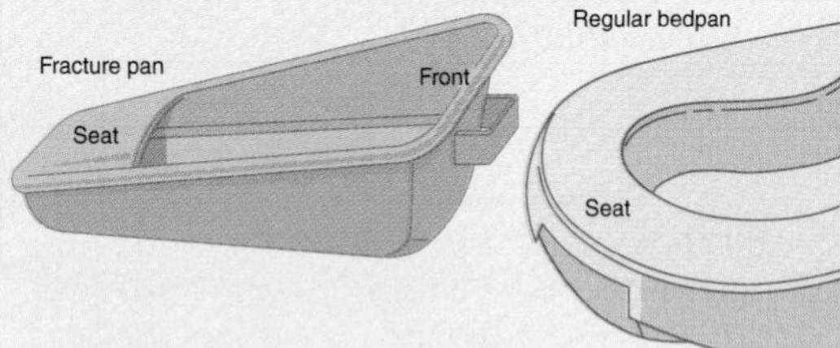

9. Empty bedpan or urinal.
10. Rinse and place in a convenient place for night-time use.
11. Remove and dispose of gloves.
12. Wash patient's hands and face.
13. Put on gloves.
14. Provide for oral hygiene.
15. Change gown, if soiled.

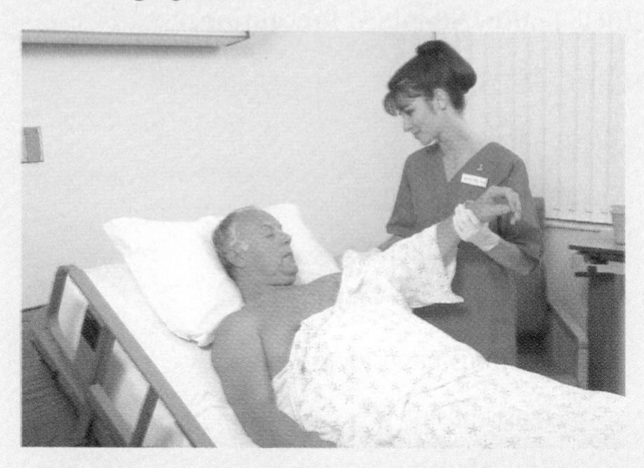

16. Transfer patient from chair or wheelchair into bed, if out of bed.
17. Give back rub with lotion.
18. Observe skin for irritations or breakdown.
19. Smooth the sheets.
20. Change draw sheets if necessary.
21. Provide extra blankets if necessary.
22. Position side rails as ordered after patient is in bed.

POSTPROCEDURE

23. Remove and discard gloves.
24. Wash hands.
25. Provide fresh drinking water.
26. Place bedside table within patient's reach.
27. Secure call light within patient's reach.

8/30/11	2045
	PM care given
	No complaints
	________ *S. Gomez CNA*

PROCEDURE **18.13**

Skin Care—Giving a Back Rub

BACKGROUND: Giving a back rub provides an opportunity to help the patient relax and to check for any skin changes. It is also a good time to listen to any complaints or concerns the patient might have.

CAUTION: Check with team leader for permission to give a back rub.

ALERT: Follow Standard Precautions.

PREPROCEDURE

1. Wash hands.
2. Assemble equipment:
   a. Lotion
   b. Powder
   c. Towel
   d. Washcloth
   e. Soap
   f. Water (105°F)
   g. Disposable gloves
3. Tell patient what you are going to do.
4. Provide privacy by pulling privacy curtains.

PROCEDURE

5. Place lotion container in warm water to help warm it.
6. Raise bed to a comfortable working height.
7. Lower side rail on the side you are working on.
8. Put on disposable gloves.
9. Position patient on side or in prone position.
10. Place a towel along back to protect linen if patient is in a side-lying position.
11. Wash back thoroughly.
12. Rub a small amount of lotion into your hands.
13. Begin at base of spine and apply lotion over entire back.
14. Use firm, long strokes, beginning at buttocks and moving upward to neck and shoulders.
15. Use firm pressure as you stroke upward, and light circular strokes returning to buttocks.

NOTE: Pay special attention to bony prominences.

16. Use a circular motion over each area (shoulder blades, backbone).

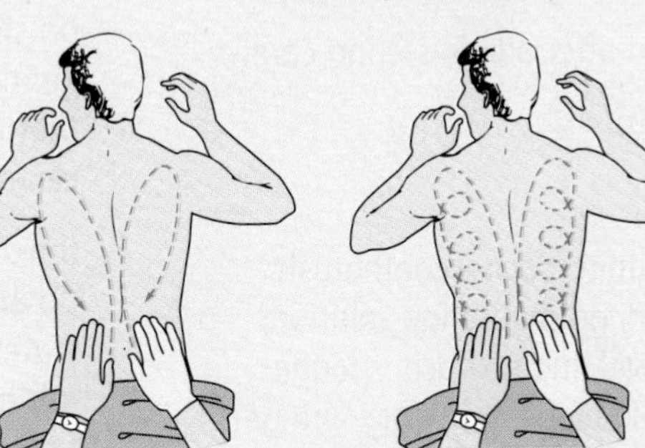

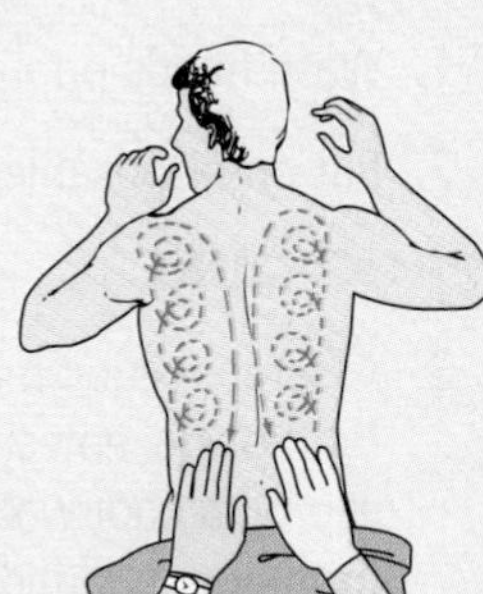

17. Observe skin for irritation or breakdown.

NOTE: Do not rub or apply lotion to any open area on the skin.

18. Repeat several times (3 to 5 minutes).
19. Dry back.
20. Adjust gown for comfort.
21. Remove towel.
22. Position patient comfortably.
23. Return bed to lowest height.
24. Put up side rail if required.
25. Secure call light in reach of patient.

POSTPROCEDURE

26. Remove and discard gloves.
27. Wash hands.
28. Record procedure and any observations (e.g., redness, broken areas, dry skin).

7/15/12	1350
	Back rub given
	No shin change noted
	Rails up
	——— *R. Johnson CNA*

PROCEDURE 18.14 Giving Special Mouth Care to the Unconscious Patient

BACKGROUND: The mouth must be cared for during illness. If the patient is helpless, the nurse needs to make certain the patient receives the care necessary to keep the mouth clean and moist, every 1 to 2 hours as necessary.

PREPROCEDURE

1. Wash hands prior to and after administering care.
2. Put on disposable gloves.

PROCEDURE

3. Assemble equipment within reach—toothbrush, toothpaste, emesis basin, normal saline solution, cup with cool water, towel, mouthwash, sponge toothette, padded tongue blade, irrigating syringe with rubber tip, petroleum jelly, suction catheter with suction apparatus.
4. Provide privacy for the patient. Adjust the height of the bed to a comfortable position for the nurse. Lower the side rail next to the nurse and position the patient on their side with the head of the bed lowered. Place the towel across the patient's chest and emesis basin in position under the chin.
5. Open the patient's mouth and gently insert a padded tongue blade between the back molars if necessary.

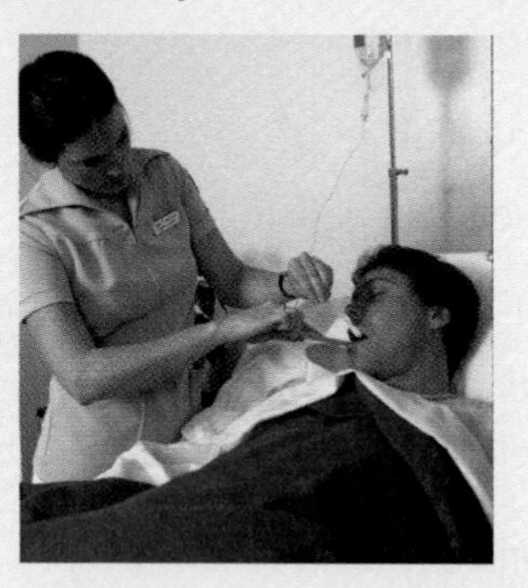

6. If teeth are present, brush carefully with toothbrush and paste. If dentures are present, remove gently and cleanse before replacing. Use a toothette moistened with normal saline to gently cleanse gums, mucous membranes, and tongue.
7. If necessary, use the irrigating syringe with rubber tip and rinse mouth gently with a small amount of water. Position the patient's head to allow for the return of water or use suction apparatus to remove the water from the oral cavity.
8. Apply petroleum jelly to the patient's lips.
9. Remove equipment and return the patient to a comfortable position. Raise the siderail and lower the bed.

POSTPROCEDURE

10. Document the nursing assistant's oral assessment and any unusual findings.

Some patients may have **dentures**. Often patients are sensitive about removing their dentures. Provide privacy and encouragement for oral care. Learn the correct method of handling dentures so that you do not break them.

PROCEDURE 18.15 Oral Hygiene—Self-Care

BACKGROUND: A clean mouth and clean teeth help prevent oral problems, freshen the breath, and give an overall feeling of well-being.

ALERT: Follow Standard Precautions.

PREPROCEDURE

1. Wash hands.
2. Assemble equipment:
   a. Toothbrush
   b. Toothpaste
   c. Mouthwash
   d. Cup of water with straw, if needed
   e. Emesis basin
   f. Bath towel
   g. Tissues
3. Identify patient and explain what you are going to do.
4. Screen patient by pulling privacy curtain around bed.

PROCEDURE

5. Raise head of the bed if patient is allowed to sit up.
6. Place towel over blanket and patient's gown.
7. Place toothbrush, toothpaste, mouthwash, emesis basin, and glass of water on overbed table.
8. Remove overbed table when patient has completed brushing.
9. Put away towel and make patient comfortable.
10. Put up side rails if required.
11. Secure call bell within patient's reach.
12. Put away all equipment and tidy unit.

POSTPROCEDURE

13. Wash hands.
14. Chart procedure.

6/14/11	0640
	Set up equipment on overbed table
	Brushed teeth without assistance
	________ *S. Gomez CNA*

PROCEDURE 18.16 Oral Hygiene—Brushing the Patient's Teeth

BACKGROUND: A clean mouth and clean teeth help prevent oral problems, freshen the breath, and give an overall feeling of well-being.

ALERT: Follow Standard Precautions.

PREPROCEDURE

1. Wash hands.
2. Assemble equipment:
   a. Toothbrush
   b. Toothpaste
   c. Mouthwash
   d. Cup of water with straw, if needed
   e. Emesis basin
   f. Bath towel
   g. Tissues
   h. Disposable nonsterile gloves
3. Identify patient and explain what you are going to do.
4. Screen patient by pulling privacy curtain around bed.

PROCEDURE

5. Raise head of bed if patient is allowed to sit up.
6. Place a towel over blanket and patient's gown.
7. Put on gloves.
8. Pour water over toothbrush; put toothpaste on brush.
9. Insert brush into the mouth carefully.
10. Place brush at an angle on upper teeth and brush in an up-and-down motion starting at rear of mouth.
11. Repeat on lower teeth
12. Give patient water to rinse mouth. If necessary, use a straw.
13. Hold emesis basin under chin. Have patient expectorate (spit) water into the basin.
14. Offer tissues to patient to wipe mouth and chin. Discard tissues.
15. Provide mouthwash if available. Use emesis basin and tissues as above.
16. Put up side rails before turning away from patient.
17. Return all equipment.
18. Remove gloves and put in hazardous waste.

POSTPROCEDURE

19. Wash hands.
20. Tidy up unit.
21. Secure call bell within patient's reach.
22. Make patient comfortable before leaving the room.
23. Chart procedure and how patient tolerated it.

5/14/12	0825
	Brushed teeth, provided oral hygiene
	Tolerated well
	No oral problems noted
	R. Johnson CNA

PROCEDURE 18.17 Oral Hygiene—Ambulatory Patient

BACKGROUND: A clean mouth and clean teeth help prevent oral problems, freshen the breath, and give an overall feeling of well-being.

ALERT: Follow Standard Precautions.

PREPROCEDURE

1. Wash hands.
2. Tell patient what you are going to do.

PROCEDURE

3. Set up equipment at sink.
   a. Toothbrush
   b. Toothpaste
   c. Tablets or powder to soak dentures in
   d. Towel
   e. Glass

POSTPROCEDURE

4. Rinse equipment and put away.
5. Wash hands.

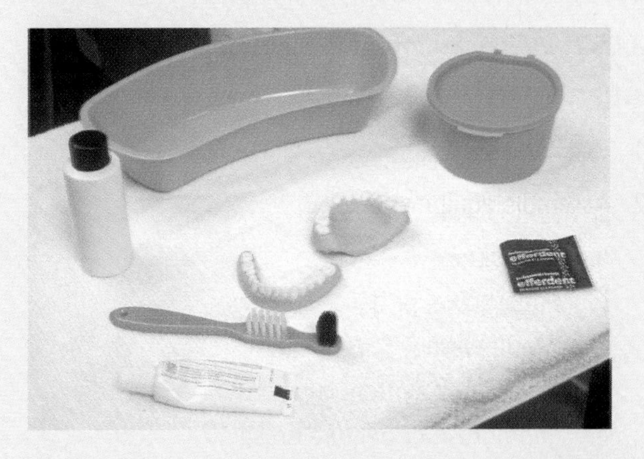

5/24/11 0745
Brushed teeth without assistance
________ S. Gomez CNA

PROCEDURE 18.18 Oral Hygiene—Denture Care

BACKGROUND: Food and bacteria collect under dentures causing discomfort due to tissue breakdown and mouth odor. Clean dentures protect against oral problems and refresh the mouth.

ALERT: Follow Standard Precautions.

PREPROCEDURE

1. Wash hands.
2. Assemble equipment:
   a. Tissues
   b. Paper towel or gauze squares
   c. Mouthwash
   d. Disposable denture cup
   e. Toothbrush or denture brush
   f. Denture paste or toothpowder
   g. Towel
   h. Disposable nonsterile gloves
   i. Emesis basin
3. Identify patient.
4. Explain what you are going to do.

PROCEDURE

5. Pull privacy curtain.
6. Lower side rails.
7. Raise head of bed if allowed.
8. Place towel across patient's chest.
9. Prepare emesis basin by placing tissue, paper towel or washcloth in bottom of basin.
10. Put on gloves.
11. Have patient remove his or her dentures.
12. Remove dentures if patient cannot.

    Upper Denture

    a. Explain what you are going to do.
    b. Use a gauze square to grip upper denture.
    c. Place your index finger between top ridge of denture and cheek.
    d. Gently pull on denture to release suction.
    e. Remove upper denture.

    Lower Denture

    a. Use a gauze square to grip lower denture.
    b. Place your index finger between lower ridge and cheek.
    c. Gently pull on denture to release suction.
    d. Remove lower denture.
13. Place dentures in lined emesis basin and take to sink or utility room.
14. Remember to pull side rails up if you walk away from the bed.
15. Hold dentures firmly in palm of hand.
16. Put toothpowder or toothpaste on toothbrush.
17. Rinse dentures in cool water.
18. Hold dentures under cold running water and brush dentures on all surfaces until clean.
19. Rinse dentures under cold running water.
20. Remember to rinse denture cup with cold water before placing clean dentures in the cup.
21. Place in denture cup.
22. Place some mouthwash and cool water in cup.

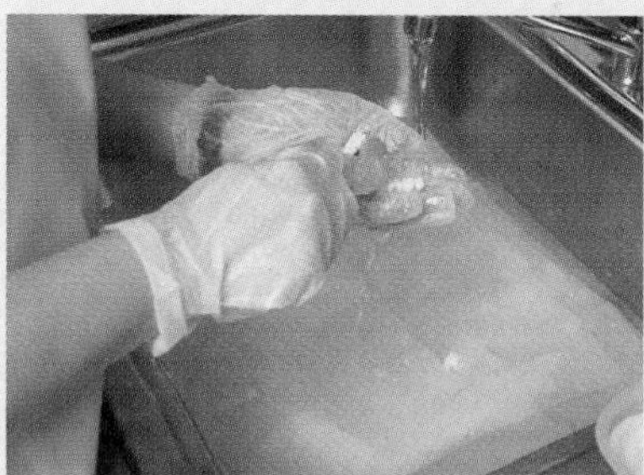

(continued)

23. Help patient rinse mouth with mouthwash; if food particles are between cheek and gumline, gently swab away with gauze. Clean gums with toothette.
24. Have patient replace dentures.
25. Place dentures in labeled denture cup next to bed, if dentures are to be left out.
26. Rinse equipment and put away.

POSTPROCEDURE

27. Remove gloves; dispose of in hazardous waste.
28. Wash hands.
29. Position patient.
30. Secure call bell within patient's reach.
31. Chart procedure and how it was tolerated.

NOTE: The patient may want to soak dentures ov ernight after PM care has been given. Place dentures in a solution in a denture cup and store in a safe place.

7/07/11	0725
	Set out equipment for denture care
	Able to clean dentures
	Or: Removed dentures, cleaned,
	and freshened
	Provided oral hygiene
	No oral problems noted
	R. Johnson CNA

PROCEDURE 18.19 Oral Hygiene—For the Unconscious Patient

BACKGROUND: The unconscious patient often mouth breathes causing very dry lips and mucous membrane. Careful care and observation help prevent oral problems.

ALERT: Follow Standard Precautions.

PREPROCEDURE

1. Wash hands.
2. Tell patient what you are going to do. When patient is unconscious he or she may hear even if he or she cannot respond.
3. Provide privacy.
4. Assemble equipment:
   a. Emesis basin
   b. Towel
   c. Lemon glycerin swabs
   d. Tongue blades
   e. 4 × 4 gauze
   f. Lip moisturizer
   g. Disposable nonsterile gloves
5. Position bed at a comfortable working height.
6. Put on gloves.

PROCEDURE

7. Position patient's head to side and place towel on bed under patient's cheek and chin.
8. Secure emesis basin under patient's chin.
9. Wrap a tongue blade with 4 × 4 gauze and slightly moisten. Swab mouth being certain to clean gums, teeth, tongue, and roof of mouth.
10. Apply lip moisturizer to lips and swab mouth with lemon and glycerin if available.
11. Remove towel and reposition patient.
12. Make sure side rails are up and bed is in low position.
13. Discard disposable equipment in hazardous waste.
14. Clean basin and put away.
15. Remove gloves and put in hazardous waste.

POSTPROCEDURE

16. Wash hands.
17. Report and document patient's tolerance of procedure.

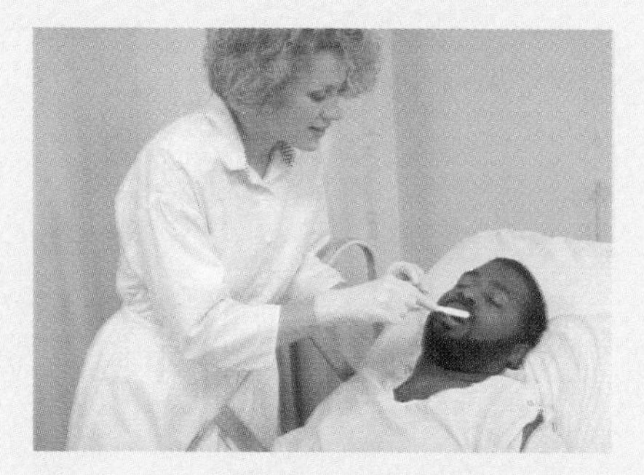

6/16/11	1040
	Cleaned teeth, moistened lips,
	provided oral hygiene
	Noted small canker sore on palate
	Reported to team leader
	_________ *S. Gomez CNA*

PROCEDURE 18.20 Elimination—Offering the Bedpan

BACKGROUND: Carefully placing the bedpan prevents discomfort. This procedure allows observations for skin breakdown and elimination.

ALERT: Follow Standard Precautions.

PREPROCEDURE

1. Wash hands.
2. Assemble equipment:
   a. Bedpan with cover
   b. Toilet tissue
   c. Soap and water
   d. Towel and washcloth
   e. Disposable nonsterile gloves (two pairs)
3. Ask visitors to wait outside room.
4. Provide privacy for patient with curtain, screen, or door.
5. Put on clean gloves before handling the bedpan.
6. Remove bedpan from storage space.
7. Warm metal bedpans by running warm water over them and drying.

PROCEDURE

8. Lower head of bed if it is elevated.
9. Fold top covers back enough to see where to place the pan. Do not expose patient.
10. Ask patient to raise hips off bed. Help support patient by placing your hand at patient's midback.
    a. Roll the patient onto his or her side if the patient is unable to lift the hips.
    b. Place bedpan on buttocks. For a standard bedpan: Position bedpan so wider end of pan is aligned with patient's buttock; for a fracture pan: position bedpan with handle toward the foot of the bed.
    c. Hold in place with one hand and help patient roll back onto bedpan.
11. Slide bedpan into place.

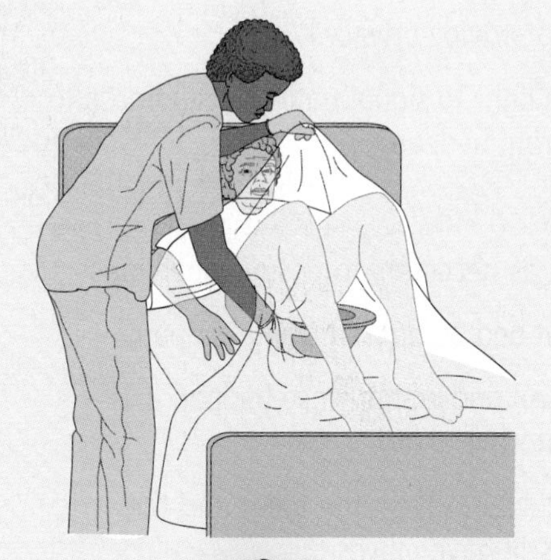

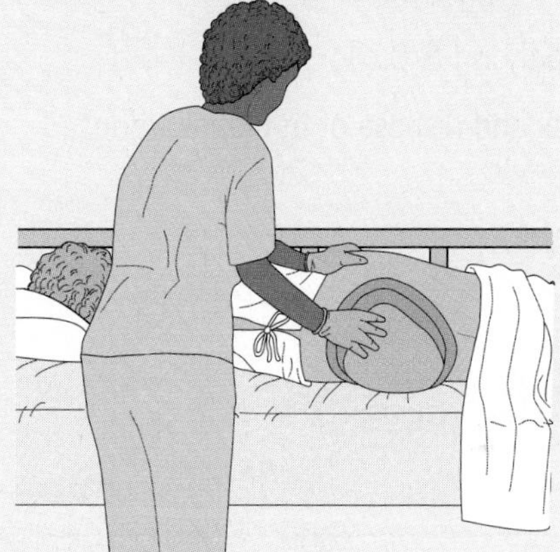

12. Cover patient again.
13. Raise head of bed for comfort.

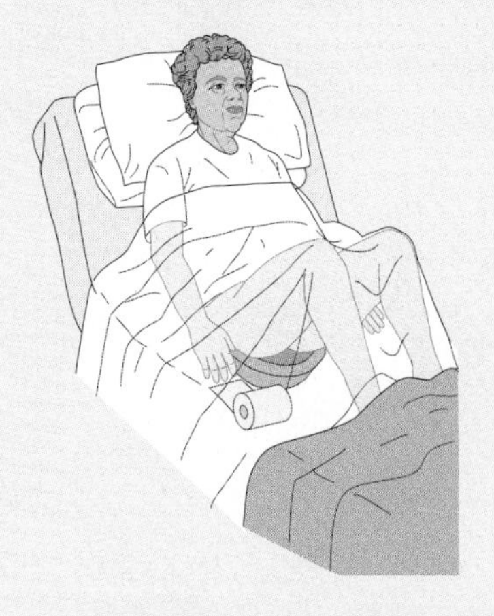

14. Put toilet tissue within patient's reach.

(continued)

PROCEDURE 18.20 Elimination—Offering the Bedpan (continued)

15. Remove gloves.
16. Wash your hands.
17. Leave call light with patient and ask patient to signal when finished.
18. Leave room to provide privacy.
19. Watch for call light to signal patient's readiness to be removed from bedpan.
20. Put on gloves.
21. Assist patient as necessary to ensure cleanliness.
22. Lower head of bed before removing bedpan.
23. Remove bedpan and empty, rinse bedpan and pours rinse into the toilet.
24. Use a paper towel to flush the toilet and the faucet, since still have gloves on.
25. Measure urine if on I & O.
26. Remove gloves and dispose of in biohazardous container.

POSTPROCEDURE

27. Wash hands.
28. Put on clean gloves.
29. Provide washcloth, water, and soap for patient to wash hands.
30. Dispose of soiled washcloth or wipes in proper container.
31. Provide comfort measures for patient.
32. Secure call light in patient's reach, make sure side rails are up and bed is in lowest position.
33. Remove and dispose of gloves in biohazardous container.
34. Wash hands.
35. Open privacy curtain.
36. Chart the following:
    a. Bowel movement amount, color, consistency
    b. Amount voided if on I & O

4/10/12	0830
	Small, light brown, dry bowel
	Complained of discomfort when eliminating
	Noted small amount bright red blood
	Reported to team leader
	R. Johnson CNA

PROCEDURE 18.21 Elimination—Offering the Urinal

BACKGROUND: Offering a urinal at the time of elimination allows the patient who is not able to go into the bathroom, a way to stay in bed or in a chair and eliminate liquid waste. Remember to provide privacy to maintain the patient's dignity.

ALERT: Follow Standard Precautions.

PREPROCEDURE

1. Wash hands.
2. Assemble equipment:
   a. Urinal with cover
   b. Soap and water
   c. Towel and washcloth
   d. Disposable nonsterile gloves
3. Ask visitors to wait outside room.
4. Provide privacy for patient.

PROCEDURE

5. Hand urinal to patient.
   a. Place call light at patient's side.
   b. Wash your hands.
   c. Leave room until patient signals with the call light.

(If the patient is unable to place urinal, place penis in urinal. If necessary, stand and hold urinal until patient has finished voiding.) Wear gloves for this step.

6. Return to room when patient has finished voiding.
7. Put on gloves.
8. Offer washcloth for patient to wash their hands.
9. Place cover over urinal and carry it into bathroom.
10. Check to see if patient is on I & O or if a urine specimen is needed. (See I & O and specimen collection in this chapter.)
11. Observe urine color, consistency, and odor.
12. Empty into toilet.
13. Use a paper towel to turn on the faucet and flush the toilet, since still have gloves on. Rinse urinal with cold water.

POSTPROCEDURE

14. Cover and place in a convenient location for the patient.
15. Remove gloves and place in biohazard container.
16. Wash hands.
17. Secure call light in reach of patient.
18. Report and document unusual color, odor, or consistency of urine.
19. Record amount if on I & O.

4/10/12	*1030*
	Voided 250 cc.
	Recorded on I & O sheet
	————— R. Johnson CNA

PROCEDURE 18.22 Elimination—Bedside Commode

BACKGROUND: A bedside commode allows patients who cannot ambulate to the toilet to eliminate body waste by sitting on a chairlike device at the bedside. Patients generally have less difficulty eliminating waste when they use a commode instead of a bedpan.

ALERT: Follow Standard Precautions.

PREPROCEDURE

1. Wash hands.
2. Assemble equipment:
   a. Bedside commode
   b. Toilet tissue
   c. Washcloth
   d. Warm water
   e. Soap
   f. Towel
   g. Disposable nonsterile gloves
3. Identify patient.
4. Explain what you are going to do.

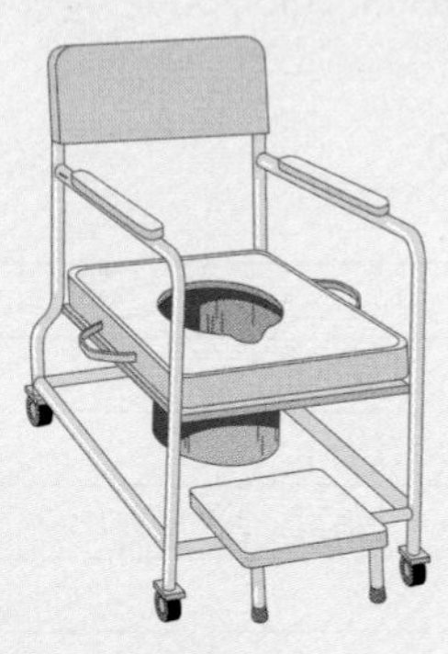

PROCEDURE

5. Place commode chair next to bed facing head of bed. *Lock wheels!*
6. Check to see if receptacle is in place under seat.
7. Provide privacy by pulling privacy curtains.
8. Lower bed to lowest position.
9. Lower side rail.
10. Help patient to sitting position.
11. Help patient swing legs over side of bed.
12. Put on patient's slippers and assist to stand.
13. Have patient place hands on your shoulders.
14. Support under patient's arms, pivot patient to right, and lower to commode. (See the procedure "Transferring—Pivot Transfer from Bed to Wheelchair.")
15. Place call bell within reach.
16. Place toilet tissue within reach.
17. Remain nearby if patient seems weak.
18. Return immediately when patient signals.
19. Put on gloves.
20. Assist patient to stand.
21. Clean anus or perineum if patient is unable to help self.
22. Remove gloves and put in hazardous waste.
23. Help patient wash hands. Remember to do this before you stand the patient up.
24. Assist back to bed and position comfortably.
25. Put up side rail if required.
26. Put on gloves.
27. Put down cover on commode chair and remove receptacle.
28. Empty contents, measuring if on I & O.
29. Empty and clean per hospital policy.
30. Remove gloves and put in hazardous waste.

(continued)

POSTPROCEDURE

31. Wash hands.
32. Replace equipment and tidy unit.
33. Record the following:
    a. Bowel movement
        (1) Amount
        (2) Consistency
        (3) Color
    b. Any unusual observations, such as
        (1) Weakness
        (2) Discomfort

11/24/11	1030
	Eliminated moderate amount of brown,
	formed stool and 200 cc of urine Returned
	to bed, positioned for comfort; Tolerated
	activity well
	________ S. Gomez CNA

PROCEDURE 18.23 Assisting to Bathroom

BACKGROUND: It is the nurse's responsibility to obtain an assessment of the patient's baseline functional status at the time that care for the patient is assumed. Understanding the baseline functional status of the patient enables the nurse to establish goals for activities of daily living. The goal must always be to maintain or improve the baseline function of the patient.

Institutionalization where staff may take over these activities promotes decreased self mobility and may contribute to the future dependency of the patient. Assisting the patient with toileting activities can maintain continence as well as provide opportunities for the patient to ambulate and build strength.

ALERT: Follow Standard Precautions.

PREPROCEDURE

1. Establish the baseline function of the patient. Determine the amount of assistance required (one nurse, two nurses).
2. Establish the need for assertive devices such as cane, walker, gait belt.

   NOTE: The use of a gait belt for any patient that is not fully independent is highly recommended. This a protective device for both the patient and the nurse.
3. Assure that the path to be used is clear of obstruction.
4. Explain to the patient what is to be done. Instruct the patient to alert the nurse of any lightheadedness or discomfort.

PROCEDURE

5. Assist the patient to an erect position at the edge of the bed.
6. Pause at the edge of the bed (and again after the patient arises) to ensure that the patient feels steady. You should stand in front of and face the patient. Brace the patient's lower extremities. Place belt around the patient's waist.
7. Elevate the bed to a height that allows the patient's legs to rest firmly on the ground but not to have to lift his body from a low position as the patient rises.
8. With your hands under the gait belt assist the patient to rise.
9. Patients who are fearful of walking may tend to bend forward and look at their feet. They will need to be reminded to stand erect and hold their head high.
10. Guide the patient to the bathroom with one hand under the gait belt at the patient's back and the other hand guiding the patient's free arm. Walk slightly behind and to one side of the patient for the full distance, while holding on to the belt. Assist with lowering the patient onto the toilet seat. For those patients who have functional disabilities it is advisable to obtain and use an elevated toilet seat. This will enable the patient to sit and rise with the least amount of energy use and the greatest degree of safety.
11. Instruct the patient on using the nurse call light to call for assistance after toileting is complete.
12. After toileting is complete assist the patient with completing personal hygiene as necessary.
13. Return the patient to the bedside and assist as necessary with positioning the patient back into bed.

POSTPROCEDURE

14. Assure that all needs are met and that the patient is comfortable prior to leaving the area.
15. Document in the medical record the patient's level of activity, any problems with independent function, and the level of assistance required.

PROCEDURE 18.24 Assist to Dangle, Stand, and Walk

BACKGROUND: Patients that have been immobile for a period of time may need assistance from the nurse to sit, stand, and walk. Determining what the patient's baseline activity level has been, any recent changes in mobility, and goals of care are the first steps to improving the patient's functional level.

The goal must always be to maintain or improve baseline function. A patient who has not been walking at all may have a goal of taking one independent step. One who has diminished tolerance of activity may have a goal of increasing the number of feet walked without an increase in fatigue. The goal should always be individualized to the particular patient.

ALERT: Follow Standard Precautions.

PREPROCEDURE

1. Assess the functional level of the patient. Include the patient when determining the plan of care and goals.
2. Explain the procedure to the patient.
3. Provide privacy for the patient.
4. Ensure a clear path for ambulation.
5. Place a chair midway of the distance to be traveled to facilitate a rest spot if necessary.

PROCEDURE

6. Assist the patient to an erect position on the side of the bed. Pause to determine the patient's tolerance of the activity.
7. Place a gait belt around the patient's waist to ensure safety for the patient and the nurse.
8. Stand the patient at the bedside. Pause to determine the patient's tolerance of the activity.
9. With the nurses nearest hand placed under the gait belt at the patient's back and the other hand grasping the patient's nearest elbow: (a) Guide the patient forward. (b) Assess the patient's gait and tolerance of activity as the patient progresses forward.

10. If the patient should faint or begin to fall the nurse can use the gait belt to pull the patient towards the nurse and ease the patient to the ground.
11. Return the patient to the bedside and assist the patient into a chair or back into the bed. Assure that the patient is comfortable and has no further needs.
12. Reassure and encourage the patient to continue the mobility program for increasing functional status.

POSTPROCEDURE

13. Wash hands.
14. Document in observation note patient's gait, feet walked and tolerance of activity.

NOTE: If the patient has numerous tethers and ambulation is problematic an alternative activity can be marching in place at the bedside.

PROCEDURE 18.25 Transferring—Pivot Transfer from Bed to Wheelchair

BACKGROUND: Pivot transfer allows you to move the patient in one easy, safe motion into or out of a wheelchair. Use good body mechanics, explain each step, and reassure the patient of his/her safety.

ALERT: Follow Standard Precautions.

PREPROCEDURE

1. Wash hands.
2. Explain procedure to patient, speaking clearly, slowly and directly, maintaining face-to-face contact whenever possible.
3. Provide for patient's privacy during the procedure, using a curtain, screen or door.
4. Make sure that wheels on bed are locked.
5. Lift foot rests or swing leg supports out of way.
6. Position wheelchair alongside bed. (See teacher for directions in working with stroke patients.) *Lock wheels.*

PROCEDURE

7. Place bed at a safe and appropriate level for the patient. Support patient's back and hips and assist patient to sitting position with feet flat on the floor.
8. Move patient to edge of bed, with legs over side (see top right).
9. Before transferring patient, put non-skid footwear on patient and securely fasten.
10. Have patient dangle legs for a few minutes and take slow, deep breaths. Observe for dizziness.
11. Remember to use a gait belt. Stand in front of patient, positioning yourself to ensure your safety and that of your patient during transfer (e.g., knees bent, feet apart, back straight), place belt around patient's waist, and grasp belt.
12. Brace patient's lowest extremities to prevent slipping.
13. Count to three (or say other prearranged signal) to alert patient to begin transfer.
14. Support him or her at midriff and ask patient to stand, if patient is not dizzy.
15. Once standing, have patient pivot (turn) and hold onto armrest of wheelchair with both arms or one strong arm (see bottom right).

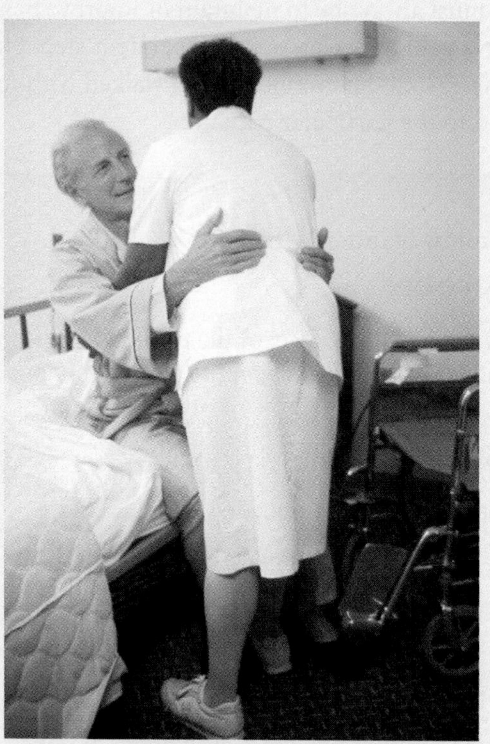

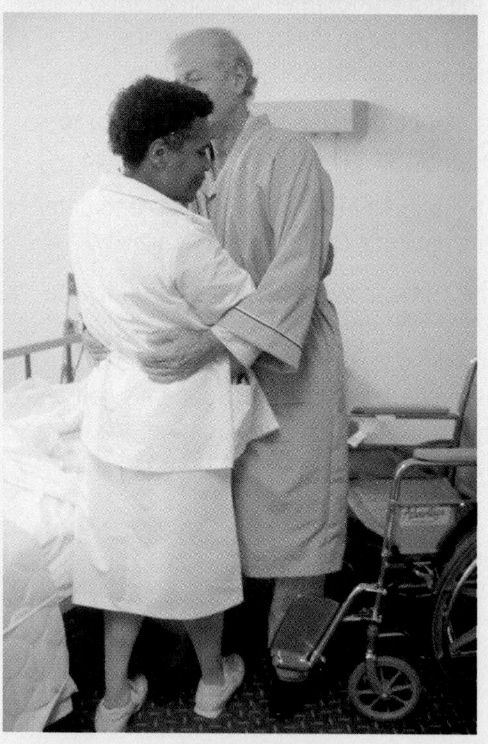

(continued)

16. Gently ease patient into a sitting position, as shown in the following two pictures.

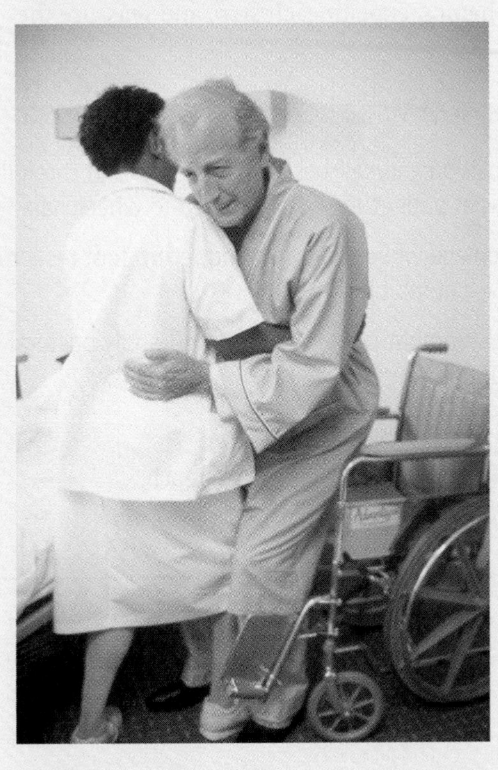

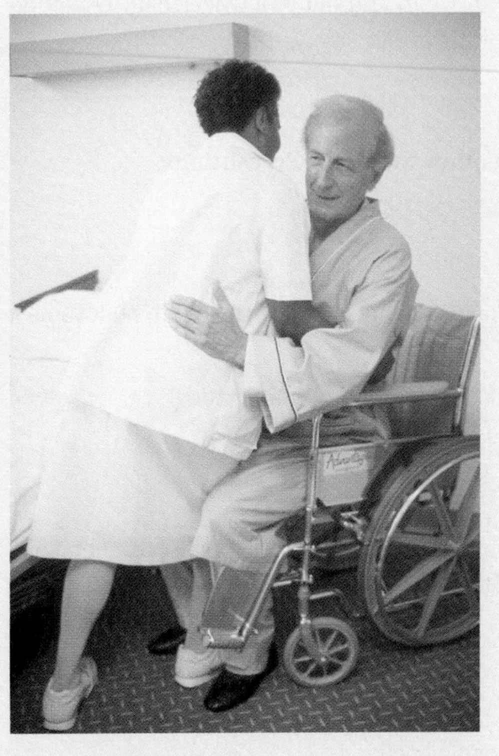

17. Position yourself at back of wheelchair. Ask patient to push on the floor with feet as you lift gently under each arm to ease patient into a comfortable position against backrest. Make sure patient's hips are touching the back of the wheelchair and then remove the transfer belt, if used.
18. Return foot rests to normal position and place feet and legs in a comfortable position on rests. Make sure the signaling device is within the patient's reach.
19. Do not leave a patient who requires a postural support until it is in place.
20. Reverse above procedure to return patient to bed.

POSTPROCEDURE

21. Wash hands

PROCEDURE 18.26

Transferring—Sliding from Bed to Wheelchair and Back

BACKGROUND: Sliding transfer allows you to assist the patient who is paralyzed from the waist down to easily move in and out of a wheelchair. Use good body mechanics, explain each step, and reassure the patient of his or her safety.

ALERT: Follow Standard Precautions.

PREPROCEDURE

1. Wash hands.
2. Assemble equipment: wheelchair with removable arms.
3. Explain the procedure to the patient.
4. Provide privacy for the patient.

PROCEDURE

5. Position wheelchair at bedside with back parallel to head of bed. *Lock* wheels. Move foot rests out of the way.
6. Remove wheelchair arm nearest to bedside.
7. Place bed level to chair seat height if possible. *Lock* bed wheels.
8. Raise head of bed so that patient is in sitting position.
9. Position yourself beside wheelchair and carefully assist patient to slide from bed to wheelchair.
10. Replace wheelchair arm and return foot rests to their normal position.
11. Position patient for comfort and apply postural supports.

POSTPROCEDURE

12. Make sure call bell is within reach.
13. Wash hands..

5/30/11 0945
Transferred from bed into
wheelchair
Tolerated sliding transfer well
R. Johnson CNA

PROCEDURE 18.27

Transferring—Two-Person Lift from Bed to Chair and Back

BACKGROUND: A person who is unable to bear his or her weight during a pivot transfer can be lifted by two people. Use good body mechanics, explain each step, and reassure the patient of his or her safety.

ALERT: Follow Standard Precautions.

PREPROCEDURE

1. Wash hands.
2. Assemble equipment: chair.
3. Ask one other person to help.
4. Tell patient what you are going to do.
5. Provide privacy for the patient.

PROCEDURE

6. Position chair next to bed with back of chair parallel with head of bed. *Lock wheels.*
7. Position patient near edge of bed. Lock wheels of bed.
8. Position co-worker on side of bed near feet.
9. Position yourself behind chair at head of bed.
10. Place your arms under patient's axillae and clasp your hands together at patient's midchest.
11. Co-worker places hands under patient's upper legs.

12. Count to three. On the count of three, lift patient into chair.

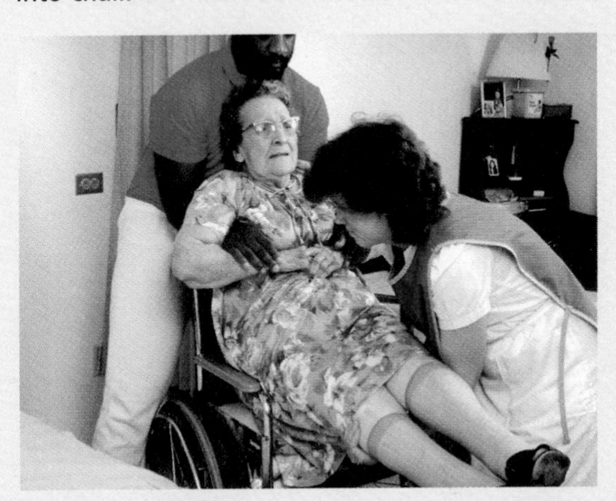

13. Position for comfort and secure postural supports PRN.

POSTPROCEDURE

14. Put call bell within reach of patient.
15. Wash hands.

11/20/11	2100
	Transferred per two-person lift from
	chair into bed, positioned for HS
	comfort
	Tolerated transfer well
	A. Chaplin, CNA

PROCEDURE 18.28 Transferring—Sliding from Bed to Gurney and Back

BACKGROUND: A sliding transfer of a patient on and off a gurney is easily and safely accomplished with two people using a pull sheet. Use good body mechanics, explain each step, and reassure the patient of his or her safety.

ALERT: Follow Standard Precautions.

PREPROCEDURE

1. Wash hands.
2. Assemble equipment:
   a. Gurney
   b. Cover sheet
3. Ask a co-worker to help.
4. Explain what you are going to do and lock wheels on bed.
5. Provide privacy for the patient.

PROCEDURE

6. Cover patient with sheet and remove bed covers.
7. Raise bed to gurney height: lower side rail and move patient to side of bed.
8. Loosen draw sheet on both sides so it can be used as a pull sheet.
9. Position gurney next to bed and *lock* wheels on gurney.
10. Position yourself on outside of gurney—one arm at the head, the other at the hips. Co-worker is on other side of bed.
11. Reach across gurney and securely hold edge of draw sheet. Pull patient onto gurney and cover. (If patient is large, a third person on the opposite side of bed may be necessary.)

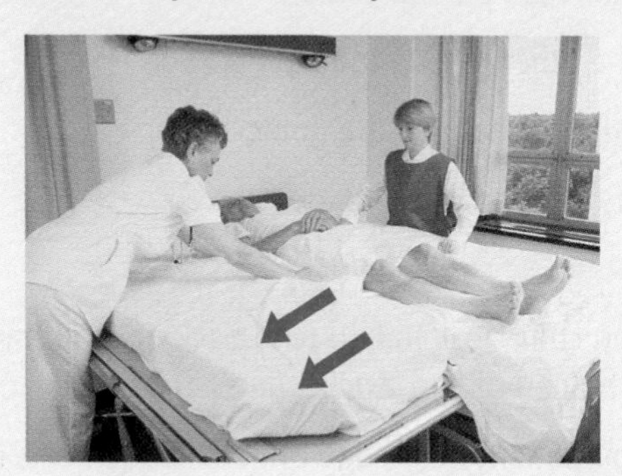

12. Position patient for comfort.
13. Secure with safety straps or raise side rails.

POSTPROCEDURE

14. Wash hands.

9/10/11	0900
	Transferred to radiology via gurney
	following a sliding transfer from bed
	Tolerated transfer well
	________ *A. Chaplin CNA*

PROCEDURE **18.29**

Transferring—Lifting with a Mechanical Lift

BACKGROUND: Patients who are paralyzed can be easily transferred with a mechanical lift. Mechanical lifts allow patients who would otherwise be bedridden to be placed into a bathtub or chair.

Your ability to use the lift safely will provide important environmental and physical stimulation for the patient. Remember to ask a co-worker to double-check all connections and positions before moving the patient to ensure their safety.

ALERT: Follow Standard Precautions.

PREPROCEDURE

1. Wash hands.
2. Gather equipment:
    a. Mechanical lift
    b. Sheet or blanket for patient comfort
    c. Sling
3. Check all equipment to be sure it is in good working order and that the sling is not damaged or torn.
4. Ask one other person to help.
5. Prepare patient's destination.
    a. Chair
    b. Gurney
    c. Bathtub
    d. Shower
6. *Lock* wheels on bed and explain what you are going to do.
7. Provide privacy for the patient.

PROCEDURE

8. Roll patient toward you.
9. Place sling on bed behind patient.
    a. Position top of sling at shoulders.
    b. Position bottom of sling under buttocks.
    c. Leave enough of sling to support body when the body is rolled back. Fan-fold remaining sling next to body. It will be pulled through when patient is rolled back.
10. Roll patient to other side of bed and pull fan-folded portion of sling flat. Remove all wrinkles and allow patient to lie flat on back.
11. Position lift over patient, being sure to broaden base of lift. This stabilizes the lift while raising patient.
12. Raise head of bed to a semi-Fowler's position.
13. Attach straps on lift to sling loops. Shorter straps must be attached to shoulder loops. Longer straps are attached to loops at hips. *(Important: If you reverse the strap attachment, the patient's head will be lower than his or her hips.)*
14. Reassure patient. Let patient know you will keep him or her from falling. Gently raise patient from bed with hand crank or pump handle.
15. Keep patient centered over base of lift as you move lift and patient to his or her destination. (It is helpful to have a helper stand by and steady patient while moving so that patient doesn't swing.)
16. Position patient over chair, commode, bathtub, shower chair, etc. Ask a co-worker to steady chair.
17. Slowly lower patient into chair using foot-pedal positioning.
18. Unhook sling from lift straps and carefully move lift away from patient.
19. Provide all comfort measures for patient.
20. Secure postural supports if necessary.
21. Return lift to storage area.

(continued)

PROCEDURE 18.29 Transferring—Lifting with a Mechanical Lift (continued)

POSTPROCEDURE

22. Wash hands.
23. Reverse procedure when returning patient to bed.

NOTE: The mechanical lift is an expensive item. Depending on the size of the facility you are in, there may be a limited number available. Always return the lift to its storage area so that it will be available for others to use.

4/20/12	0830
	Transferred via mechanical lift to bathtub
	Tolerated bath well
	Positioned in day chair and taken to patio
	________ S. Gomez CNA

PROCEDURE 18.30 Transferring—Moving a Patient on a Gurney or Stretcher

BACKGROUND: Patients who are medicated or must stay in a reclined position can be moved throughout a facility on a gurney or stretcher. It is important to secure safety rails and wheel them in a safe manner.

ALERT: Follow Standard Precautions.

PREPROCEDURE

1. Wash hands.
2. Position bed to gurney height.
3. *Lock* all the brakes on gurney and bed.
4. Follow the procedure for transferring to and from a gurney.

PROCEDURE

5. Stand at the patient's head and push the gurney with patient's feet moving first down the hallway.
6. Slow down when turning a corner. Always check the intersection mirrors for traffic.
7. Enter an elevator by standing at patient's head and pulling gurney into elevator. The feet will be the last to enter elevator.
8. Leave elevator by carefully pushing the gurney out of elevator into corridor.
9. Position yourself at patient's feet, and back a patient on a gurney down a hill.
10. Never leave a patient unattended on a gurney.
11. Raise side rails and secure a safety strap.

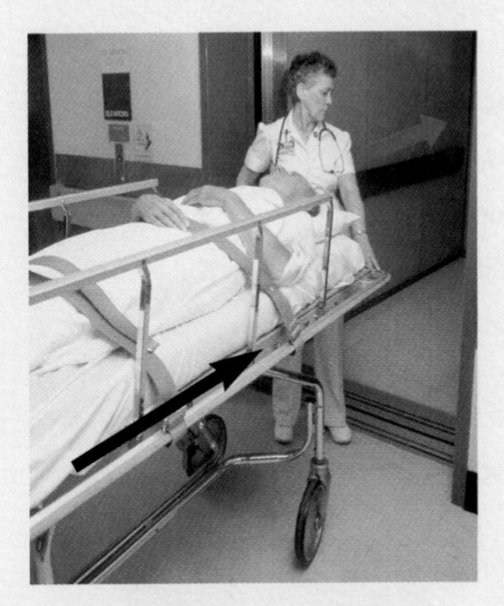

POSTPROCEDURE

13. Wash hands.

12/14/11 1320
Transferred via gurney to surgery
R. Johnson CNA

PROCEDURE 18.31 Transferring—Moving a Patient in a Wheelchair

BACKGROUND: Patients can easily be transferred from place to place in a wheelchair. It is important to move them safely and secure their transfer in and out of the wheelchair.

ALERT: Follow Standard Precautions.

PREPROCEDURE

1. Wash hands.
2. Position wheelchair.
3. *Lock* all brakes on wheelchair and bed.

PROCEDURE

4. Follow procedure for transferring patient to and from a wheelchair.
5. Push wheelchair carefully into hallway, watching for others who may be near doorway.

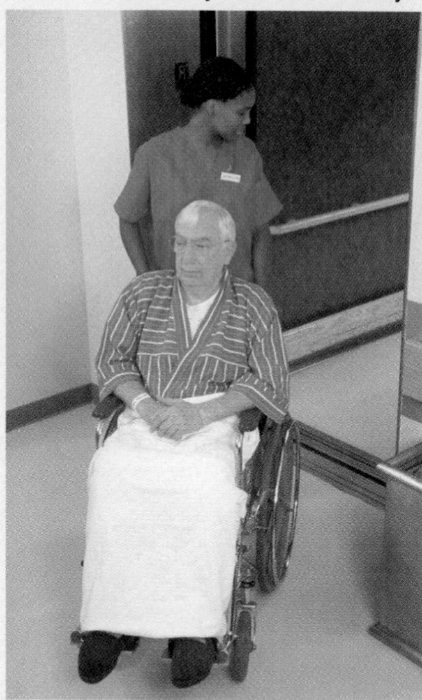

6. Move cautiously down hallway, being especially careful at intersections.
7. Always back a patient in a wheelchair over bumps, doorways, and into or out of elevators.
8. Always back a patient in a wheelchair down a hill.

9. Check patient for comfort measures before leaving.
10. Always notify appropriate person that patient has arrived.

POSTPROCEDURE

11. Wash hands.

10/10/12 1730
Transferred via wheelchair to radiology
________ S. Gomez CNA

PROCEDURE 18.32 Moving—Helping the Helpless Patient to Move Up in Bed

BACKGROUND: Keeping patients in good alignment helps prevent a decubitus, respiratory problems, and general discomfort. Following correct procedures when lifting and moving the patient prevents injury to the patient and the nurse assistant(s).

ALERT: Follow Standard Precautions.

PREPROCEDURE

1. Wash hands.
2. Ask a co-worker to help move patient. (Co-worker will work on opposite side of bed.)
3. Identify patient and explain what you are going to do. (Even if the patient seems unresponsive, he or she may be able to hear.) Provide privacy for the patient.

PROCEDURE

4. Lock wheels of bed. Raise bed to comfortable working position, and lower side rails.
5. Remove pillow and place it at head of bed or on a chair.
6. Loosen both sides of draw sheet.
7. Roll edges toward side of patient's body.
8. Face head of bed and grasp rolled sheet edge with hand closest to patient.
9. Place your feet 12 inches apart with foot farthest from the edge of bed in a forward position.
10. Place your free hand and arm under patient's neck and shoulders, supporting head.
11. Bend your hips slightly.
12. On the count of three, you and your co-worker will raise patient's hips and back with draw sheet, supporting head and shoulders, and move patient smoothly to head of bed.

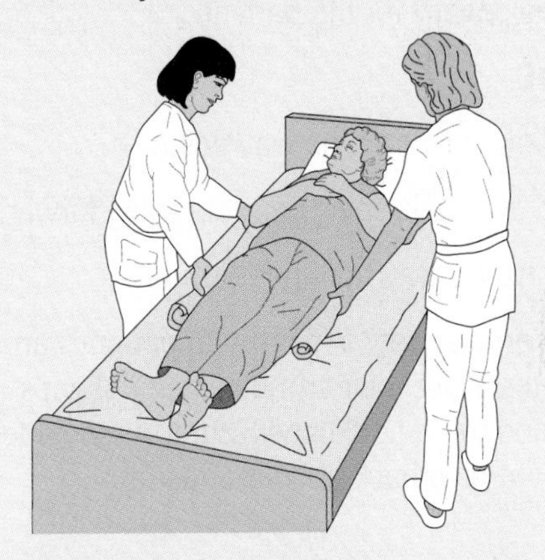

13. Replace pillow under patient's head and check for good body alignment.
14. Tighten and tuck in draw sheet and smooth bedding.
15. Raise side rails and lower bed.

POSTPROCEDURE

16. Wash hands..

PROCEDURE 18.33 Moving—Assisting Patient to Sit Up in Bed

BACKGROUND: Some patients are too weak to adjust themselves in bed. Sitting up comfortably helps prevent fatigue and poor body alignment. Using correct procedure prevents injury to the patient and the nurse assistant(s).

ALERT: Follow Standard Precautions.

PREPROCEDURE

1. Wash hands.
2. Identify patient and explain what you are going to do. Provide privacy for the patient.

PROCEDURE

3. Lock bed and lower all the way down.
4. Face head of bed, keeping your outer leg forward.
5. Turn your head away from patient's face.
6. Lock your arm nearest patient with patient's arm. To lock arms, place your arm between patient's arm and body, and hold upper arm near shoulder. Have patient hold back of your upper arm.
7. Support patient's head and shoulder with your other arm.
8. Raise patient to sitting position. Adjust head of bed and pillows.

POSTPROCEDURE

9. Wash hands.

5/10/11	0850
	Helped to sitting position
	No complaints of discomfort
	________ *R. Johnson CNA*

PROCEDURE 18.34 Moving—Logrolling

BACKGROUND: Maintaining alignment is essential to prevent injury. Logrolling helps prevent movement of the back following surgery.

ALERT: Follow Standard Precautions.

PREPROCEDURE

1. Wash hands.
2. Identify patient and explain what you are going to do.
3. Provide privacy by pulling privacy curtain.

PROCEDURE

4. Lock wheels of bed. Raise bed to a comfortable working position.
5. Lower side rail on side you are working on.
6. Be certain that side rail on opposite side of bed is in up position.
7. Leave pillow under head.
8. Place a pillow lengthwise between patient's legs.
9. Fold patient's arms across chest.
10. Roll patient onto his or her side like a log, turning body as a whole unit, without bending joints.
11. Check for good body alignment.
12. Tighten and tuck in draw sheet and smooth bedding.
13. Tuck pillow behind back for support.
14. Raise side rails and lower bed.
15. Secure call light in patient's reach.

POSTPROCEDURE

16. Wash hands.
17. Chart position of patient and how procedure was tolerated.

10/24/11	1145
	Logrolled to left side
	Moved every 2 hours
	Skin in good condition
	Complained of slight pain in left leg
	when moved
	Pillows placed behind back to maintain
	alignment
	Made comfortable with rails up
	________ *A. Chaplin CNA*

PROCEDURE 18.35 Moving—Turning Patient Away from You

BACKGROUND: Following correct procedure for turning patients away from you when bed changing, bathing, and positioning provides good alignment and prevents injury.

ALERT: Follow Standard Precautions.

PREPROCEDURE

1. Wash hands.
2. Identify patient and explain what you are going to do. Provide privacy for the patient.

PROCEDURE

3. Lock bed and elevate to a comfortable working height.
4. Lower side rail on side you are working from.
5. Have patient bend knees. Cross arms on chest.
6. Place arm nearest head of bed under patient's shoulders and head. Place other hand and forearm under small of the patient's back. Bend your body at hips and knees, keeping your back straight. Pull patient toward you.
7. Place forearms under patient's hips and pull patient toward you.
8. Place one hand under ankles and one hand under knees and move ankles and knees toward you.

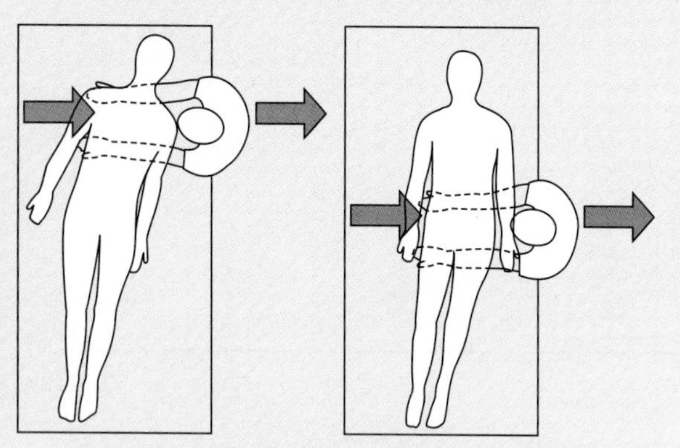

As a safety measure, this procedure must be done before turning a patient onto his side. It ensures that the patient, when turned, is located in the center of the mattress.

9. Cross patient's leg closest to you over other leg at ankles.

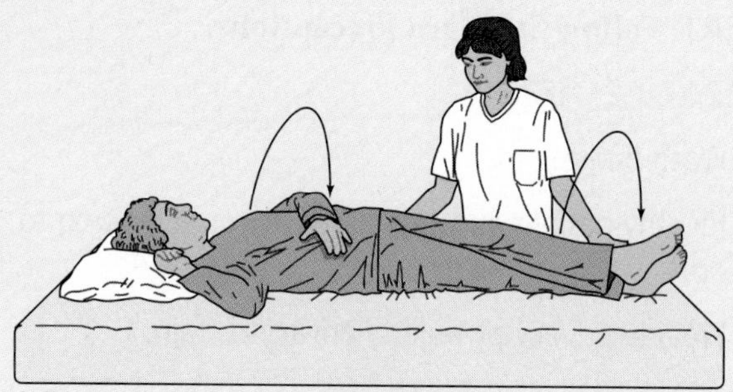

A Bend the resident's farthest arm next to her head and place the other arm across her chest. Cross her near leg over the other leg.

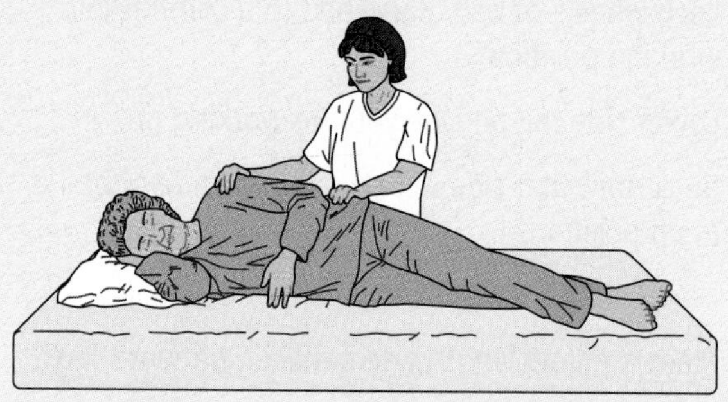

B Place one hand on the resident's shoulder and the other on her hip. Turn her away from you onto her side.

C Place pillows under her upper arm and leg for support.

10. Roll patient away from you by placing one hand under hips and one hand under shoulders.
11. Place one hand under patient's shoulders and one hand under patient's head. Draw patient back toward center of bed.
12. Place both hands under patient's hips and move hips toward center of bed.
13. Put a pillow behind patient's back to give support and keep patient from falling onto his or her back.

(continued)

PROCEDURE 18.35 Moving—Turning Patient Away from You (continued)

14. Be certain patient is in good alignment.
15. Place upper leg on a pillow for support.
16. Replace side rail on near side of bed and return bed to lowest height.
17. You may place a turning sheet under a helpless or heavy patient to help with turning. Use a folded large sheet or half sheet and place it so that it extends just above shoulders and below hips.

POSTPROCEDURE

18. Wash hands.

8/04/11	1145
	Turned to left side
	Pillows placed behind back to
	maintain good body alignment
	Resting comfortably
	Side rails up
	________ A. Chaplin CNA

PROCEDURE 18.36 Turning Patient on Side

BACKGROUND: The nurse's responsibility is to determine baseline function of the patient and to strive to maintain and/or improve function. Prolonged periods of bedrest are harmful to the overall status of the patient and must be avoided whenever possible. However, when a patient cannot turn in bed without assistance nurses need to use their knowledge of correct body mechanics and correct alignment to change the patient from one position to another.

ALERT: Follow Standard Precautions.

PREPROCEDURE

1. Wash hands.
2. Explain procedure to patient.
3. Provide privacy for the patient with curtain, screen, or door.

PROCEDURE

4. Raise the bed to a height that allows the nurse to remain in an erect posture while moving patient. Adjust the bed to a flat position or as low as the patient can tolerate. Make sure side rails on side to which patient's body will be turned are raised. Lower the side rail nearest to nurse.
5. Use a pull sheet or pad for moving the patient in order to avoid the effects of friction on the patient's skin integrity.
6. Place the patient's arms across the chest and cross the patient's far leg over the near one. Grasping the pull sheet on the far side of the patient pull the patient towards the nurse.
7. Slowly roll patient onto side toward raised side rail while supporting patient's body.
8. Place a pillow under the head and the neck to prevent lateral flexion of the neck.
9. Place a pillow behind the patient's back to promote the side lying position. Ensure that the shoulders are aligned with the hips.
10. Place a pillow under the upper arm. The lower arm should be flexed and positioned comfortably. Make sure patient is not lying on their arm.
11. Use one or two pillows as needed to support the leg from the groin to the foot. Avoid having bony prominences resting against hard surfaces.
12. Assure that the two shoulders are aligned with the two hips.
13. For the completely immobile patient it is important that passive range of motion exercises by provided during the time used to reposition the patient.
14. Readjust the bed height and position and raise the side rail if appropriate. Put the bed in the lowest position.
15. Assure that the patient is comfortable and has no further needs before leaving the bedside.
16. Put the call signal within the patient's reach.

POSTPROCEDURE

17. Wash your hands.

PROCEDURE 18.37 Moving—Turning Patient Toward You

BACKGROUND: Following correct procedure for turning patients toward you when bed changing, bathing, and positioning provides good alignment and prevents injury.

ALERT: Follow Standard Precautions.

PREPROCEDURE

1. Wash hands.
2. Identify patient and explain what you are going to do. Provide privacy for the patient.

PROCEDURE

3. Lock bed and elevate to a comfortable working height.
4. Lower side rail on side you are working from.
5. Cross patient's far leg over leg that is closest to you.
6. Place one hand on patient's far shoulder. Place your other hand on the hip.

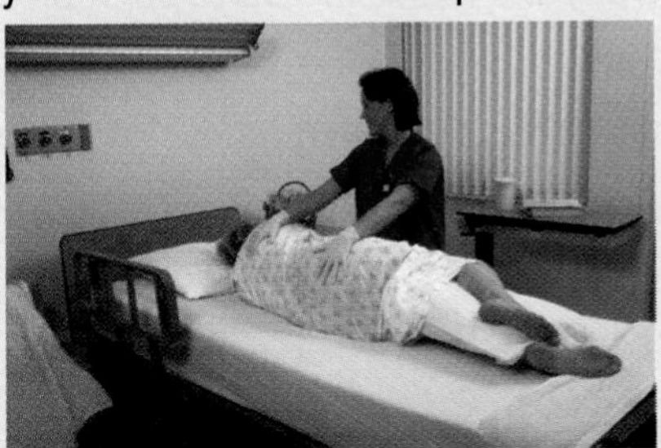

7. Brace yourself against side of bed. Roll patient toward you in a slow, gentle, smooth movement.
8. Help patient bring upper leg toward you and bend comfortably (Sims position).
9. Put up side rail. Be certain it is secure.
10. Go to other side of bed and lower side rail.
11. Place hands under patient's shoulders and hips. Pull toward center of bed. This helps maintain side-lying position.
12. Be certain to align patient's body properly.
13. Use pillows to position and support legs if patient is unable to move self.
14. *Check tubing to make certain that it is not caught between legs or pulling in any way if patient has an indwelling catheter.*
15. Tuck a pillow behind patient's back. This forms a roll and prevents patient from rolling backward onto back.
16. Return bed to low position.
17. Secure call light in patient's reach.

POSTPROCEDURE

18. Wash hands.

5/05/11	1000
	Repositioned on right side
	Skin care given
	Skin is clean and dry
	________ S. Gomez CNA

PROCEDURE 18.38 Applying Restraints

BACKGROUND: Restraints should be used only as a last resort when alternative measures have failed, and the patient is at an increased risk for harming himself or others. Alternative measures might include: assuring that basic patient needs have been met; providing a sitter; providing distraction.

CAUTION: Physically restraining a patient can escalate the patient's confusion and their level of agitation.

ALERT: Follow Standard Precautions.

PREPROCEDURE

1. Determine the need for restraints and that alternative measures have been attempted.
2. Assess patient's physical condition, behavior and mental status.

PROCEDURE

3. Determine the agency's policy for application of restraints. Secure a physician's order.
4. Explain the reason for use to patient and family. Clarify how the patient's needs will be met and that the use of restraints is only temporary.
5. Wash your hands.
6. Apply restraints according to manufacturer's directions (each type of restraint may require a different type of application).
   a. Choose the least restrictive type of device that allows the greatest degree of mobility.
   b. Pad bony prominences. Ensure that two fingers can be inserted between the restraint and the patient's wrist or ankle.
   c. Maintain restrained extremity in normal anatomical position.
   d. Use a quick release tie for all restraints.
   e. Fasten restraint to bed not side rail.
   f. Remove restraint every two hours or according to agency policy and patient need.
   g. While removed check for signs of decreased circulation, impaired function of limb, or impaired skin integrity.
   h. Perform range-of-motion exercises before reapplying.
   i. Reevaluate the need for use of physical restraints, alternative measures attempted before reapplying.
   j. Document procedure and rationale.
   k. Obtain a new physician's order for restraint every 24 hours if continued need.

POSTPROCEDURE

7. Assure that patient safety and comfort has been maintained throughout the period that restraints are in place.

PROCEDURE 18.39 How to Tie Postural Supports

BACKGROUND: Postural supports must be secured with a quick-release knot that allows the patient to be moved quickly in the event of an emergency.

ALERT: Follow Standard Precautions.

PREPROCEDURE

1. Wash hands.

PROCEDURE

2. Assemble equipment: a postural support that has been ordered.
3. Tie a half-bow knot or quick-release knot. Tie the same way you tie a bow on a shoe. Once bow is in place, grasp one loop and pull end of tie through knot.
4. Knot can be easily released pulling end of loop.

NOTE: Half-bow knot/quick-release knot is always used when a restraint is attached to wheelchair or mattress support. This allows quick release if it is necessary to move patient in a hurry.

POSTPROCEDURE

5. Wash hands.

9/09/11	0930
	Transferred to wheelchair
	Vest postural support applied and
	secured with a quick-release knot
	at back of chair
	________ S. Gomez CNA

PROCEDURE 18.40 Postural Supports: Limb

BACKGROUND: Postural supports for the limbs are necessary to prevent some patients from causing injury to themselves or others.

ALERT: Follow Standard Precautions.

PREPROCEDURE

1. Check for physician's order.
2. Wash hands.
3. Assemble equipment: a limb support.
4. Identify patient. Provide privacy for the patient by curtain, screen, or door.

PROCEDURE

5. Explain what you are going to do, even if the patient is confused.
6. Place soft side of limb support against skin. Check to make sure the wrinkles are out.
7. Wrap around limb and put one tie through opening on other end of support (see Figure 18.16a).
8. Gently pull until it fits snugly around limb.
9. Buckle or tie in place so that support stays on limb.
10. Tie out of patient's reach. (See the procedure "How to Tie Postural Supports.")
    a. Tie to bed frame *(not side rails).*
    b. Tie to wheelchair *(not to stationary chair).*
11. Check for proper alignment and comfort of patient.
12. Check to be certain that knots or wrinkles are not causing pressure.
13. Check to be certain that support is snug but does not bind. *(You should be able to put two fingers under edges.)*
14. Place call light where it can be easily reached.

POSTPROCEDURE

15. Wash hands.
16. Circulation under restraint should be checked every 15–30 minutes and documented.
17. Check patient frequently and move at least every 2 hours. Restraints should be removed every 2 hours for at least 5–10 minutes.
18. Chart the following:
    a. Reason for use of support
    b. Type of support used
    c. When it was applied
    d. When it was released
    e. Times of repositioning
    f. How patient tolerated it
    g. Condition of skin

10/14/11	0200
	Resident disoriented; swinging arms and
	legs against side rails
	Limb postural supports applied and
	secured with a quick-release knot
	to legs and arms, to prevent injury
	per physician's order
	R. Johnson CNA

PROCEDURE 18.41 Postural Supports: Mitten

BACKGROUND: Mitten postural supports prevent the hands from grasping objects.

ALERT: Follow Standard Precautions.

PREPROCEDURE

1. Check for physician's order.
2. Wash hands.
3. Assemble equipment: a soft cloth mitten.
4. Identify patient.
5. Explain what you are going to do.

PROCEDURE

6. Slip mitten on hand with padded side against palm and net on top of hand.
7. Lace mitten (see **Figure 18.16c**).
8. Gently pull until it fits snugly around wrist.
9. Tie with a double bow knot so that support stays on hand.

NOTE: Double bow knot helps secure the restraint to the patient. Use only a half-bow/quick-release knot to tie a postural support to a bed, wheelchair, or other furniture.

10. Check for proper alignment and comfort of patient.
11. Check to be certain knots or wrinkles are not causing pressure.
12. Check to be certain support is snug but does not bind. *(You should be able to put two fingers under edges.)*
13. Place call light where it can be easily reached.

POSTPROCEDURE

14. Wash hands.
15. Check circulation and document every 15–30 minutes.
16. Remove mitten restraint every 2 hours for at least 5–10 minutes.
17. Check patient frequently and move at least every 2 hours.
18. Chart the following:
    a. Reason for use of support
    b. Type of support used
    c. When it was applied
    d. When it was released
    e. Times of repositioning
    f. How patient tolerated it
    g. Condition of skin

11/07/11	1400
	Bilateral mitten postural supports applied
	and secured with a quick-release knot to
	prevent the resident from removing
	abdominal dressing and IV per physician's
	order
	________ *S. Gomez CNA*

PROCEDURE 18.42 Postural Supports: Vest or Jacket

BACKGROUND: Vest postural support is necessary to prevent some patients from injuring themselves.

ALERT: Follow Standard Precautions.

PREPROCEDURE

1. Check for physician's order.
2. Wash hands.
3. Assemble equipment: a vest support.
4. Identify patient.
5. Explain what you are going to do.

PROCEDURE

6. Put arms through armholes of vest with opening to back (see **Figure 18.16b**).
7. Cross back panels by bringing tie on left side over to right and right tie to left.
8. Carefully smooth material so that there are no wrinkles.
9. Tie where patient cannot reach. (See the procedure "How to Tie Postural Supports.")
    a. Tie to bed frame *(not side rails).*
    b. Tie to wheelchair *(not stationary chair).*
10. Check for proper alignment and comfort of patient.
11. Check to be certain that knots or wrinkles are not causing pressure.
12. Check to be certain that support is snug but does not bind. *(You should be able to put two fingers under edges.)*
13. Place call light where it can be easily reached.

POSTPROCEDURE

14. Wash your hands.
15. Check skin condition and circulation every 15–30 minutes.
16. Remove restraint every 2 hours for 5–10 minutes.
17. Check patient frequently and move at least every 2 hours.
18. Chart the following:
    a. Reason for use of support
    b. Type of support used
    c. When it was applied
    d. When it was released
    e. Times of repositioning
    f. How patient tolerated it
    g. Condition of skin

9/14/11 1700
Vest postural support applied to
protect resident from getting out of
bed and falling, per physician's order
A. Chaplin CNA

PROCEDURE 18.43 Giving a Bed Bath

BACKGROUND: Providing a bed bath improves circulation, relaxes the patient, provides an opportunity to examine the skin, and enables you to interact with the patient.

ALERT: Follow Standard Precautions.

PREPROCEDURE

1. Wash hands.
2. Assemble equipment:
   a. Soap and soap dish
   b. Face towel
   c. Bath towel. Will need at least 2.
   d. Washcloth. Will need at least 2.
   e. Hospital gown or patient's sleepwear
   f. Lotion or powder
   g. Nailbrush and emery board
   h. Comb and brush
   i. Bedpan or urinal and cover
   j. Bed linen
   k. Bath blanket
   l. Bath basin, water at 105° F
   m. Disposable nonsterile gloves
3. Place linens on chair in order of use and place towels on overbed table.

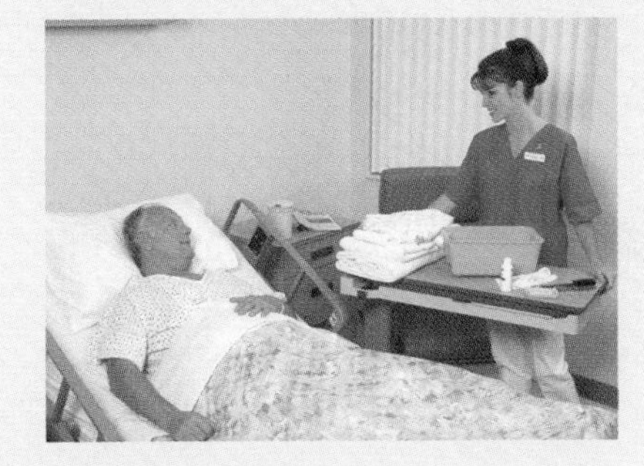

4. Identify patient.
5. Explain what you are going to do.

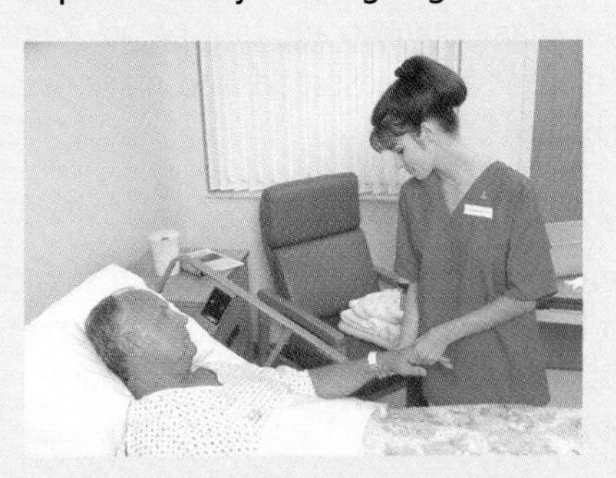

6. Provide for privacy by pulling the privacy screen curtain, or door.

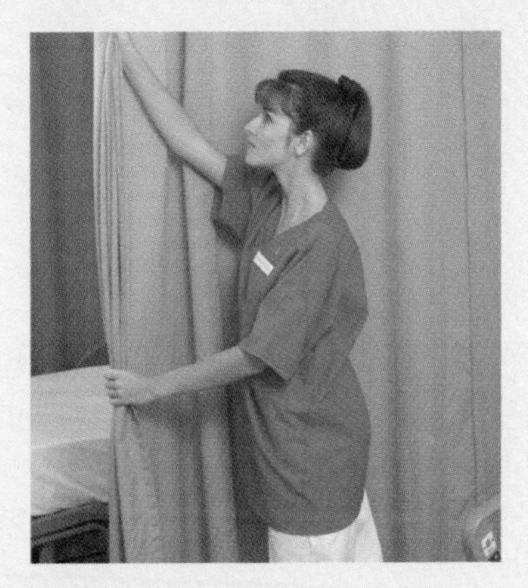

PROCEDURE

7. Raise bed to a comfortable working height.

8. Offer bedpan or urinal. Empty and rinse before starting bath. Wash your hands. (Remember to wear gloves when handling urine.)

(continued)

PROCEDURE 18.43 Giving a Bed Bath (continued)

9. Lower headrest and knee gatch (raised knee area/bed) so that bed is flat.
10. Lower the side rail only on side where you are working.
11. Put on gloves.
12. Loosen top sheet, blanket, and bedspread. Remove and fold blanket and bedspread, and place over back of chair.
13. Cover patient with a bath blanket.
14. Ask patient to hold bath blanket in place. Remove top sheet by sliding it to foot of bed. *Do not expose patient.* (Place soiled linen in laundry container.)

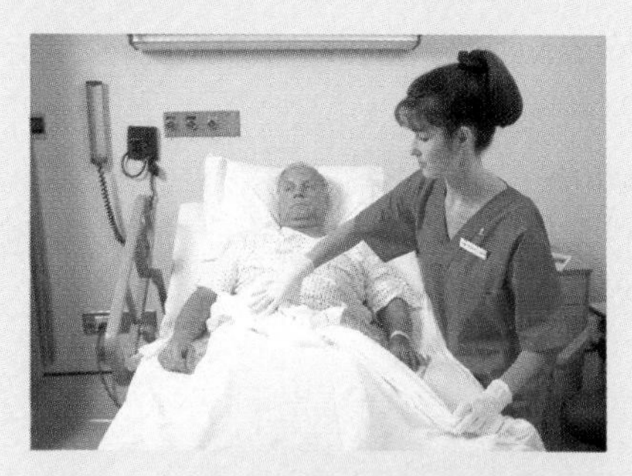

15. Leave a pillow under patient's head for comfort.
16. Remove patient's gown and place in laundry container. If nightwear belongs to patient, follow hospital policy (i.e., send home with family or to hospital laundry).
17. To remove gown when the patient has an IV:

NOTE: Most facilities provide gowns with snaps for easy removal around existing intravenous tubing.

   a. Loosen gown from neck.
   b. Slip gown from free arm.
   c. Be certain that patient is covered with a bath blanket.
   d. Slip gown away from body toward arm with IV.
   e. Gather gown at arm and slip downward over arm and tubing. *Be careful not to pull on tubing.*
   f. Gather material of gown in one hand and slowly draw gown over tip of fingers.
   g. Lift IV free of stand with free hand and slip gown over bottle.
   h. *Do not lower bottle! Raise gown.*

18. Fill bath basin two-thirds full with warm water. Test water temperature and ensure it is safe and comfortable before bathing patients and adjust if necessary.
19. Help patient move to side of bed nearest you.
20. Fold face towel over upper edge of bath blanket. This will keep it dry.
21. Form a mitten by folding washcloth around your hand.

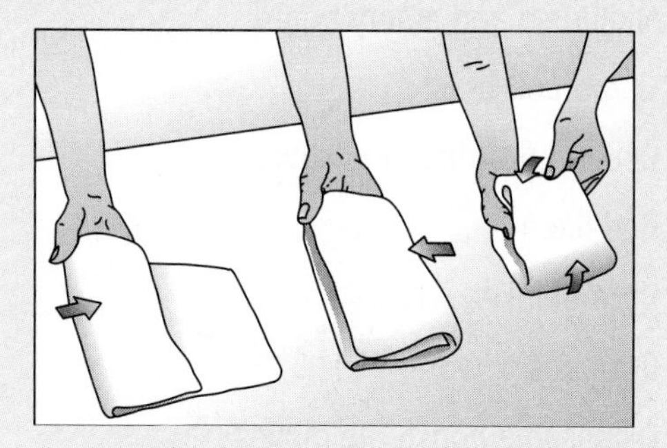

22. Wash patient's eyes from nose to outside of face. Use different corners of washcloth.

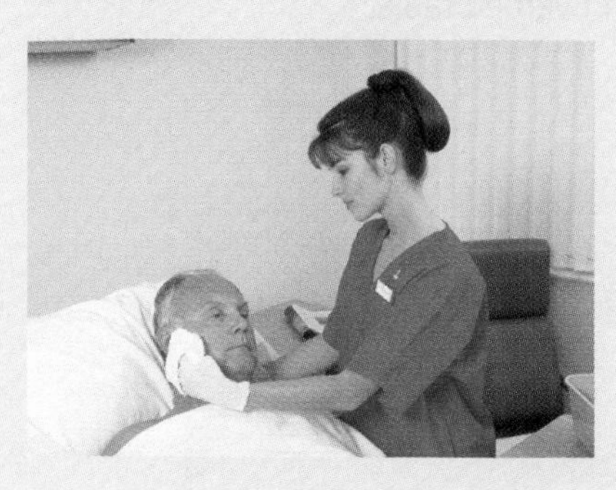

(continued)

23. Ask patient if he or she wants soap used on the face. Gently wash and rinse face, ears, and neck. Be careful not to get soap in eyes. Dry face with towel, using a blotting motion.
24. To wash patient's arms, shoulders, axilla:
    a. Uncover patient's far arm (one farthest from you).

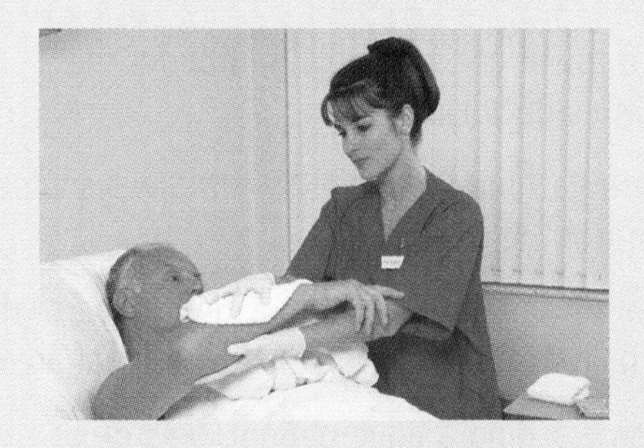

    b. Protect bed from becoming wet with a bath towel placed under arm. Wash with long, firm, circular strokes, rinse, and dry.
    c. Wash and dry armpits (axillae). Apply deodorant and powder.

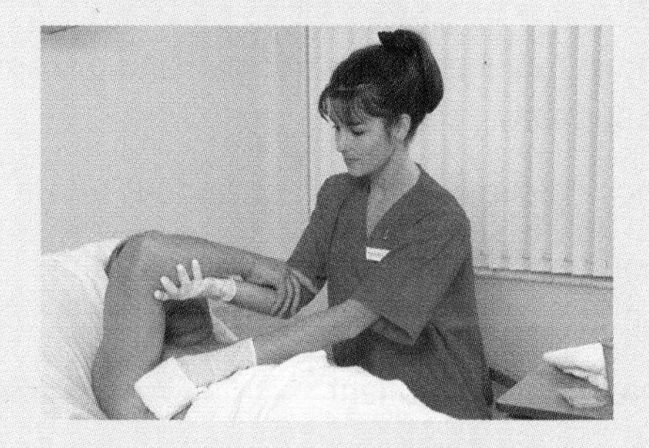

25. To wash hand:
    a. Place basin of water on towel.
    b. Put patient's hand into basin.
    c. Wash, rinse, and dry and push back cuticle gently.
26. Repeat on other arm.
27. To wash chest:
    a. Place towel lengthwise across patient's chest.
    b. Fold bath blanket down to patient's abdomen.
    c. Wash chest. Be especially careful to dry skin under female breasts to prevent irritation. Dry area thoroughly.
28. To wash abdomen:
    a. Fold down bath blanket to pubic area.
    b. Wash, rinse, and dry abdomen.

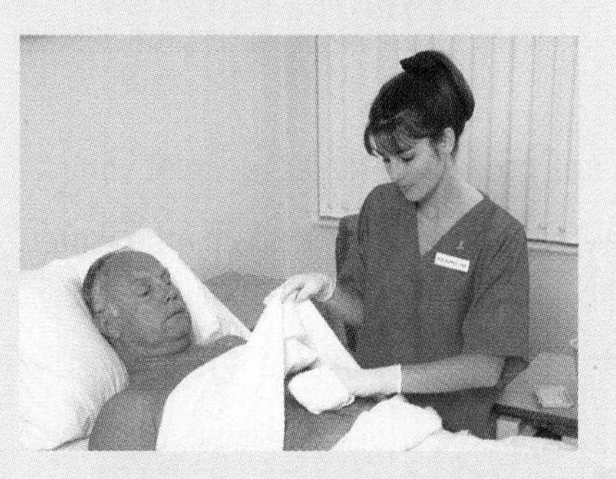

    c. Pull up bath blanket to keep patient warm.
    d. Slide towel out from under bath blanket.
29. To wash thigh, leg, and foot:
    a. Ask patient to flex knee if possible.
    b. Fold bath blanket to uncover thigh, leg, and foot of leg farthest from you.
    c. Place bath towel under leg to keep bed from getting wet.
    d. Place basin on towel and put foot into basin.
    e. Wash and rinse thigh, leg, and foot.

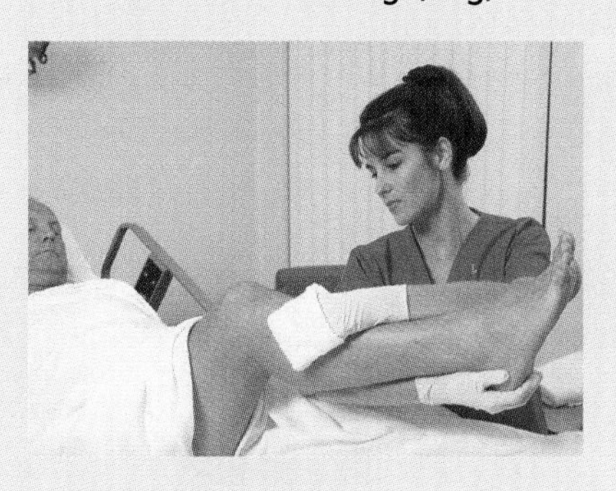

(continued)

f. Dry well between toes. Be careful to support the leg when lifting it.

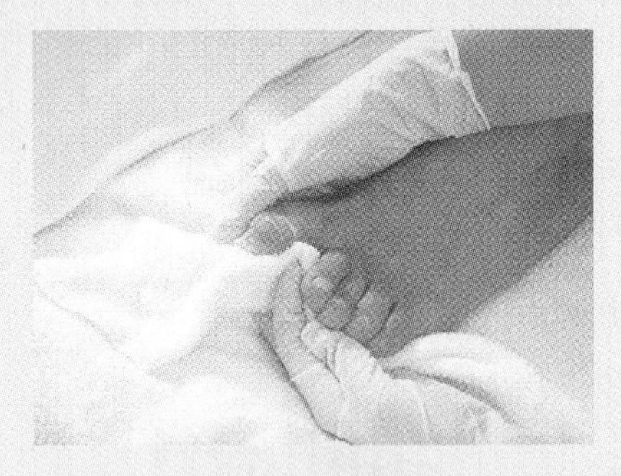

30. Follow same procedure for leg nearest you.
31. Change water. You may need to change water before this time if it is dirty or cold.
32. Raise side rail on opposite side if it is down.
33. To wash back and buttocks:
    a. Help patient turn on side away from you.
    b. Have patient move toward center of bed.
    c. Place a bath towel lengthwise on bed, under patient's back.
    d. Wash, rinse, and dry neck, back, and buttocks.
    e. Give patient a back rub. Help patient turn back on their back and make sure they are still covered with a bath blanket. Massage back for at least a minute and a half, giving special attention to shoulder blades, hip bones, and spine. *Observe for reddened areas.* (See the procedure "Skin Care—Giving a Back Rub.")

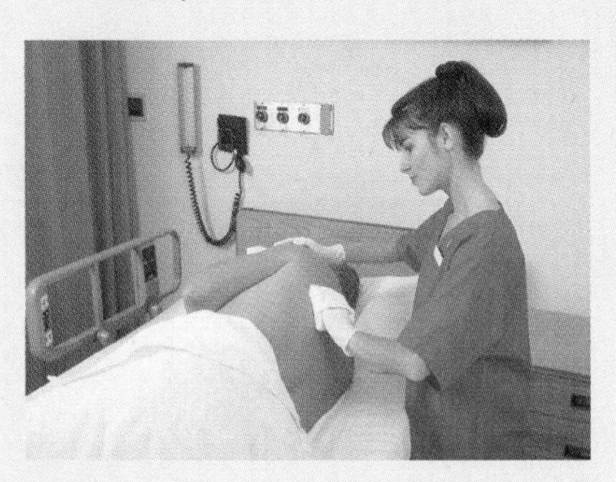

34. To wash genital area:
    a. Offer patient a clean, soapy washcloth to wash genital area.
    b. Give the person a clean, wet washcloth to rinse with and a dry towel to dry with.
35. Clean the genital area thoroughly if patient is unable to help. To clean the genital area:
    a. Put a towel or disposable pad under the patient's buttock.
    b. When washing a female patient always wipe from front to back.
    c. Separate the labia and use a clean area of the wash cloth for each side of the perineal area.
    d. When washing a male patient, be sure to wash and dry penis, scrotum, and groin area carefully. Clean the tip of the penis using a circular motion and clean the shaft of the penis from top to bottom. Remember to pull back the foreskin if the patient is not circumcised.
    e. Remove towel or disposable pad and discard appropriately.
    f. Remove gloves and put in hazardous waste.
36. If range of motion is ordered, complete at this time. (See the procedure "Range of Motion.")
37. Put a clean gown on patient.

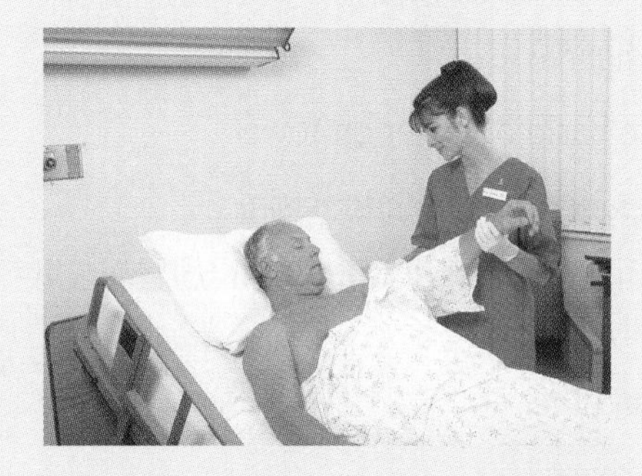

(continued)

PROCEDURE 18.43 Giving a Bed Bath (continued)

38. If patient has an IV:
    a. Gather the sleeve on IV side in one hand.
    b. Lift bottle free of stand. Do not lower bottle.
    c. Slip bottle through sleeve from inside and rehang.
    d. Guide gown along the IV tubing to bed.
    e. Slip gown over the patient's hand. Be careful not to pull or crimp tubing.
    f. Put gown on arm with IV, then on opposite arm.
39. Comb or brush hair.

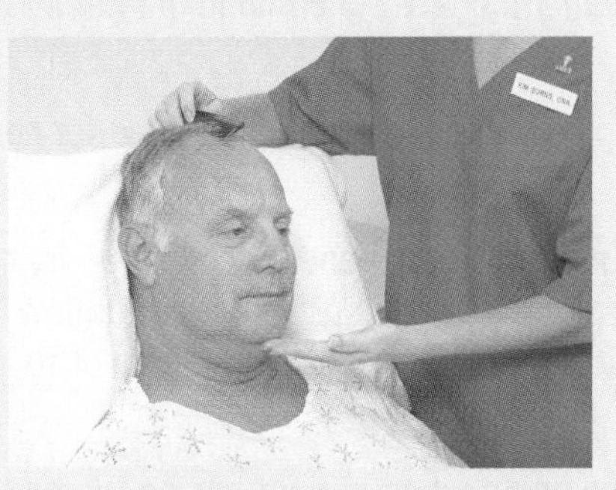

40. Follow hospital policy for towels and washcloths. Some have you hang them for later use; others have you place them in the laundry containers immediately.

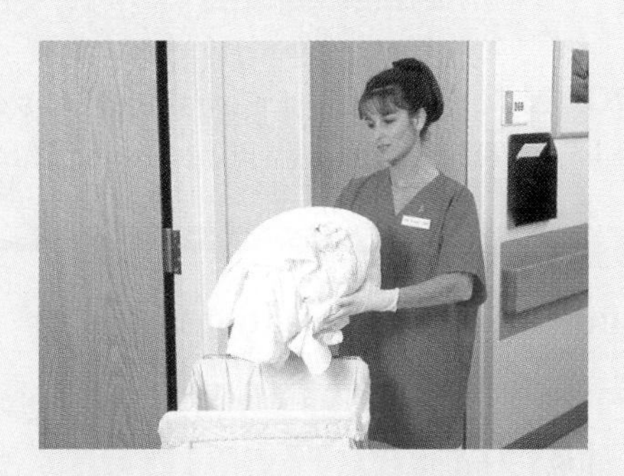

41. Leave patient in a comfortable position and in good body alignment.
42. Place call bell within reach. Replace furniture and tidy unit.

POSTPROCEDURE

43. Wash hands.
44. Chart procedure and how patient tolerated it. Note any unusual skin changes or patient complaints.

10/24/11	0945
	Completed bed bath
	Dime-sized red area on sacrum
	Reported to charge nurse
	No complaints of discomfort
	Resting quietly with rails up
	________ *A. Chaplin CNA*

PROCEDURE 18.44

Giving a Partial Bath (Face, Hands, Axillae, Buttocks, and Genitals)

BACKGROUND: Providing a partial bath relaxes the patient and prevents odors. The interaction with the patient is important through communication and touch.

ALERT: Follow Standard Precautions.

PREPROCEDURE

1. Wash hands.
2. Assemble equipment:
   a. Soap and soap dish
   b. Face towel
   c. Bath towel
   d. Washcloth
   e. Hospital gown or patient's sleepwear
   f. Lotion or powder
   g. Nail brush and emery board
   h. Comb and brush
   i. Bedpan or urinal and cover
   j. Bath blanket
   k. Bath basin, water at 105°F
   l. Clean linen, as needed
   m. Disposable gloves
3. Identify patient.
4. Explain what you are going to do.
5. Provide privacy by pulling privacy screen, curtain, or door.
6. Offer bedpan or urinal. Empty and rinse before starting bath. (Wear gloves if handling body fluid.)
7. Raise headrest to a comfortable position, if permitted.
8. Lower side rails if permitted. If they are to remain up, lower only side rail on side where you are working.

PROCEDURE

10. Loosen top sheet, blanket, and bedspread. Remove and fold blanket and bedspread and place over back of chair.
11. Cover patient with a bath blanket.
12. Ask patient to hold bath blanket in place. Remove top sheet by sliding it to the foot of bed: *Do not expose patient.* (Place soiled linen in laundry container.)
13. Leave a pillow under the patient's head for comfort.
14. Remove patient's gown and place in laundry container. If nightwear belongs to patient, follow hospital policy (i.e., send home with family or to hospital
15. To remove gown when patient has an IV, see the procedure "Giving a Bed Bath."
16. Fill bath basin two-thirds full with warm water and place on overbed table. Test water temperature and ensure it is safe and comfortable before bathing patients; adjust if necessary.
17. Put overbed table where patient can reach it comfortably.
18. Place towel, washcloth, and soap on overbed table.
19. Ask patient to wash as much as he or she is able to and tell the person that you will return to complete bath.
20. Place call bell where patient can reach it easily. Ask patient to signal when ready.
21. Remove glove, wash your hands, and leave unit.
22. When patient signals, return to unit, wash your hands, and put on gloves.

(continued)

PROCEDURE 18.44 Giving a Partial Bath (Face, Hands, Axillae, Buttocks, and Genitals) (continued)

23. Change water. Test water temperature and ensure it is safe and comfortable before bathing patients and adjust if necessary.
24. Complete bathing areas the patient was unable to reach. Make sure that face, hands, axillae, genitals, and buttocks are dry. To wash the genital area:
    a. Offer the patient a clean, soapy washcloth to wash genital area. Provide a clean, wet washcloth to rinse with and a dry towel to dry with. If patient is unable to help, you will need to clean the genital area thoroughly.
    b. When washing a female patient, always wipe from front to back.
    c. Separate the labia and use a clean area of the wash cloth for each side of the perineal area.
    d. When washing a male patient, be sure to wash and dry penis, scrotum, and groin area carefully. Clean the tip of the penis using a circular motion and clean the shaft of the penis from top to bottom. Remember to pull back the foreskin if the patient is not circumcised.
    e. Remove gloves and put in hazardous waste. If range of motion is ordered, complete it at this time. (See the procedure "Range of Motion.")
25. Give a back rub. (See the procedure "Skin Care—Giving a Back Rub.")
26. Put a clean gown on patient.
27. If patient has an IV, see the procedure "Giving a Bed Bath."
28. Assist patient in applying deodorant and putting on a clean gown.
29. Change bed according to hospital policy. Not all facilities change linen every day.
30. Put up side rails if required.
31. Leave patient in a comfortable position and in good body alignment.

POSTPROCEDURE

32. Remove and discard gloves.
33. Wash hands.
34. Place call bell within reach. Replace furniture and tidy unit.
35. Chart procedure and how it was tolerated.

9/23/11	0730
	Partial bath
	No skin breakdown noted
	Complained of headache
	Reported to charge nurse
	________ S. Gomez CNA

PROCEDURE 18.45 Tub/Shower Bath

BACKGROUND: Providing a relaxing tub/shower bath gives one-on-one time to the patient. It is an opportunity to check for skin and other problems. Careful observation is essential.

ALERT: Follow Standard Precautions.

PREPROCEDURE

1. Wash hands.
2. Assemble equipment on a chair near the tub. Be certain the tub is clean.
   a. Bath towels
   b. Washcloths
   c. Soap
   d. Bath thermometer
   e. Wash basin
   f. Clean gown
   g. Bathmat
   h. Disinfectant solution
   i. Shower chair if necessary
3. Identify patient and explain what you are going to do.
4. Provide privacy by pulling privacy curtain, screen, or door.

PROCEDURE

5. Help patient out of bed.
6. Help with robe and slippers.
7. Check with head nurse to see if the patient can ambulate or if a wheelchair or shower chair is needed. If a shower chair is used, always do the following:
   a. Cover patient with a bath blanket or sheet so that patient is not exposed in any way.
   b. Provide adequate clothing for patient, such as a robe or extra cover.

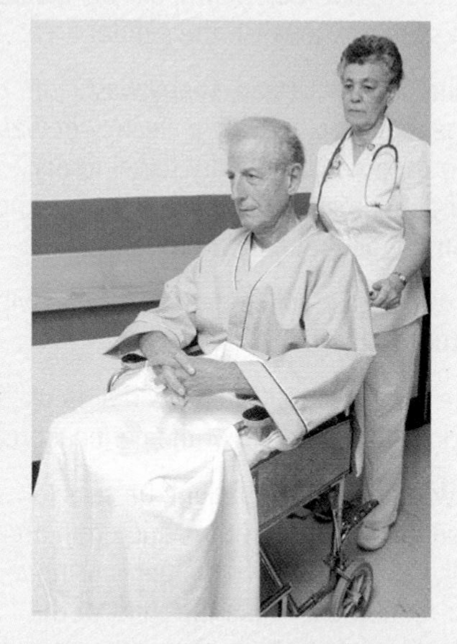

8. Take patient to shower or tub room.
9. For tub bath, place a towel in bottom of tub to help prevent falling.

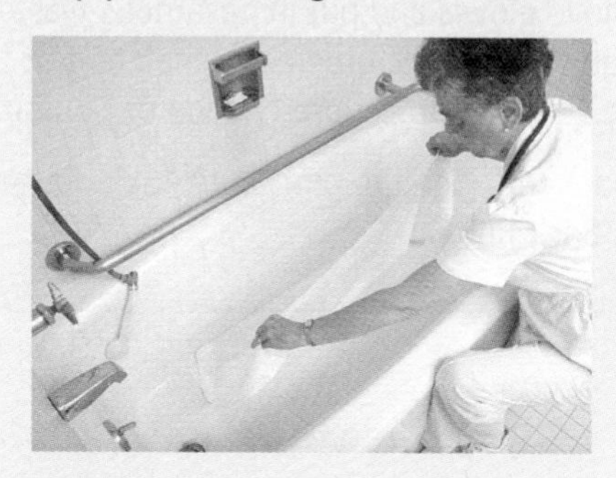

10. Fill tub with water or adjust shower flow (95–105°F).
11. Help patient undress. Give a male patient a towel to wrap around his midriff.
12. Assist patient into tub or shower. If shower, leave weak patient in shower chair.

NOTE: Remember to put on gloves.

(continued)

PROCEDURE 18.45 Tub/Shower Bath (continued)

13. Wash patient's back. Observe carefully for reddened areas or breaks in skin.
14. Patient may be left alone to complete genitalia area if feeling strong.

NOTE: If patient shows signs of weakness, remove plug from tub and drain water, or turn off shower. Allow patient to rest until feeling better.

15. Assist patient from tub or shower.
16. Wrap bath towel around patient to prevent chilling.

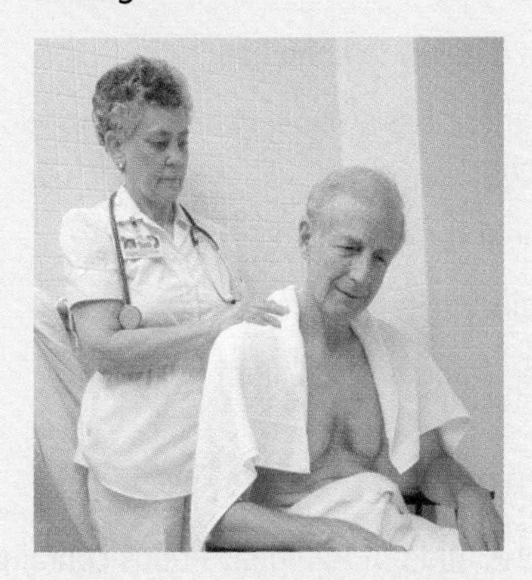

17. Remove gloves and put in biohazardous container.
18. Assist in drying and dressing.
19. Return to unit and make comfortable. Make sure call bell is within patient's reach.
20. Put away equipment.
21. Clean bathtub with disinfectant solution.

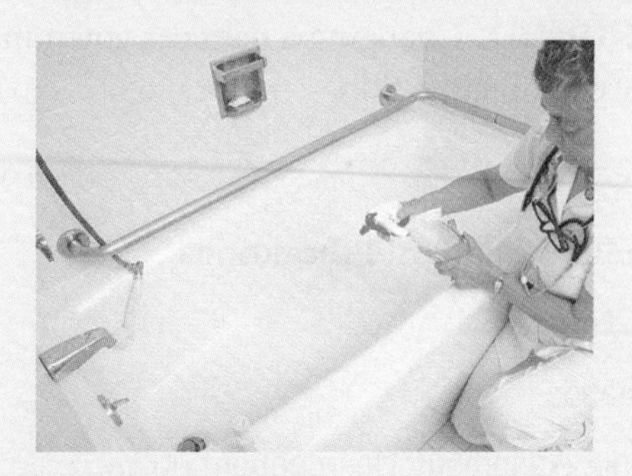

POSTPROCEDURE

22. Wash hands.
23. Chart procedure and how patient tolerated it.

NOTE: Use gloves if you are in contact with body fluids.

7/07/11	0900
	Assisted with shower
	Taken to shower on shower chair
	No skin problems noted
	Tolerated well
	________ *A. Chaplin CNA*

PROCEDURE 18.46 Patient Gown Change

BACKGROUND: Changing a patient's gown makes the patient feel clean and refreshed. It also allows you to visually examine the skin.

ALERT: Follow Standard Precautions.

PREPROCEDURE

1. Wash hands.
2. Assemble equipment: clean patient gown.
3. Tell patient what you are going to do.
4. Provide privacy by pulling privacy curtain.
5. Put on gloves in case you come in contact with bodily fluids.

PROCEDURE

6. Untie strings of gown at neck and midback. (It may be necessary to assist patient onto side.)
7. Pull soiled gown out from sides of patient.
8. Unfold clean gown and position over patient.
9. Remove soiled gown one sleeve at a time.
10. Leave soiled gown laying over patient's chest; insert one arm into sleeve of clean gown.

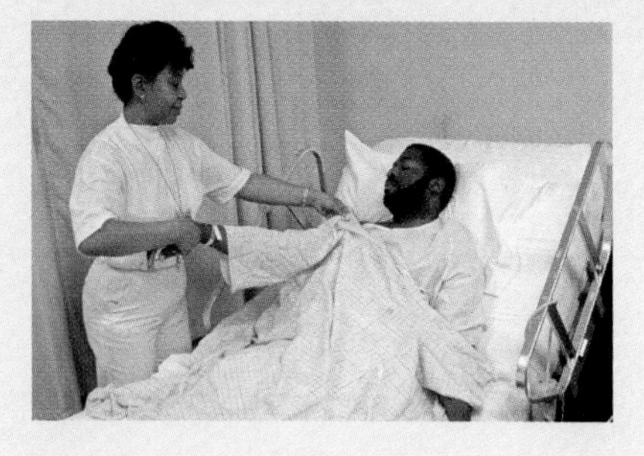

11. Fold soiled gown to one side as clean gown is placed over patient's chest.
12. Insert other arm in empty sleeve of gown.
13. Tie neck string on side of neck.
14. Tie midback tie if patient desires.
15. Remove soiled gown to linen hamper.
16. Slip gown under covers, being careful not to expose patient.
17. Position patient for comfort.
18. Raise side rails when necessary.
19. Place bedside stand and call light in patient's reach.

POSTPROCEDURE

20. Remove gloves and put in biohazardous container.
21. Wash hands.

PROCEDURE 18.47 Perineal Care

BACKGROUND: Perineal care provides cleansing around areas where body waste is eliminated. The perineal area is dark, warm, and moist, providing an environment for bacterial growth. Keeping the perineum free of drainage and bacteria is an important preventive health measure and helps patients feel more comfortable.

ALERT: Follow Standard Precautions.

PREPROCEDURE

1. Wash hands.
2. Assemble equipment.
   a. Bath blanket
   b. Bedpan and cover
   c. Basin
   d. Solution, water, or other if ordered
   e. Cotton balls
   f. Waterproof protector for bed
   g. Disposable gloves
   h. Perineal pad and belt if needed
3. Identify patient.
4. Explain what you are going to do.
5. Provide privacy by pulling privacy curtain.

PROCEDURE

6. Put warm water in basin.
7. Raise bed to a comfortable working height.
8. Lower side rail.
9. Put on disposable gloves.
10. Remove spread and blanket.
11. Cover patient with bath blanket.
12. Have patient hold top of bath blanket, and fold top sheet to bottom of bed.
13. Place waterproof protector under patient's buttocks.
14. Pull up bath blanket to expose perineal area.
15. Provide male and female pericare.
    a. Circumcised male: Wipe away from urinary meatus as you wash with soap and water, rinse, and dry in a circular motion. Clean the shaft of the penis from top to bottom.

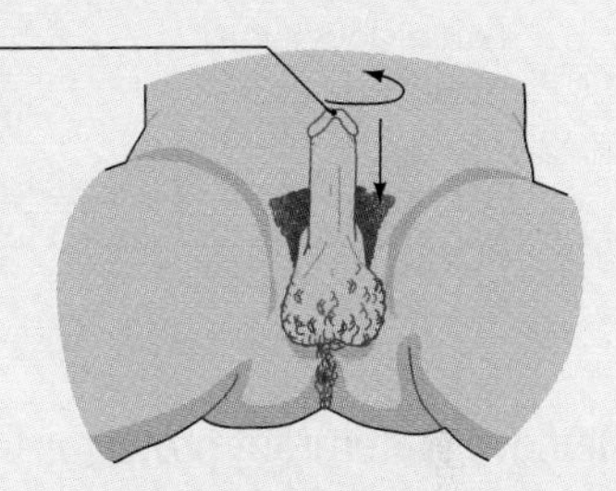

    b. Uncircumcised male: Gently move foreskin back away from tip of penis. Wash as directed in step a. After drying, gently move foreskin back over tip of penis.

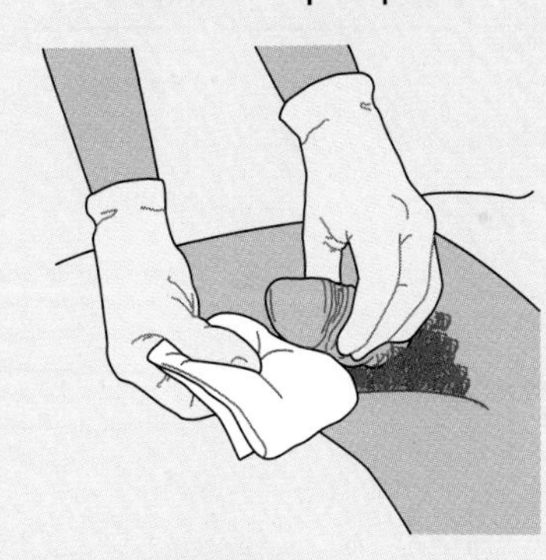

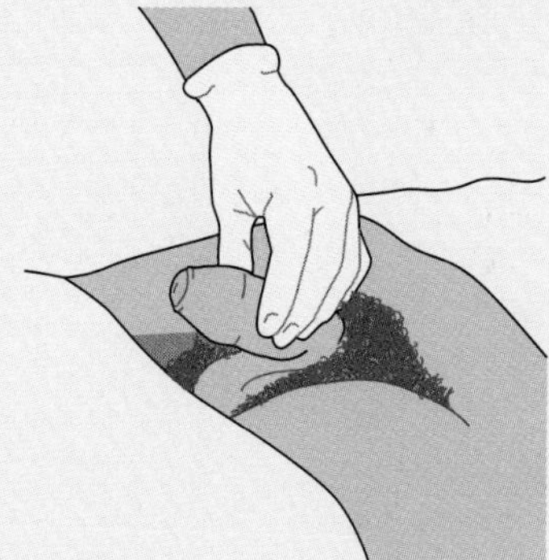

(continued)

PROCEDURE 18.47 Perineal Care (continued)

c. Female:

(1) Instruct patient to bend knees with feet flat on bed.

(2) Separate patient's knees.

(3) Separate the labia and wipe from front to back away from the urethra as you wash with soap and water, rinse, and dry. Use a clear part of the washcloth for each stroke.

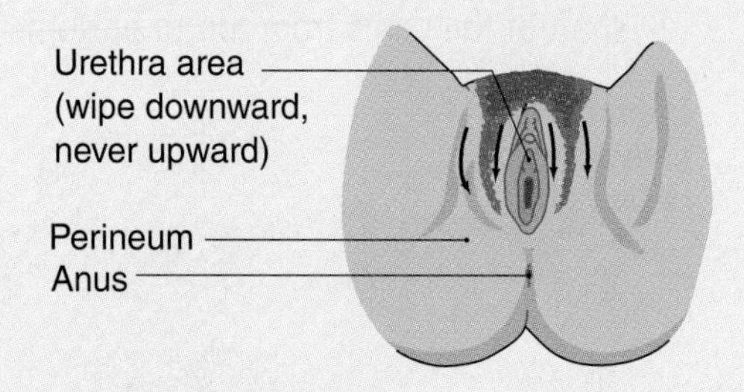

16. Remove waterproof protector from bed and dispose of gloves.
17. Cover patient with sheet and remove bath blanket.
18. Return top covers.
19. Return bed to lowest position and put up side rails if required.
20. Secure call bell within patient's reach.

POSTPROCEDURE

21. Clean equipment; dispose of disposable material according to hospital policy.
22. Discard gloves and put in biohazardous container.
23. Wash hands.

4/14/12	1045
	Perineal care provided
	Observed a dime-sized reddened area
	on the interior left thigh approximately
	2 inches below the groin
	________ *R. Johnson CNA*

PROCEDURE 18.48 Shampooing the Hair in Bed

BACKGROUND: Clean hair makes a patient feel fresh and provides a sense of well-being. Your careful attention to the steps below will make this a pleasant experience for the patient and yourself.

ALERT: Follow Standard Precautions.

PREPROCEDURE

1. Wash hands.
2. Assemble equipment:
   a. Chair
   b. Basin of water (105°F)
   c. Pitcher of water (115°F)
   d. Paper or Styrofoam cup
   e. Large basin
   f. Shampoo tray or plastic sheet
   g. Waterproof bed protector
   h. Pillow with waterproof cover
   i. Bath towels
   j. Small towel
   k. Cotton balls
3. Identify patient.
4. Explain what you are going to do.
5. Provide privacy by pulling privacy curtain.

PROCEDURE

6. Raise bed to a comfortable working position.
7. Place a chair at side of bed near patient's head.
8. Place small towel on chair.
9. Place large basin on chair to catch water.
10. Put cotton in patient's ears to keep water out of ears.
11. Have patient move to side of bed with head close to where you are standing.
12. Remove pillow from under head. Lower head of bed and remove pillows. Cover pillow with waterproof case.
13. Place pillow under patient's back so that when he or she lies down the head will be tilted back.
14. Place bath blanket on bed.
15. Have patient hold top of bath blanket, and pull top covers to foot.
16. Place waterproof protector under head.
17. Put shampoo tray under patient's head (i.e., plastic bag with both ends open).
18. Place end of plastic in large basin.
19. Have patient hold washcloth over eyes.
20. Put basin of water on bedside table with paper cup. Have pitcher of water for extra water. Test water temperature to ensure it is safe and comfortable before wetting patient's hair. Adjust if needed.
21. Brush patient's hair thoroughly.
22. Fill cup with water from basin.
23. Pour water over hair; repeat until completely wet.
24. Apply small amount of shampoo; use both hands to massage the patient's scalp with your fingertips. Be careful not to scratch the scalp with your fingernails.
25. Rinse soap off hair by pouring water from cup over hair. Have patient turn head from side to side. Repeat until completely rinsed.
26. Dry patient's forehead and ears.
27. Remove cotton from ears.
28. Lift patient's head gently and wrap with bath towel.
29. Remove equipment from bed.
30. Change patient's gown and be certain patient is dry.
31. Gently dry patient's hair with towel. (Use a hair dryer if allowed by your facility.)

(continued)

PROCEDURE 18.48 Shampooing the Hair in Bed (continued)

32. Comb or brush hair and arrange neatly.
33. Remove bath blanket and cover patient with top covers.
34. Make patient comfortable.
35. Lower bed to its lowest position.
36. Put up side rail if required.

POSTPROCEDURE

37. Return equipment.
38. Tidy unit.
39. Wash hands.
40. Record procedure.

9/06/11	1130
	Hair washed while in bed
	There is a dime-sized red scaly area
	on scalp directly above left ear
	Resident denies pain or itching at site
	Notified charge nurse
	Hair dried with hair dryer and styled
	to suit resident
	________ R. Johnson CNA

PROCEDURE 18.49 Shampooing in Shower or Tub

BACKGROUND: Clean hair makes a patient feel fresh and provides a sense of well-being. Your careful attention to the steps below will make this a pleasant experience for the patient and yourself.

ALERT: Follow Standard Precautions.

PREPROCEDURE

1. Wash hands.
2. Assemble equipment:
   a. Shampoo
   b. Washcloth
   c. Towel
   d. Cream rinse, if desired
3. Provide privacy by pulling curtain or door.
4. Explain what you are going to do.

PROCEDURE

5. Instruct patient to tip head back.
6. Wet hair with water, being careful not to get eyes wet.
7. Give patient a washcloth to wipe his or her face as needed.
8. Apply a moderate amount of shampoo to hair. Massage head and hair until a lather develops. (Be careful not to use fingernails.)
9. Rinse hair with clean, clear water until shampoo has disappeared.
10. Repeat shampooing procedure a second time. When rinsing, be sure to remove all shampoo.
11. If a cream rinse is used, apply a small amount to hair, paying special attention to ends of hair.
12. Allow rinse to remain on hair for a few seconds before rinsing.
13. Rinse thoroughly with clean, clear water.
14. Towel dry.
15. Gently comb or brush hair to remove tangles.
16. Use a hair dryer to dry hair.
17. Arrange in an appropriate hairstyle for the patient's age and manner. (Remember that ponytails, pigtails, etc. are not appropriate for a 70-year-old patient.)

POSTPROCEDURE

18. Return equipment.
19. Wash hands.
20. Record procedure.

10/13/11 0830
Hair washed while in shower
Scalp is clean and there is no
evidence of sores or scratches present
Upon return to room, hair styled
according to resident's preference
________ A. Chaplin CNA

PROCEDURE 18.50 Arranging the Hair

BACKGROUND: A patient's outward appearance plays a significant role in his or her self-image. Arranging the hair is a key part of the daily grooming routine for every patient. It is important to arrange your patient's hair according to their preferences.

ALERT: Follow Standard Precautions.

PREPROCEDURE

1. Wash hands.
2. Assemble equipment.
   a. Comb and/or brush
   b. Towel
3. Identify patient.
4. Explain what you are going to do.
5. Provide privacy by pulling privacy curtain.
6. Raise bed to a comfortable working height.

PROCEDURE

7. Assist as needed.
8. If total assistance is needed:
   a. Section the hair, starting at one side, working around to other side.
   b. Comb or brush hair thoroughly, being careful not to pull it.
   c. Arrange hair neatly.
9. Lower bed to lowest position.
10. Put up side rail if required.
11. Secure call light in patient's reach.

POSTPROCEDURE

12. Clean and replace all equipment.
13. Wash hands.
14. Report procedure and observations (e.g., dry scalp, reddened areas).

PROCEDURE 18.51 Nail Care

BACKGROUND: A patient's outward appearance plays a significant role in his or her self-image. Nail care is a key part of the daily grooming routine for every patient. Keeping nails clean and trimmed prevents sores from developing around the nail beds and eliminates unintentional scratches that could become infected.

ALERT: Follow Standard Precautions.

PREPROCEDURE

1. Wash hands.
2. Assemble equipment.
   a. Warm water
   b. Orange sticks
   c. Emery board
   d. Nail clippers

NOTE: Do not clip a diabetic patient's nails.

3. Identify the patient and explain the procedure.
4. Provide privacy for the patient by pulling a curtain or closing the door.
5. Test water temperature and ensure it is safe and comfortable before immersing patient's fingers in water; adjust if needed.
6. Place basin of water at a comfortable level for patients. Cleanse nails by soaking in water.
7. Put on gloves.

PROCEDURE

8. Use slanted edge of orange stick to clean dirt out from under nails. Wipe orangewood stick on towel after each nail and dry patient's hand/fingers, including between fingers.

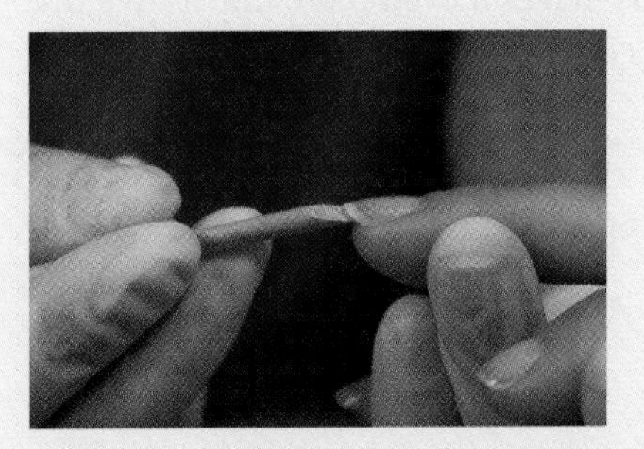

9. File nails with emery board to shorten. (Clip if permitted by your facility.)
10. Use smooth edge of emery board to smooth.
11. Apply lotion to help condition cuticle.
12. Massage hands and feet with lotion.
13. Make patient comfortable.
14. Raise side rail if required. Make sure call bell is within reach.

POSTPROCEDURE

15. Empty, rinse and wipe basin
16. Return equipment.
17. Remove and dispose of gloves in biohazardous container.
18. Wash hands.
19. Record procedure and any unusual conditions (e.g., hangnails, broken nails).

PROCEDURE 18.52 Foot Care

BACKGROUND: Providing and assisting with foot care is an important part of total patient care. For elderly patients and the diabetic patient improper foot care can lead to decreased mobility and even loss of mobility.

Both the elderly and the diabetic may experience decreased circulation and decreased sensation to the lower extremities. This makes it even more imperative that the condition of the feet are checked frequently for any change in status or acute problems.

ALERT: Follow Standard Precautions.

PREPROCEDURE

1. Wash hands.
2. Put on disposable gloves.
3. Explain procedure to patient and provide for patient privacy with curtain, screen, or door.

PROCEDURE

4. Inspect the feet for any problems/change in skin integrity. Check for the presence of pulses and note their strengths. Assess for any patient complaints.
5. Test water temperature and ensure it is safe and comfortable before placing patient's foot in water and adjust if needed.
6. Place basin at a comfortable position on protective barrier.
7. Completely submerge and soak foot in water
8. Bathe the feet thoroughly in tepid water with a mild soap. Be sure to clean the interdigital areas.
9. Dry the feet thoroughly, paying particular attention to the interdigital areas. Apply lotion to feet but avoid leaving lotion in the interdigital areas as it could provide a moist environment for bacteria and fungal growth. Support foot and ankle throughout the procedure.
10. If nails are overgrown use a file instead of scissors or clippers. If the patient is a diabetic and a file is not sufficient refer the patient to a Podiatrist for further nail care.
11. Empty, rinse and wipe bath basin and return to proper storage.
12. Dispose of soiled linens in proper container. Remove glove and place in biohazardous container.
13. Make sure the patient is comfortable and the call bell is within reach.
14. Discourage the patient from going barefoot. Decreased sensation may allow an injury to occur without the patient noting it.
15. Encourage the patient to use appropriate footwear. Ill fitting shoes may contribute to skin breakdown. All new footwear should be broken in gradually over time. All shoes that are rough or worn or do not provide adequate foot support should be discarded.
16. Clean, dry socks that provide warmth, absorb perspiration and protect the feet should be worn.

POSTPROCEDURE

17. Return equipment.
18. Remove and dispose of gloves in biohazardous container.
19. Wash hands.
20. Report any signs of foot problems to the physician. Early interventions will diminish the magnitude of any problems noted.

NOTE: It is always the caregiver's responsibility to provide education to the patient during the process of providing care.

PROCEDURE 18.53 Shaving the Patient

BACKGROUND: A patient's outward appearance plays a significant role in his or her self-image. Shaving facial hair is a key part of the daily grooming routine for many patients. Carefully follow the steps below as you groom your patient each day.

ALERT: Follow Standard Precautions.

PRETPROCEDURE

1. Wash hands.
2. Assemble equipment:
   a. Electric shaver or safety razor
   b. Shaving lather or an electric preshave lotion
   c. Basin of warm water
   d. Face towel
   e. Mirror
   f. Aftershave
   g. Disposable gloves
3. Identify patient and explain what you are going to do.
4. Provide privacy by pulling privacy curtains.

PROCEDURE

5. Raise head of bed if permitted.
6. Place equipment on overbed table.
7. Place a towel over patient's chest.
8. Adjust light so that it shines on patient's face.
9. Shave patient.
   a. If you are using a safety razor:
      (1) Put on gloves.
      (2) Moisten face and apply lather.
      (3) Start in front of ear; hold skin taut and bring razor down over cheek toward chin. Use short firm strokes. Repeat until lather on cheek is removed and skin is smooth.
      (4) Repeat on other cheek.
      (5) Wash face and neck. Dry thoroughly.
      (6) Apply aftershave lotion or powder if desired.
      (7) Discard gloves according to facility policy.
   b. If you are using an electric shaver:
      (1) Put on gloves.
      (2) Apply preshave lotion.
      (3) Gently shave until beard is removed.
      (4) Wash face and neck. Dry thoroughly.
      (5) Apply aftershave lotion or powder if desired.
      (6) Remove gloves.
10. Lower bed if you raised it and make sure side rails are up.
11. Make sure patient is comfortable and call bell is within reach.

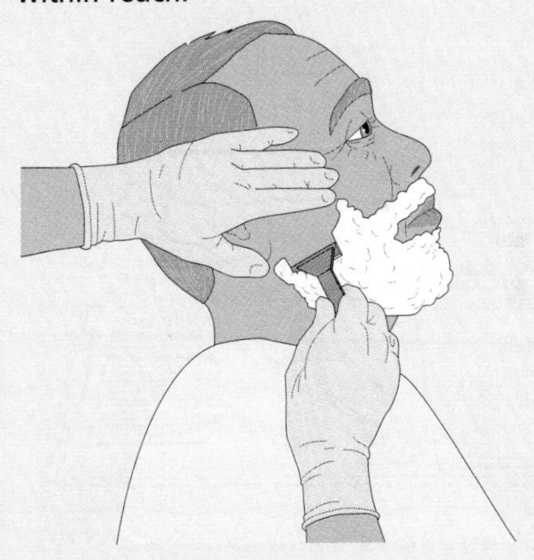

POSTPROCEDURE

12. Wash hands.
13. Chart procedure and how procedure was tolerated.

12/10/11	0730
	Face shaved with a safety razor
	Skin is clear and free of irritation
	R. Johnson CNA

PROCEDURE **18.54** Postmortem Care

BACKGROUND: Provides direction for the preparation of the body following death.

ALERT: Follow Standard Precautions.

PREPROCEDURE

1. Wash hands.
2. Assemble equipment.
   a. Wash basin with warm water
   b. Washcloth and towel
   c. Shroud/postmortem set:
      (1) Sheet or plastic container
      (2) Identification tags
      (3) Large container for personal belongings
      (4) Plastic pad
   d. Gurney or morgue cart
   e. Nonsterile disposable gloves

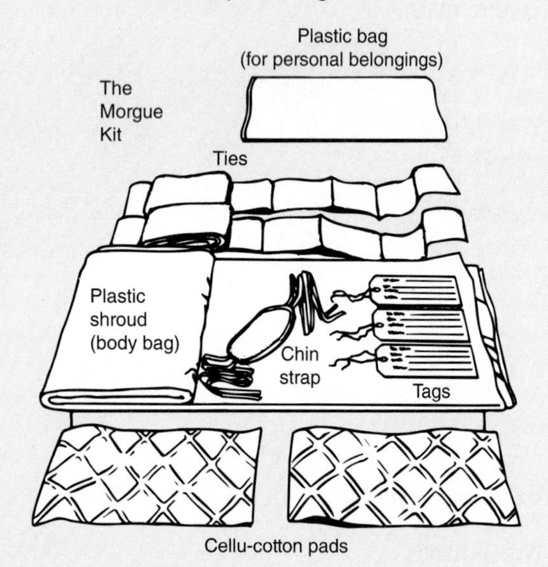

3. Close privacy curtains.
4. Put on gloves.

PROCEDURE

5. Position body in good alignment in supine position.
6. Keep one pillow under head.
7. Straighten arms and legs.
8. Gently close each eye. Do not apply pressure to eyelids.

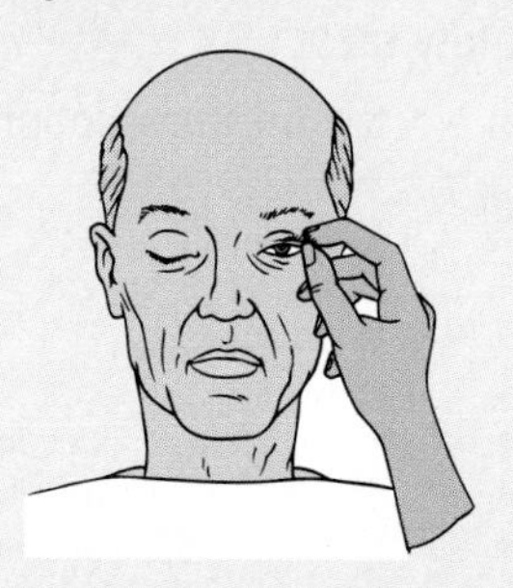

9. Put dentures in mouth or in a denture cup. If placed in a denture cup, put cup inside shroud so that mortician can find.
10. Remove all soiled dressings or clothing.
11. Bathe body thoroughly.
12. Apply clean dressings where needed.
13. Attach identification tags to wrists and ankles. Tag is usually placed on the right great toe and also on the outside of the shroud. Fill in tags with:
    a. Name
    b. Sex
    c. Hospital ID number
    d. Age

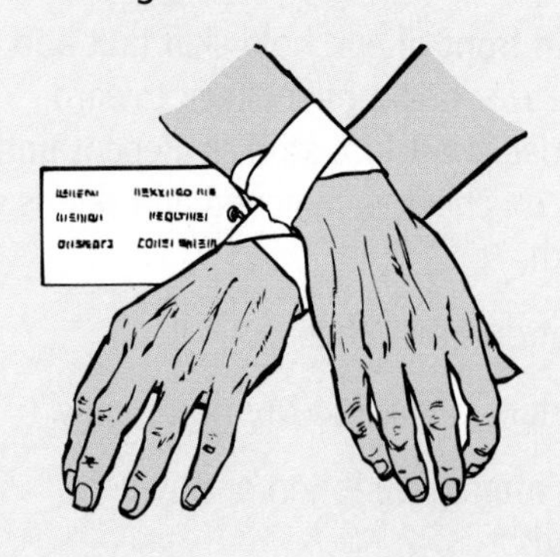

(continued)

PROCEDURE 18.54 Postmortem Care (continued)

14. Place body in a shroud, sheet, or other appropriate container. Do this in the following way:
    a. Ask for assistance from a co-worker.
    b. Logroll body to one side. Place shroud behind body leaving enough material to support body when rolled back. Fan-fold remaining shroud next to body.
    c. Place a plastic protection pad under buttocks.
    d. Roll body on its back and then to the other side.
    e. Pull fan-folded portion of shroud until flat.
    f. Roll body on its back.
    g. Cover entire body with shroud.
    h. Tuck in all loose edges of cover.
    i. Position a tie above elbows and below knees and secure around body.
    j. Attach ID tag to tie just above elbows.
15. Remove gloves and discard according to facility policy and procedure.
16. Wash hands.
17. Place all personal belongings in a large container. Label container with:
    a. Patient's name
    b. Age
    c. Room number
18. Place list of belongings in container and on patient's chart.
19. Follow your facility's procedure for transporting body and belongings through hallways.
20. Remove all linen and other supplies from room.

POSTPROCEDURE

21. Wash hands.
22. Report procedure completed to charge nurse.

12/07/11	0430
	Postmortem care completed
	Belongings listed and placed in bag,
	given to family
	Charge nurse notified
	________ *R. Johnson CNA*

PROCEDURE 18.55 Making a Closed Bed

BACKGROUND: Clean linens help prevent the spread of bacteria in the health care environment. A closed bed is made ready for new admissions or when a patient is not expected to return to bed until evening. Neatly made beds create a sense of order.

ALERT: Follow Standard Precautions.

PREPROCEDURE

1. Wash hands.
2. Assemble equipment:
   a. Fitted bottom sheet and one large sheet
   b. Draw sheet or large pad
   c. Blankets as needed
   d. Spread
   e. Pillow
   f. Pillowcase
3. Raise bed to a comfortable working height. Lock wheels on bed.
4. Place a chair at the side of bed.
5. Put linen on chair in the order in which you will use it. (First things you will use go on top.)

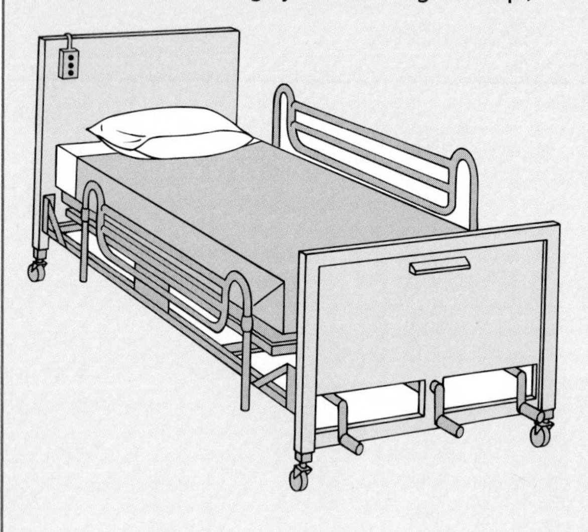

PROCEDURE

6. Position mattress at head of bed until it is against head board.
7. Work on one side of bed until that side is completed. Then go to other side of bed. This saves you time and energy.
8. Tuck edges of fitted bottom sheet under bed.

Tuck the entire side of the sheet under the mattress.

9. Place pad midway on bed or tuck in draw sheet.

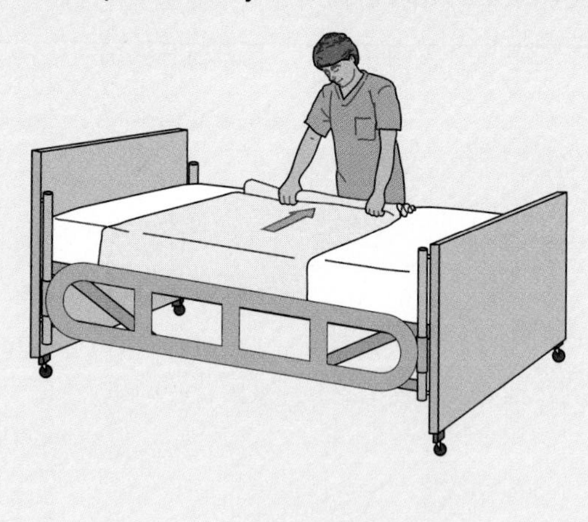

(continued)

PROCEDURE 18.55 Making a Closed Bed (continued)

10. Top sheet is folded lengthwise. Place on bed.
    a. Place the center fold at center of bed from head to foot.
    b. Put large hem at head of bed, even with top of mattress.
    c. Open the sheet. Be certain rough edge of hem is facing up.
    d. Tightly tuck the sheet under at foot of bed.
    e. Make a mitered corner at foot of bed.
    f. Do not tuck in sheet at side of bed.

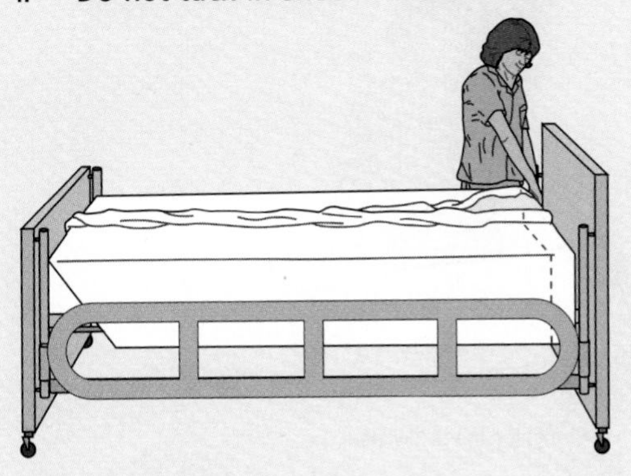

11. Blanket is folded lengthwise. Place it on bed.
    a. Place center fold of blanket on center of bed from head to foot.
    b. Place upper hem 6 inches from top of mattress.
    c. Open blanket and tuck it under foot tightly.
    d. Make a mitered corner at foot of bed.
    e. Do not tuck in at sides of bed.
12. Bedspread is folded lengthwise. Place it on bed.
    a. Place center fold in center of bed from head to foot.
    b. Place upper hem even with upper edge of mattress.
    c. Have rough edge down.
    d. Open spread and tuck it under at foot of bed.
    e. Make a mitered corner.
    f. Do not tuck in at sides.
13. Go to other side of bed. Start with bottom sheet.
    a. Pull sheet tight and smooth out all wrinkles.
    b. Make a mitered corner at top of bed.
    c. Pull draw sheet tight and tuck it in.
    d. Straighten out top sheet. Make a mitered corner at foot of bed.
    e. Miter foot corners of blanket and bedspread.
14. Fold top hem of spread over top hem of blanket.
15. Fold top hem of sheet back over edge of spread and blanket to form cuff. The hem should be on the underside so that a rough surface does not come in contact with patient's skin and cause irritation.
16. Put pillowcase on pillow.
    a. Hold pillowcase at center of end seam. Do not tuck pillow under the chin.
    b. With your other hand, turn pillowcase back over hand holding end seam.
    c. Grasp pillow through case at center of end of pillow.

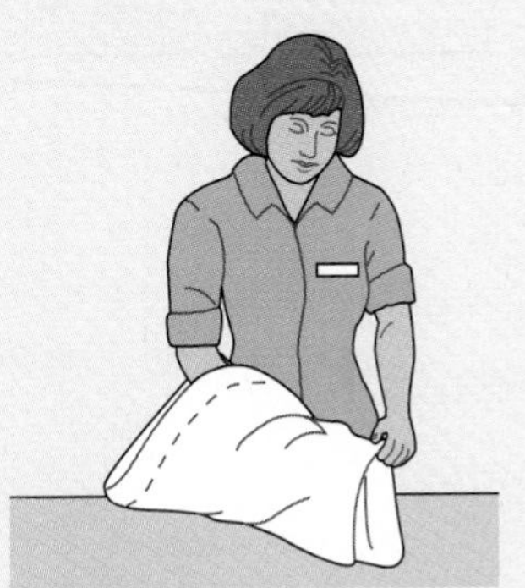

With one hand, hold the pillowcase at the center of the seamed end.

(continued)

PROCEDURE 18.55 Making a Closed Bed (continued)

Turn the pillowcase back over that hand with your free hand.

Grasp the pillow at the center of one end with the hand that is inside the pillowcase.

Pull the pillowcase down over the pillow with your free hand.

Straighten the pillowcase.

d. Bring case down over pillow and fit pillow into corners of case.

e. Fold extra material over open end of pillow and place it on bed with open end away from door.

17. Put bed in lowest position.

POSTPROCEDURE

18. Wash hands.

PROCEDURE 18.56 Making an Occupied Bed

BACKGROUND: Clean linens help prevent the spread of bacteria in the health care environment. Making an occupied bed with fresh linen will provide cleanliness, comfort, and will help the patient maintain a healthy skin condition.

ALERT: Follow Standard Precautions.

PREPROCEDURE

1. Wash hands.
2. Assemble equipment:
   a. Draw sheet or large pad
   b. Two large sheets or fitted bottom sheet and one large sheet
   c. Two pillowcases
   d. Blankets as needed
   e. Bedspread (if clean one is needed)
   f. Pillow
   g. Disposable gloves if needed
3. Identify patient and explain what you are going to do.
4. Raise bed to comfortable working height. Lock wheels on bed.
5. Place chair at side of bed.
6. Put linen on chair in the order in which you will use it. (First things you will use go on top.)
7. Provide for privacy by pulling privacy curtain.

PROCEDURE

8. Lower headrest and kneerest until bed is flat, if allowed.
9. Loosen linens on all sides by lifting edge of mattress with one hand and pulling out bedclothes with the other. *Never shake linen: This spreads microorganisms.*
10. Push mattress to top of bed. Ask for assistance if you need it.
11. Remove bedspread and blanket by folding them to the bottom, one at a time. Lift them from center and place over back of chair.
12. Place bath blanket or plain sheet over top sheet. Ask patient to hold top edge of clean cover if he or she is able to do so. If patient cannot hold the sheet, tuck it under patient's shoulders.
13. Slide soiled sheet from top to bottom and put in dirty linen container. Be careful not to expose patient.
14. Ask patient to turn toward the opposite side of bed. Have patient hold onto the side rail. Assist patient if he or she needs help. Patient should now be on far side of bed from you.

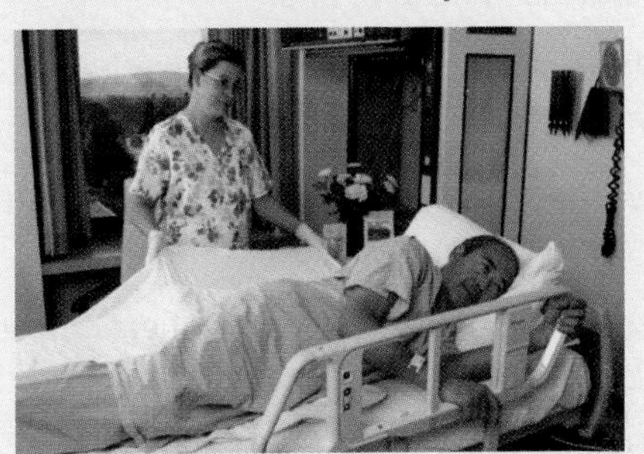

15. Adjust pillow for patient to make him or her comfortable.
16. Fan-fold soiled draw sheet and bottom sheet close to patient and tuck against patient's back. This leaves mattress stripped of linen.
17. Work on one side of bed until that side is completed. Then go to other side of bed. This saves you time and energy.
18. Take fitted bottom and fold it lengthwise. Be careful not to let it touch floor.
19. Place sheet on bed, still folded, with fold on middle of mattress.

(continued)

PROCEDURE 18.56 Making an Occupied Bed (continued)

20. Fold top half of sheet toward patient. Tuck folds against patient's back.
21. Miter corner at head of mattress. Tuck bottom sheet under mattress on your side from head to foot of mattress.
22. Place clean bottom draw sheet or large pad that has been folded in half with fold along middle of mattress. Fold top half of sheet toward patient. Tuck folds against patient's back.
23. Raise side rail and lock in place.
24. Lower side rail on opposite side.
25. Ask patient to roll away from you to other side of bed and onto clean linen. Tell patient that there will be a bump in the middle. (Be careful not to let patient become wrapped up in bath blanket.)
26. Remove old bottom sheet and draw sheet from bed and put into laundry container.
27. Pull fresh linen toward edge of mattress. Tuck it under mattress at head of bed.
28. Tuck bottom sheet under mattress from head to foot of mattress. Pull firmly to remove wrinkles.
29. Pull draw sheet very tight and tuck under mattress. If pad used, pull from patient and straighten.
30. Have patient roll on back, or turn patient yourself. Loosen bath blanket as patient turns.
31. Change pillowcase.
    a. Hold pillowcase at center of end seam.
    b. With your other hand turn pillowcase back over hand, holding end seam.
    c. Grasp pillow through case at center of end of pillow.
    d. Bring case down over pillow and fit pillow into corners of case.
    e. Fold extra material over open end of pillow and place pillow under patient's head.
32. Spread clean top sheet over bath blanket with wide hem at the top. Middle of sheet should run along middle of bed with wide hem even with top edge of mattress. Ask patient to hold hem of clean sheet. Remove bath blanket by moving it toward foot of bed. Be careful not to expose patient.
33. Tuck clean top sheet under mattress at foot of bed. Make to epleat in top sheet so that patient's feet can move freely. To make a toepleat, make 3-inch fold toward foot of bed in topsheet before tucking in sheet. Tuck in and miter corner.
34. Place blanket over patient, being sure that it covers the shoulders.
35. Place bedspread on bed in same way. Tuck blanket and bedspread under bottom of mattress and miter corners.
36. Make cuff.
    a. Fold top hem edge of spread over blanket.
    b. Fold top hem of top sheet back over edge of bedspread and blanket, being certain that rough hem is turned down.
37. Position patient and make comfortable.
38. Put bed in lowest position.
39. Open privacy curtains.
40. Raise side rails, if required.
41. Place call light where patient can reach it.

POSTPROCEDURE

42. Tidy unit.
43. Wash hands.
44. Chart linen change and how the patient tolerated procedure.

PROCEDURE 18.57 Making an Open Bed

BACKGROUND: Clean linens help prevent the spread of bacteria in the health care environment. An open bed provides easy access for patients returning to bed within a short period.

ALERT: Follow Standard Precautions.

PREPROCEDURE

1. Wash hands.

PROCEDURE

2. Grasp cuff of bedding in both hands and pull to foot of bed.

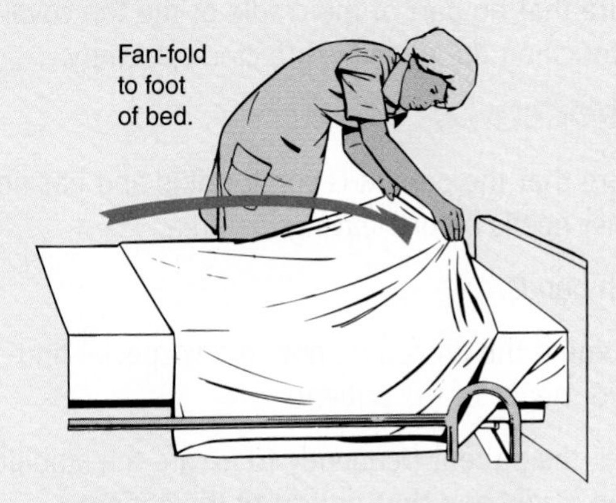
Fan-fold
to foot
of bed.

3. Fold bedding back on itself toward head of bed. The edge of cuff must meet fold. (This is called fan-folding.)

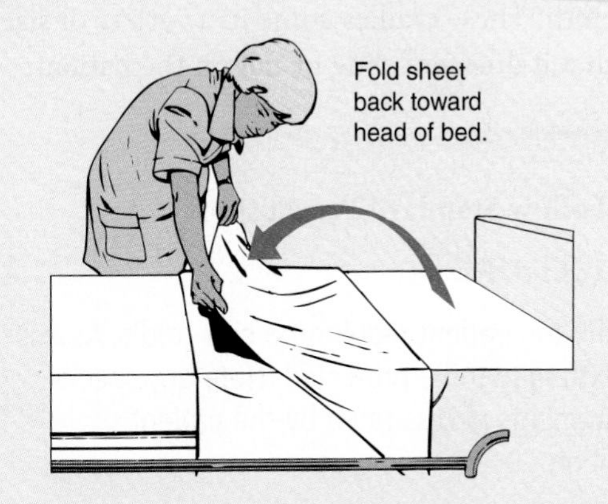
Fold sheet
back toward
head of bed.

4. Smooth the hanging sheets on each side into folds.

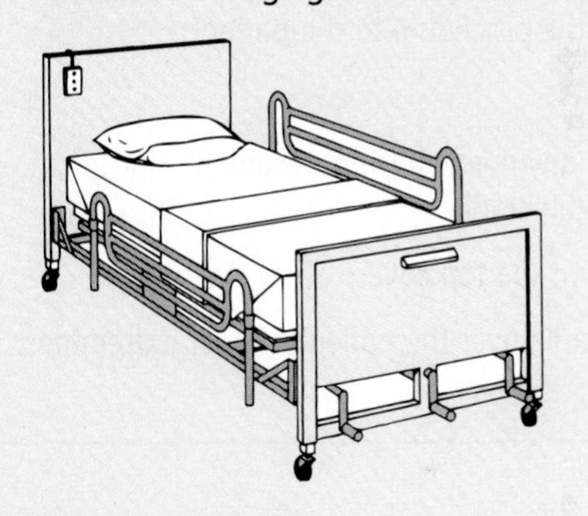

POSTPROCEDURE

5. Wash hands.

PROCEDURE 18.58 Placing a Bed Cradle

BACKGROUND: There can be situations where having the top bed linens touching the patient's lower extremities could be harmful to the patient. In this case, an apparatus called a bed cradle can be used.

A cradle is usually a metal frame that supports the bed linens away from the patient while providing privacy and warmth. These cradles come in a variety of sizes and shapes. If used, the cradle should be fastened to the bed so that it does not slide or fall on the patient.

ALERT: Follow Standard Precautions.

PREPROCEDURE

1. Identify the patient requiring a bed cradle. Assess the extremity to be protected. Note any special requirements necessitated by the patient's condition.
2. Wash hands.
3. Explain the procedure to the patient.

PROCEDURE

4. Address any needs for repositioning prior to placing the cradle.
5. Fold down the top covers off of the patient.
6. Place cradle over the patient's lower extremities.
7. Secure the cradle to the bed frame so that it will not collapse on to the patient.
8. Replace the top covers over the top of the cradle
9. Assure that no part of the cradle or the top covers are touching the patient's affected extremity.

POSTPROCEDURE

10. Assure that the patient is comfortable and has no further needs before leaving the area.
11. Wash hands.
12. Document the procedure noting any special findings or needs of the patient.
13. Check the patient frequently to assure the stability of the cradle and the comfort of the patient.

PROCEDURE 18.59 Preparing the Patient to Eat

BACKGROUND: Meals are an important part of every culture. Preparing patients for a meal by providing clean, neat surroundings and encouraging toileting and washing hands before eating can help patients enjoy their meal and promote their appetites.

ALERT: Follow Standard Precautions.

PREPROCEDURE

1. Wash hands.
2. Assemble equipment:
   a. Bedpan or urinal
   b. Toilet tissue
   c. Washcloth
   d. Hand towel
3. Assist patient as needed to empty bladder and wash hands and face.
4. Explain that you are getting ready to give patient a meal.

PROCEDURE

5. Clear bedside table.
6. Position patient for comfort and a convenient eating position.
7. Wash your hands.
8. Identify patient and check name on food tray to ensure that you are delivering the correct diet to patient.
9. Place tray in a convenient position in front of patient.

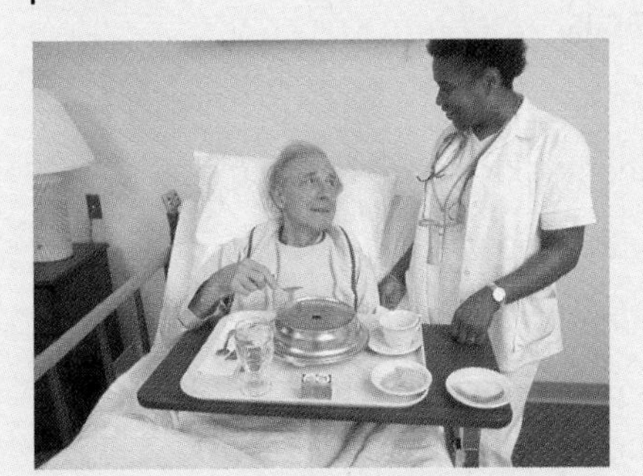

10. Open containers if patient cannot.
11. If patient is unable to prepare food, do it for patient.
    a. Butter the bread
    b. Cut meat
    c. Season food as necessary
12. Follow the procedure for feeding a patient if patient needs to be fed.

POSTPROCEDURE

13. Wash hands.

PROCEDURE 18.60 Preparing the Patient to Eat in the Dining Room

BACKGROUND: Eating in the dining room provides a more normal environment for patients, creating an opportunity to visit with others during the meal.

ALERT: Follow Standard Precautions.

PREPROCEDURE

1. Wash hands.

PROCEDURE

2. Help patient take care of toileting needs.
3. Assist with handwashing.
4. Take patient to dining room.
5. Position patient in wheelchair at table that is proper height for wheelchair.
6. Be certain patient is sitting in a comfortable position in wheelchair.
7. Provide adaptive feeding equipment if needed.
8. Bring patient tray.
9. Identify patient.
10. Serve tray and remove plate covers.
11. Provide assistance as needed (e.g., cut meat, butter bread, open containers).
12. Remove tray when finished, noting what patient ate.
13. Assist with handwashing and take patient to area of choice.

POSTPROCEDURE

14. Wash hands.
15. Record what patient ate.
16. Record I & O if necessary. (See the section "Measuring Intake and Output" later in the section.)

8/10/11	0800
	Taken by wheelchair to dining room
	80% of breakfast eaten, and
	tolerated well
	S. Gomez CNA

PROCEDURE 18.61 Assisting the Patient with Meals

BACKGROUND: Food is essential to maintain health. As a health care worker you are responsible to encourage patients to maintain their health by eating routine meals. Your attitude and willingness to assist patients who require your attention during meals can encourage their intake of a balanced diet.

ALERT: Follow Standard Precautions.

PREPROCEDURE

1. Wash hands.
2. Check patient's ID band with name on food tray to ensure that you will be feeding correct diet to patient.

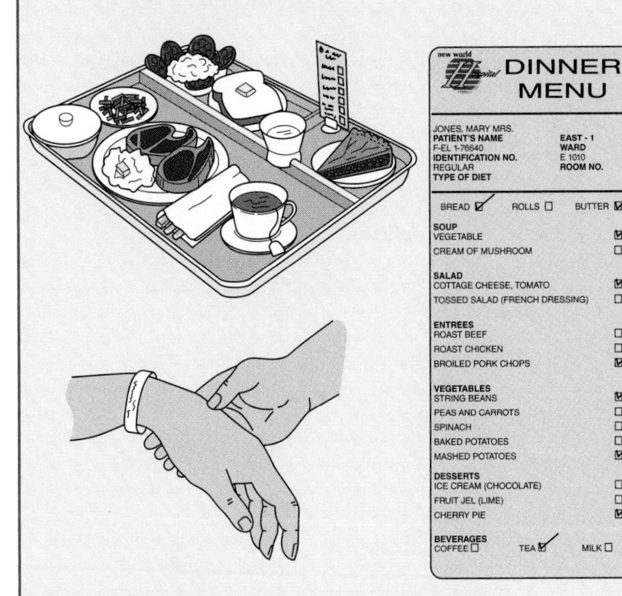

PROCEDURE

3. Tell patient what food is being served.
4. Ask patient how he or she prefers food to be prepared (e.g., salt, pepper, cream or sugar in coffee).
5. Position patient in a sitting position, as allowed by physician. If ordered to lie flat, turn patient on side.
6. Position yourself in a comfortable manner, facing the patient, so that you won't be rushing patient because you are uncomfortable. (Do not sit on bed.)
7. Cut food into small bite-sized pieces.
8. Place a napkin or small hand towel under patient's chin.
9. Put a flex straw in cold drinks. Hot drinks tend to burn mouth if taken through a straw.
10. Use a spoon to feed patient small to average-sized bites of food. (Encourage patient to help self as much as possible.)

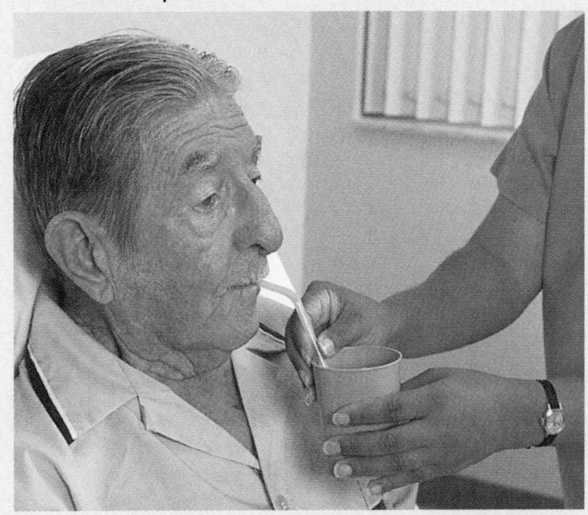

11. Always feed patient at a slow pace. It may take more time for him or her to chew and swallow than you think is necessary.
12. Always be sure that one bite has been swallowed before you give another spoonful to patient.
13. Tell patient what is being served and ask which item he or she prefers first, if patient cannot see food.
14. Offer beverages to patient throughout the meal.
15. Talk with patient during meal.
16. Encourage patient to finish eating, but do not force.
17. Assist patient in wiping face as necessary and when patient is finished eating.

(continued)

PROCEDURE 18.61 Assisting the Patient with Meals (continued)

18. Observe amount of food eaten.

POSTPROCEDURE

19. Remove tray from room.
20. Position patient for comfort and safety.
21. Place call light in a convenient place.
22. Wash hands.
23. Record amount of food eaten (half, three-fourths, one-fourth, etc.) on chart, and indicate if food was tolerated well or not.

10/10/11	1800
	50% of meal taken with assistance and
	tolerated well.
	Resident stated that he doesn't like beef
	Dietitian notified of resident's request for
	meat other than beef.
	________ *R. Johnson CNA*

PROCEDURE 18.62 Serving Food to the Patient in Bed (Self-Help)

BACKGROUND: As a health care worker you are required to identify the right diet for each patient and recognize what they need assistance with. Your opening packages and cartons or cutting food into bite-sized pieces may make the difference between a patient eating or refusing his or her food.

ALERT: Follow Standard Precautions.

PREPROCEDURE

1. Wash hands.
2. Assemble equipment:
   a. Food tray with diet card
   b. Flex straws
   c. Towel

PROCEDURE

3. Assist patient with bedpan or urinal.
4. Place in a sitting position if possible.
5. Help patient wash hands and face.
6. Remove unsightly or odor-causing articles.
7. Clean overbed table.
8. Check tray with diet card for
   a. Patient's name
   b. Type of diet
   c. Correct foods according to diet (e.g., diabetic, puréed, chopped, regular)
9. Set up tray and help with foods if needed (e.g., cut meat, butter bread, open containers). *Do not add foods to the tray until you check on diet.*

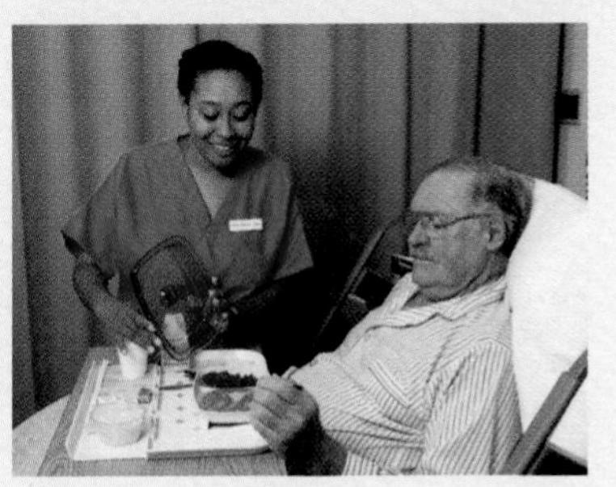

10. Encourage patient to eat all foods on tray.
11. Remove tray when finished and note what patient ate.
12. Help patient wash hands and face.
13. Position patient comfortably and make sure call bell is within reach.

POSTPROCEDURE

14. Remove tray.
15. Be certain that water is within reach.
16. Wash hands.
17. Record I & O if required.
18. Record amount eaten.

11/03/11	*1230*
	Lunch served with meat and vegetables
	cut into bite-sized pieces.
	Mr. Axel struggled to butter the bread
	without assistance. He said, "I knew
	I could butter it without help." 90% of
	lunch eaten, tolerated well.
	S. Gomez CNA

PROCEDURE 18.63 Providing Fresh Drinking Water

BACKGROUND: Providing fluids for the patient is an integral part of the process of returning the patient to an optimal health status. The elderly patient may experience a diminished sense of thirst and may require additional encouragement and assistance to maintain adequate oral intake. Recording the volume of oral intake is the responsibility of the nurse assigned to the patient's care.

ALERT: Follow Standard Precautions.

PREPROCEDURE

1. Identify any patients whose fluids may be restricted as a medical necessity.
2. Wash hands.
3. Assemble equipment: the container to be used for patient's water supply.

PROCEDURE

4. Collect and discard any of the containers previously used for the patient's water supply.
5. Establish the temperature of water preferred by the patient, i.e., iced, tepid, etc.
6. Provide a clean container and fresh water for the patient.
7. Establish that the patient has no further needs before leaving the bedside.

POSTPROCEDURE

8. Wash hands.

PROCEDURE 18.64 Feeding the Helpless Patient

BACKGROUND: Patients must routinely eat a balanced diet. You are required to feed patients who are not able to feed themselves. Your patience and willingness to feed them in a gentle, caring, compassionate manner could make the difference in their eating or not eating.

ALERT: Follow Standard Precautions.

PREPROCEDURE

1. Wash hands.
2. Bring patient's tray.
3. Check name on card with patient ID band.
4. Explain to patient what you are going to do.

PROCEDURE

5. Sit comfortably, facing patient.
6. Tuck a napkin under patient's chin.
7. Season food the way patient likes it.
8. Use a spoon and fill only half full.
9. Give food from tip, not side of spoon.
10. Name each food as you offer it, if patient cannot see food.

INTAKE AND OUTPUT SHEET

Hospital #________ Patient Name ________

Date ________ Room #________

INTAKE				OUTPUT			
				URINE		GASTRIC	
Time 7-3	BY MOUTH	TUBE	PARENTERAL	VOIDED	CATHETER	EMESIS	SUCTION
TOTAL							
Time 3-11							
TOTAL							
Time 11-7							
TOTAL							
24 HOUR TOTAL							
24 Hour Grand Total • Intake				24 Hour Grand Total • Output			

11. Describe position of food on plate (e.g., hot liquids in right corner, peas at the position of 3 o'clock on a clock) if patient cannot see but can feed self.
12. Tell patient if you are offering something that is hot or cold.
13. Use a straw for giving liquids.

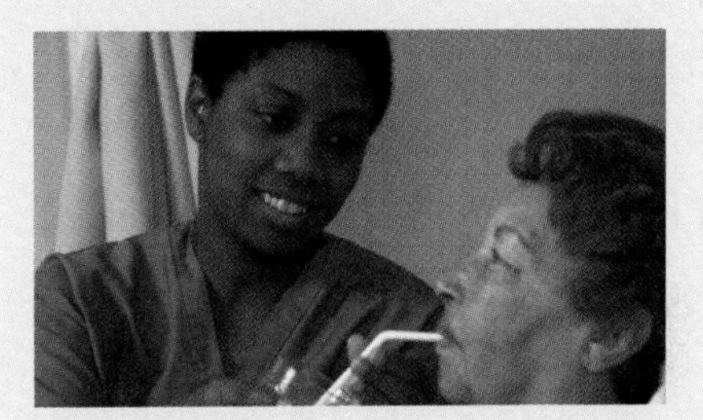

14. Feed patient slowly and allow time to chew and swallow. Offer beverages throughout the meal.
15. Note amount eaten and remove tray when finished.
16. Help with washing hands and face.
17. Position patient comfortably and place call bell within reach.

POSTPROCEDURE

18. Wash hands.
19. Record amount eaten and I & O if required. See following pages for directions on recording I & O.

12/12/11	1830
	Ate 60% of food and drank
	240cc of tea
	Chokes easily when drinking liquids
	Reported choking incidents to team
	leader
	________ *A. Chaplin CNA*

PROCEDURE 18.65 Serving Nourishments

BACKGROUND: Between-meal nourishments are served to people who need additional nutrients to maintain or improve their health. People with diabetes need nourishments to maintain balanced glucose levels. Some may need protein to build and repair body tissue and others may need specific vitamins.

ALERT: Follow Standard Precautions.

POSTPROCEDURE

1. Wash hands.
2. Assemble equipment:
   a. Nourishment
   b. Cup, dish, straw, spoon
   c. Napkin
3. Identify patient.

PROCEDURE

4. Take nourishment to patient.
5. Help if needed.
6. After patient is finished, collect dirty utensils.

POSTPROCEDURE

7. Return utensils to dietary cart or kitchen.
8. Record intake on I & O sheet if required.
9. Wash hands.
10. Record nourishment taken.

9/15/11	1500
	Took 50% of afternoon nourishment
	R. Johnson CNA

PROCEDURE 18.66 Measuring Urinary Output

BACKGROUND: All body systems rely on fluid balance to maintain normal functioning. By measuring urinary output, you can determine the body's ability to maintain fluid balance and observe characteristics of urine that indicate normalcy or potential abnormalities.

ALERT: Follow Standard Precautions.

PREPROCEDURE

1. Wash hands.
2. Assemble equipment:
   a. Bedpan, urinal, or special container
   b. Graduate or measuring cup
   c. Disposable nonsterile gloves
3. Put on gloves.

PROCEDURE

4. Pour urine into measuring graduate.
5. Place graduate on flat surface and read amount of urine.
6. Observe urine for:
   a. Unusual color
   b. Blood
   c. Dark color
   d. Large amounts of mucus
   e. Sediment
7. Save the specimen and report to nurse immediately if you notice any unusual appearance.
8. Discard in toilet if urine is normal. Use a paper towel to flush toilet and turn on faucet.
9. Rinse graduate or pitcher and put away.

POSTPROCEDURE

10. Remove gloves and discard according to facility policy.
11. Wash hands.
12. Record amount of urine in cc's on I & O sheet.

11/23/12 1200
Voided 300 cc dark,
amber-colored urine
S. Gomez CNA

11/23/12 1600
Voided 100 cc pink-tinged urine
Complained of pain upon urination
Team leader notified
S. Gomez CNA

PROCEDURE 18.67 Oil Retention Enema

BACKGROUND: Oil retention enema solutions stimulate the bowl and lubricate the colon and rectum, which facilitates the release of stool from the colon.

ALERT: Follow Standard Precautions.

PREPROCEDURE

1. Wash your hands.
2. Assemble equipment:
   a. Prepackaged oil retention enema
   b. Bedpan and cover
   c. Waterproof bed protector
   d. Toilet tissue
   e. Towel, basin of water, and soap
   f. Disposable gloves
3. Identify patient.
4. Ask visitors to leave the room. Provide privacy with curtain, screen, or door.
5. Explain what you are going to do.
6. Put on gloves.

PROCEDURE

7. Cover patient with a bath blanket, and fan-fold linen to foot of bed.
8. Put bedpan on foot of bed.
9. Elevate the bed to a comfortable working height and lower the side rail on the side you are working on.
10. Place bed protector under buttocks.
11. Help patient into the Sims' position.

NOTE: The Sim's position is a position in which the patient lies on one side with the under arm behind the back and the upper thigh flexed.

12. Tell patient to retain enema as long as possible.
13. Open a prepackaged oil retention enema.
14. Fold the bath blanket back to expose the buttock.
15. Lift patient's upper buttock and expose anus.
16. Tell patient when you are going to insert prelubricated tip into anus. (Instruct patient to take deep breaths and try to relax.) Insert tip 2–4 inches into the rectum.
17. Squeeze container slowly and steady until all solution has entered rectum.
18. Remove container; place in original package to be disposed of in contaminated waste according to facility policy and procedure.
19. Instruct patient to remain on side and retain the solution for at least 30 minutes.
20. Lower the bed and pull the side rail up. Leave the call bell in place.
21. Remove gloves and discard according to facility policy.
22. Check patient every 5 minutes until fluid has been retained for at least 20 minutes. Usually it is at least 30 minutes.
23. Position patient on bedpan or assist to bathroom. Instruct patient not to flush toilet.
24. Raise head of bed, if permitted, if using a bedpan.
25. Place toilet tissue and call bell within easy reach.
26. Stay nearby if patient is in bathroom.
27. Put on gloves.
28. Remove bedpan or assist patient to return to bed. Observe contents of toilet or bedpan for
    a. Color, consistency, unusual materials, odor
    b. Amount of return
29. Cover bedpan and dispose of contents. Use paper towel to flush toilet and turn on faucet.
30. Remove gloves and discard in biohazardous container.

(continued)

PROCEDURE 18.67 Oil Retention Enema (continued)

31. Replace top sheet and remove bath blanket and plastic bed protector.
32. Give patient soap, water, and towel for hands and face.

POSTPROCEDURE

33. Wash your hands.
34. Chart the following:
    a. Type of enema given
    b. Consistency and amount of bowel movement
    c. How the procedure was tolerated

5/13/12	1930
	16 oz oil retention enema administered
	and retained 12 minutes
	Passed large amount of dark brown
	formed stool
	_______ R. Johnson CNA
6/07/12	0800
	Tolerated enema well
	Resting quietly
	_______ S. Gomez CNA

PROCEDURE 18.68 Prepackaged Enemas

ALERT: Follow Standard Precautions.

PREPROCEDURE

1. Wash your hands.
2. Assemble equipment.
   a. Prepackaged enema
   b. Bedpan and cover
   c. Waterproof bed protector
   d. Toilet tissue
   e. Towel, basin of water, and soap
   f. Disposable gloves
3. Identify patient.
4. Ask visitors to leave room.
5. Explain what you are going to do and provide privacy with curtain, screen, or door.

PROCEDURE

6. Cover patient with a bath blanket, and fan-fold linen to foot of bed.
7. Put on gloves.
8. Raise bed to comfortable working height and lower side rail.
9. Place bed protector under buttocks.
10. Put bedpan on foot of bed.
11. Help patient into the Sims' position.

12. Fold back blanket and expose buttock.
13. Tell patient to retain enema as long as possible.
14. Open a prepackaged enema.
15. Lift patient's upper buttock and expose anus.
16. Tell patient when you are going to insert prelubricated tip into anus. (Have patient take deep breaths and try to relax.)

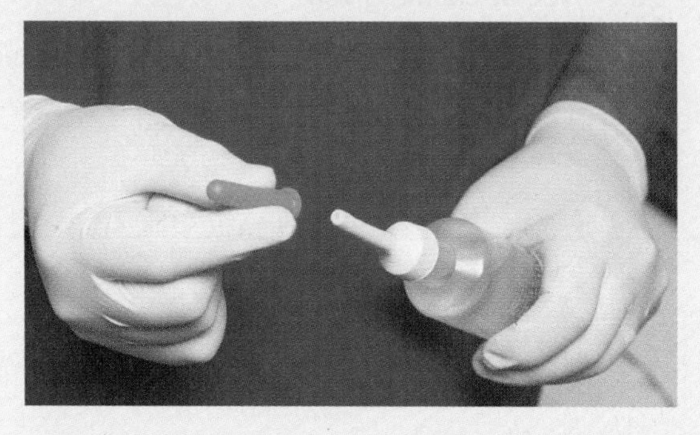

17. Squeeze container until all the solution has entered the rectum.

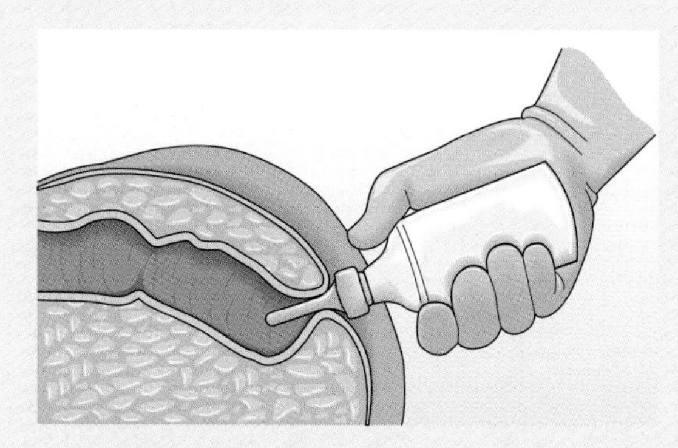

18. Remove container; place in original package to be disposed of according to facility policy.
19. Remove gloves and dispose of in biohazardous container.
20. Instruct patient to remain on side and to hold solution as long as possible. Have call bell in reach.
21. Put on gloves.
22. Position patient on bedpan or assist to bathroom. Instruct patient not to flush toilet.
23. Raise head of bed if permitted if patient is using a bedpan.

(continued)

PROCEDURE 18.68 Prepackaged Enemas (continued)

24. Place toilet tissue and call bell within easy reach.
25. Stay nearby if patient is in bathroom.
26. Remove bedpan or assist patient to return to bed.
27. Observe contents of toilet or bedpan for
    a. Color, consistency, unusual materials, odor
    b. Amount of return
28. Cover bedpan and dispose of contents. Use paper towels to flush toilet and turn on facet.

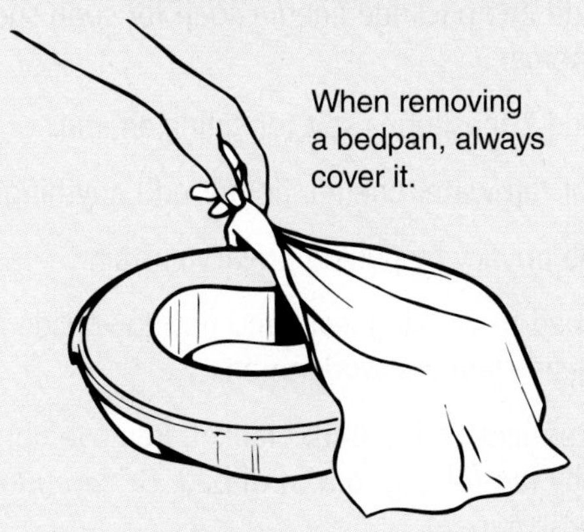
When removing
a bedpan, always
cover it.

POSTPROCEDURE

29. Remove gloves and dispose of according to facility policy.
30. Replace top sheet and remove bath blanket and plastic bed protector.
31. Give the patient soap, water, and towel for hands and face.
32. Wash hands.
33. Chart the following:
    a. Type of enema given
    b. Consistency and amount of bowel movement
    c. How the procedure was tolerated

9/10/12	*1430*
	12 oz prepackaged enema
	administered and retained 5 minutes
	Complained of severe abdominal cramps.
	Passed 12 oz watery, tan-colored fluid.
	Reported to team leader
	_________ *A. Chaplin CNA*
9/10/12	*1515*
	Restless
	Continues to complain about abdominal
	cramps
	Team leader notified
	_________ *A. Chaplin CNA*

PROCEDURE **18.69**

Tap Water, Soap Suds, Saline Enemas

BACKGROUND: Tap water, soap suds, and saline solutions stimulate the bowel and facilitate the release of stool from the colon.

ALERT: Follow Standard Precautions.

PREPROCEDURE

1. Wash your hands.
2. Assemble equipment.
   a. Disposable gloves
   b. Disposable enema equipment
      (1) Plastic container
      (2) Tubing
      (3) Clamp
      (4) Lubricant
   c. Enema solution as instructed by the head nurse, e.g.:
      (1) Tap water, 700–1,000 cc water (105°F)
      (2) Soap suds, 700–1,000 cc (105°F), one package enema soap
      (3) Saline, 700–1,000 cc water (105°F), 2 teaspoons salt
   d. Bedpan and cover
   e. Urinal, if necessary
   f. Toilet tissue
   g. Waterproof disposable bed protector
   h. Paper towel
   i. Bath blanket
3. Identify patient.

PROCEDURE

4. Ask visitors to leave room
5. Tell patient what you are going to do.
6. Attach tubing to irrigation container. Adjust clamp to a position where you can easily open and close it. Close clamp.
7. Fill container with warm water (105° F).
   a. Add one package enema soap for soap suds enema.
   b. Add 2 teaspoons salt for saline enema.
   c. For tap water enema, do not add anything.
8. Provide privacy by pulling privacy curtain.
9. Raise bed to working level and put down side rail on the side you are working on.
10. Cover patient with a bath blanket. Remove upper sheet by fan-folding to foot of bed. *Be careful not to expose patient.*
11. Put on gloves.
12. Put waterproof protector under patient's buttocks.
13. Place bedpan on foot of bed.
14. Place patient in the Sims position.
15. Open clamp on enema tubing and let a small amount of solution run into bedpan. (This eliminates air in tubing and warms tube.) Close clamp.
16. Put a small amount of lubricating jelly on tissue. Lubricate enema tip. Check to be certain that the opening is not plugged.
17. Expose buttocks by folding back bath blanket.
18. Lift the upper buttock to expose anus.
19. Tell patient when you are going to insert lubricated tip into anus.
20. Hold rectal tube about 5 inches from tip and insert slowly into rectum.

(continued)

PROCEDURE 18.69 Tap Water, Soap Suds, Saline Enemas (continued)

21. Tell patient to breathe deeply through mouth and to try to relax.
22. Raise container 12 to 18 inches above patient's hip.

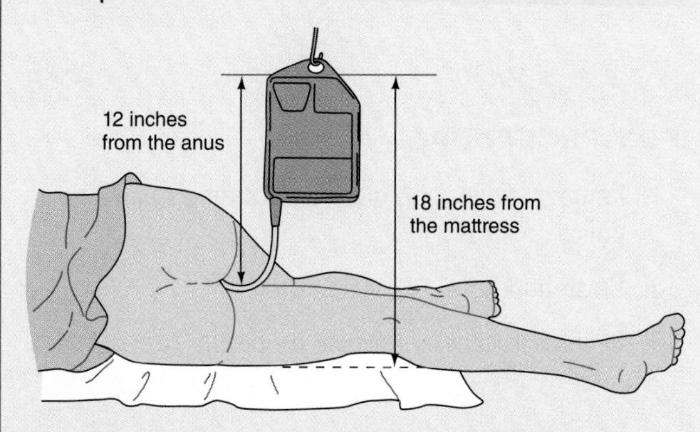

23. Open clamp and let solution run in slowly. If patient complains of cramps, clamp tubing for a minute and lower bag slightly.
24. When most of solution has flowed into rectum, close clamp. Gently withdraw rectal tube. Wrap tubing with paper towel and place into enema can.
25. Ask patient to hold solution as long as possible.
26. Assist patient to bathroom and stay nearby if patient can go to bathroom. Ask patient not to flush toilet.
27. Help patient onto bedpan and raise head of bed if permitted.
28. Place call light within reach and check patient every few minutes.
29. Dispose of enema equipment while you are waiting for patient to expel enema. *Follow hospital policy.*
30. Remove bedpan or assist patient back to bed.
31. Observe contents for
    a. Color, consistency, unusual materials
    b. Note amount (i.e., large or small)
32. Cover bedpan and remove bed protector.
33. Remove gloves and dispose of according to facility policy. Wash hands.
34. Replace top sheet and remove bath blanket.
35. Give patient soap, water, and a towel to wash hands.
36. Secure call light in patient's reach.

POSTPROCEDURE

37. Clean and replace all equipment used and wash your hands.
38. Chart the following:
    a. Date and time
    b. Type of enema given
    c. Results (amount, color, consistency) of bowel movement
    d. How the procedure was tolerated

4/14/12	1800
	1,000 cc soap suds enema
	administered and retained 15 minutes
	Complained about severe abdominal
	cramps
	Passed large amount of brown, formed
	stool, brown-colored liquid, and loose
	brown stool particles
	________ S. Gomez CNA
4/14/12	1845
	Resting quietly in bed, no pain
	________ S. Gomez CNA

PROCEDURE 18.70 Disconnecting an Indwelling Catheter

BACKGROUND: Disconnecting an indwelling catheter from the drainage bag and plugging the catheter keeps urine from draining out of the body. This procedure is commonly followed when the physician wants to remove the catheter and bladder retraining is necessary; or to allow the patient to participate in activities without the urinary drainage bag

ALERT: Follow Standard Precautions.

PREPROCEDURE

1. Wash hands.
2. Assemble equipment.
   a. Disinfectant (Can use an alcohol or Betadine swab.)
   b. Sterile gauze sponges
   c. Sterile cap or plug
   d. Disposable gloves
3. Identify patient and provide privacy with curtain, screen, or door.
4. Explain what you are going to do.
5. Put on gloves.

PROCEDURE

6. Place a towel under the tubing where it connects to the catheter.
7. Disinfect connection between catheter and drainage tubing where it is to be disconnected by applying disinfectant with cotton or gauze.
8. Disconnect catheter and drainage tubing. *Do not allow catheter ends to touch anything!*
9. Insert a sterile plug in end of catheter. Place sterile cap over exposed end of drainage tube.
10. Carefully secure drainage tube to bed.

POSTPROCEDURE

11. Remove gloves and discard according to facility policy.
12. Wash hands.
13. Record procedure. *Reverse procedure to reconnect.*

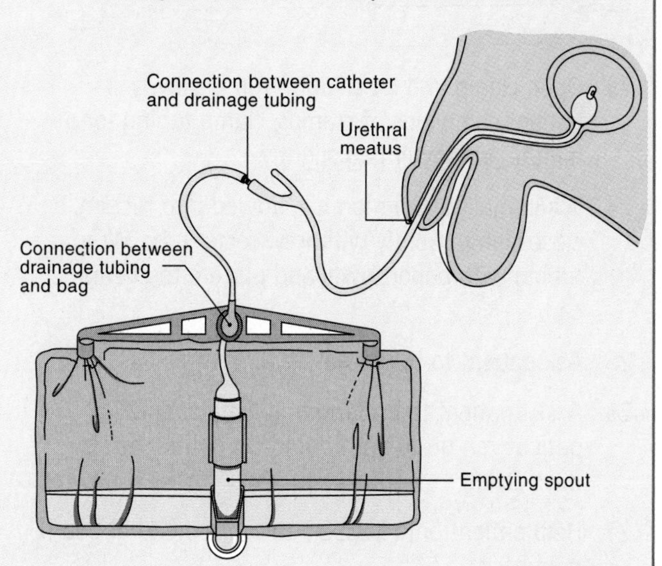

5/11/12	1000
	Urinary catheter disconnected and
	plugged with a sterile plug
	________ S. Gomez CNA
5/11/12	1130
	Lower abdominal pain
	Catheter drained 400 cc of urine
	Plug reinserted
	________ S. Gomez CNA

PROCEDURE 18.71 Giving Indwelling Catheter Care

BACKGROUND: Giving indwelling catheter care helps to prevent infection and provides an opportunity to observe the insertion site for irritation and to adjust catheter position to maximize efficient drainage.

ALERT: Follow Standard Precautions.

PREPROCEDURE

1. Wash hands.
2. Assemble equipment:
   a. Antiseptic solution or catheter care kits.
   b. Waterproof bed protector
   c. Disposable nonsterile gloves
   d. Bath Blanket
3. Identify patient.
4. Explain what you are going to do.
5. Provide privacy by pulling the privacy curtains.
6. Put on gloves. (Some facilities require you use sterile gloves.)

PROCEDURE

7. Raise bed to comfortable working level and lower side rail.
8. Put waterproof protector on bed.
9. For female patients, have them bend their knee and drape them with the bath blanket, so that only the perineum is exposed. For males, pull covers back to knee and cover top half of body with bath blanket.
10. Carefully clean perineum.
11. Observe around catheter for sores, leakage, bleeding, or crusting. Report any unusual observation to nurse.
12. For females, separate labia with forefinger and thumb. Apply antiseptic solution around area where catheter enters the urethra. Wipe from front to back and place used applicator or gauze pad in biohazardous container. Use a clean applicator or gauze with antiseptic solution each time you wipe from back to front.
13. For males, pull back foreskin on uncircumcised patient and apply antiseptic to entire area. Wipe from the meatus down the shaft of the penis. Use a clean applicator or gauze with every stroke.
14. Apply antiseptic ointment (if allowed in your facility).
15. Position patient so catheter does not have kinks and is not pulling. *Be sure the tubing is free of kinks and is draining!*
16. Remove waterproof protector.

15. Cover patient.

17. Dispose of supplies according to facility policy.
18. Remove gloves and dispose of according to facility policy.
19. Position patient comfortably. Lower bed and raise side rail.
20. Secure call light within patient's reach.

POSTPROCEDURE

21. Wash hands.
22. Record procedure.

11/02/12	0920
	Perineal care complete
	Catheter insertion site clean and free
	from irritation
	Catheter secured to left inner thigh to
	allow drainage
	________ *R. Johnson CNA*

PROCEDURE 18.72 External Urinary Catheter

BACKGROUND: An incontinent patient may use an external urinary catheter to control the flow of urine into a drainage bag in place of wearing a diaper. This is sometimes known as a condom catheter, because the device fits over the penis like a condom.

ALERT: Follow Standard Precautions.

PREPROCEDURE

1. Wash hands.
2. Assemble equipment:
   a. Basin warm water
   b. Washcloth
   c. Towel
   d. Waterproof bed protector
   e. Gloves
   f. Plastic bag
   g. Condom with drainage tip
   h. Paper towels
3. Identify patient.
4. Explain what you are going to do.

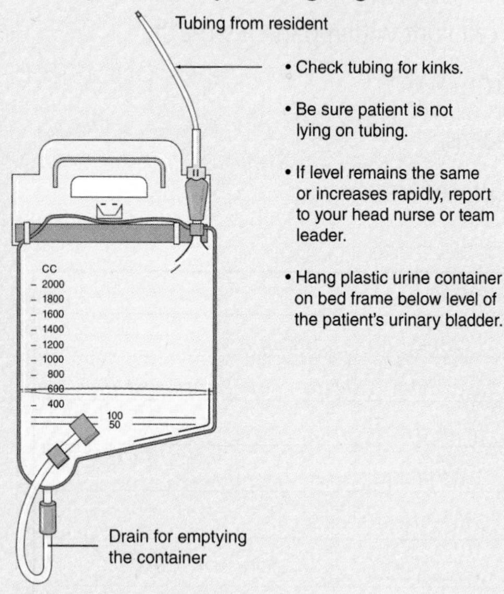
Tubing from resident
• Check tubing for kinks.
• Be sure patient is not lying on tubing.
• If level remains the same or increases rapidly, report to your head nurse or team leader.
• Hang plastic urine container on bed frame below level of the patient's urinary bladder.
cc
2000
1800
1600
1400
1200
1000
800
600
400
100
50
Drain for emptying the container

PROCEDURE

5. Provide privacy by pulling privacy curtain.
6. Raise bed to comfortable working height.
7. Cover patient with bath blanket. Have patient hold top of blanket, and fold cover to bottom of bed.
8. Put on gloves.
9. Place waterproof protector under patient's buttocks.
10. Pull up bath blanket to expose genitals only.
11. Remove condom by rolling gently toward tip of penis.
12. Wash and dry penis.
13. Observe for irritation, open areas, bleeding.
14. Report any unusual observations.
15. Check condom for "ready stick" surface. If there is none, apply a thin spray of tincture of benzoin. *Do not spray on head of penis.*
16. Apply new condom and drainage tip to penis by rolling toward base of penis.
17. Reconnect drainage system.
18. Remove and dispose of gloves in biohazardous container.
19. Pull up top bedding and remove bath blanket.
20. Replace equipment.
21. Lower bed to lowest position.
22. Put up side rail if required.
23. Secure call light within patient's reach.

POSTPROCEDURE

24. Tidy unit.
25. Wash hands.
26. Record procedure.

4/10/12	*0730*
	Shower taken and tolerated well
	Urinary condom drainage system
	applied and drains well
	______ *A. Chaplin CNA*

PROCEDURE 18.73 Emptying the Urinary Drainage Bag

BACKGROUND: Emptying the urinary drainage bag provides an opportunity to:

1. Measure urinary output for a specific period of time
2. Observe characteristics of urine

ALERT: Follow Standard Precautions.

PREPROCEDURE

1. Wash hands.
2. Identify patient and explain procedure
3. Provide privacy with curtain, screen, or door.
4. Assemble equipment.
   a. Graduate or measuring cup
   b. Disposable gloves
   c. Paper towel
   d. An alcohol swab
5. Put on disposable gloves.

PROCEDURE

6. Place towel on floor and set graduate cylinder on top of the towel.

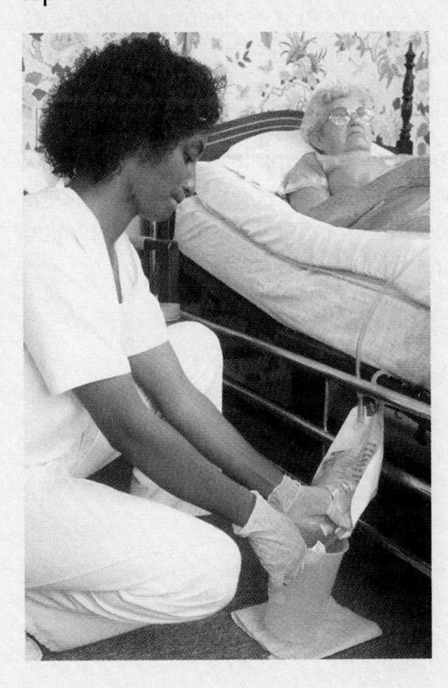

7. Carefully open drain outlet on urinary bag. *Do not allow container outlet to touch floor!* This will introduce microorganisms into bag and can cause infection.
8. Drain bag into graduate and clean drain outlet with alcohol swab. Then reattach drainage outlet securely.
9. Observe urine for:
   a. Dark color
   b. Blood
   c. Unusual odor
   d. Large amount of mucus
   e. Sediment
10. Report any unusual observations to nurse immediately (do not discard urine).
11. Hold graduate at eye level and read amount of urine on measuring scale.
12. Discard urine if normal. Flush toilet and turn on faucet with paper towel.
13. Rinse graduate and put away.

POSTPROCEDURE

14. Remove gloves and discard in hazardous waste.
15. Wash hands.
16. Record amount of urine in cc's on the I & O record.

10/10/11	0700
	15.00 Urinary drainage, 1,290 cc
	________ A. Chaplin CNA

PROCEDURE 18.74 Collect Specimen Under Transmission-Based Precautions

BACKGROUND: Concerns about the transmission of blood borne diseases, such as AIDS and the hepatitis B virus, and the increasing incidence of hospital acquired infections has caused a change in the focus of infection control programs. Since 1987 the CDC (Centers for Disease Control) has promoted the use of *universal precautions.*

It is recommended that health-care workers use gloves, gowns, masks, and protective eyewear when exposure to blood or body fluids is likely and that all patients be considered potentially infected. Universal precautions are used along with category-specific isolation systems when indicated.

Efforts have also been made to remove all sharps, such as needles, from the health-care system whenever possible, thus diminishing contamination from needle sticks. Collecting specimens requires some contact with body fluids so the prudent use of universal precautions becomes a critical part of the process.

ALERT: Follow Standard Precautions.

PREPROCEDURE

1. Collect the equipment necessary for obtaining the specimen (specimen cup, lab tubes, tourniquets, etc.).
2. Wash hands.
3. Put on disposable gloves, gowns, mask, and protective eyewear as may be required depending on the specimen to be collected.

PROCEDURE

4. Provide an explanation to the patient regarding the specimen to be collected. Answer any questions the patient may have.
5. Collect the specimen using aseptic or sterile technique as required.
6. Label the specimen with the patient's name, date, and time of collection.

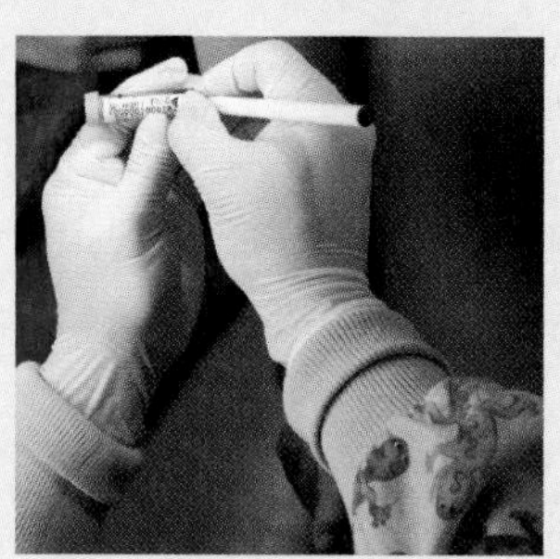

7. Place the specimen in a protective package as prescribed by the institution.
8. Assure that the patient has no further needs.
9. Dispose of any used supplies and any protective items used in the collection of the specimen in the appropriate manner, as determined by your institution.

POSTPROCEDURE

10. Wash hands.
11. Send the specimen to the laboratory.

PROCEDURE 18.75 Routine Urine Specimen

BACKGROUND: To evaluate the chemical structure of urine and determine the need for further testing.

ALERT: Follow Standard Precautions.

PREPROCEDURE

1. Wash hands.
2. Assemble equipment:
   a. Graduate (pitcher)
   b. Bedpan or urinal
   c. Urine specimen container
   d. Label
   e. Paper bag
   f. Disposable nonsterile gloves
3. Identify patient.
4. Explain what you are going to do.

PROCEDURE

5. Label specimen carefully:
   a. Patient's name
   b. Date
   c. Time
   d. Room number
6. Provide privacy by pulling privacy curtain.
7. Put on gloves.
8. Have patient void (urinate) into clean bedpan or urinal.
9. Ask patient to put toilet tissue into paper bag.
10. Pour specimen into graduate.
11. Pour from graduate into specimen container until about three-quarters full.
12. Place lid on container.
13. Discard leftover urine.
14. Clean and rinse graduate, bedpan, or urinal, and put away.
15. Remove gloves.
16. Position patient comfortably.
17. Assist patient to wash hands.

POSTPROCEDURE

18. Wash hands.
19. Store specimen according to direction for lab pickup.
20. Report and record procedure and observation of specimen.

PROCEDURE 18.76 Midstream Clean-Catch Urine, Female

BACKGROUND: A midstream clean-catch urine procedure provides a way to collect urine free of bacteria present at the urethral meatus at the beginning of urination, and in sediment in the urinary bladder which drains at the end of urination.

ALERT: Follow Standard Precautions.

PREPROCEDURE

1. Wash hands.
2. Assemble equipment:
   a. Antiseptic solution or soap and water or towelettes
   b. Sterile specimen container
   c. Tissues
   d. Nonsterile gloves

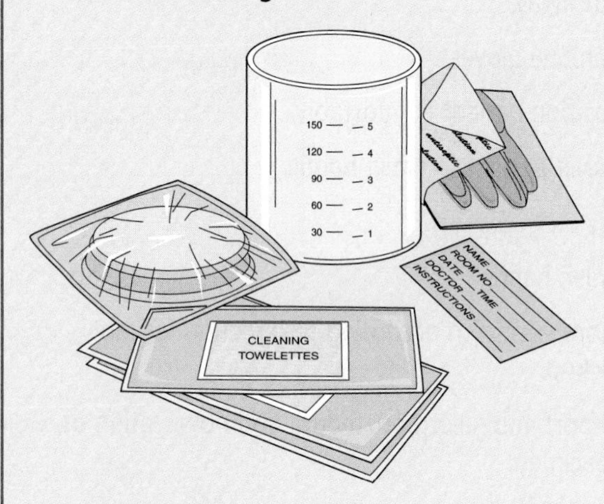

3. Identify patient.
4. Explain what you are going to do.

PROCEDURE

5. Label specimen:
   a. Patient's name
   b. Time obtained
   c. Date
6. If patient is on bedrest:
   a. Put on gloves.
   b. Lower side rail.
   c. Position bedpan under patient.
7. Have patient carefully clean perineal area if able; if not, you will be responsible for cleaning perineum:
   a. Wipe with towelette or gauze with antiseptic solution from front to back.
   b. Wipe one side and throw away wipe.
   c. Use a clean wipe for other side.
   d. Use another wipe down center.
   e. Then proceed with collecting midstream urine.
8. Explain procedure if patient can obtain own specimen.
   a. Have patient start to urinate into bedpan/toilet.
   b. Allow stream to begin.
   c. Stop stream and place specimen container to collect midstream.
   d. Remove container before bladder is empty.
9. Wipe perineum, if on bedpan.
10. Remove bedpan.
11. Rinse bedpan and put away.
12. Remove gloves and discard according to facility policy and procedure.
13. Raise side rail.
14. Secure call light in patient's reach.
15. Dispose of equipment. Never handle contaminated equipment without gloves.

POSTPROCEDURE

16. Wash hands.
17. Record specimen collection.
18. Report any unusual
    a. Color
    b. Consistency
    c. Odor

7/14/12	1300
	Clean-catch urine collected
	Urine was straw colored
	Labeled and sent to the laboratory
	R. Johnson CNA

PROCEDURE 18.77 Midstream Clean-Catch Urine, Male

BACKGROUND: A midstream clean-catch urine procedure provides a way to collect urine free of bacteria present at the urethral meatus at the beginning of urination, and in sediment in the urinary bladder which drains at the end of urination.

ALERT: Follow Standard Precautions.

PREPROCEDURE

1. Wash hands.
2. Assemble equipment:
   a. Antiseptic solution or soap and water or towelettes
   b. Sterile specimen container

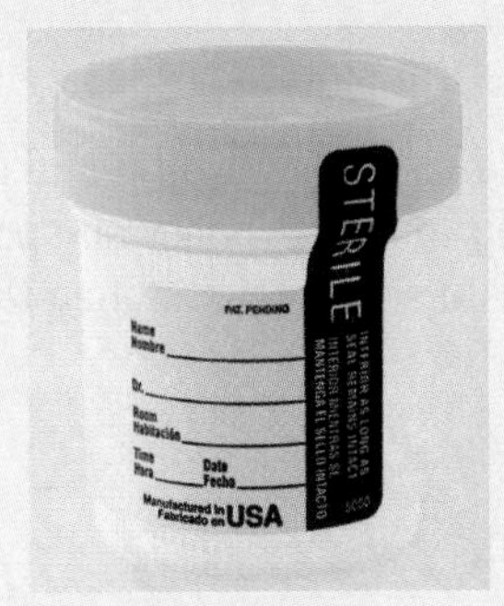

Courtesy of ShutterStock.

   c. Tissues
   d. Disposable gloves
3. Identify patient.

PROCEDURE

4. Label specimen:
   a. Patient's name
   b. Date
   c. Time obtained
5. Explain procedure (if possible allow patient to obtain his own specimen).
   a. Put on gloves.
   b. Cleanse head of penis in a circular motion with towelette or gauze and antiseptic. (If patient is uncircumcised, have him pull back foreskin before cleaning.)
   c. Have patient start to urinate into clean bedpan, urinal, or toilet. (If he is uncircumcised, have patient pull back foreskin before urinating.)
   d. Allow stream to begin.
   e. Stop stream and place specimen container to collect midstream.
   f. Remove container before bladder is empty.
6. Dispose of equipment according to facility policy.

POSTPROCEDURE

7. Remove and discard gloves according to facility policy and procedure.
8. Make patient comfortable and put call bell within reach.
9. Wash hands.
10. Record specimen collection.

5/16/12	1300
	Clean-catch urine collected
	Urine was dark amber in color with
	white sediment
	Labeled and sent to the laboratory
	A. Chaplin CNA

PROCEDURE 18.78 HemaCombistix

BACKGROUND: HemaCombistix detects the presence of blood in urine.

ALERT: Follow Standard Precautions.

PREPROCEDURE

1. Wash hands.
2. Assemble equipment.
   a. Bottle of HemaCombistix
   b. Nonsterile gloves
3. Identify patient.
4. Explain what you are going to do.
5. Put on gloves.

PROCEDURE

6. Secure fresh urine sample from patient.
7. Take urine and reagent to bathroom.
8. Remove cap and place on flat surface. Be sure top side of cap is down.
9. Remove strip from bottle by shaking bottle gently. *Do not touch areas of strip with fingers.*
10. Dip reagent stick in urine. Remove immediately.

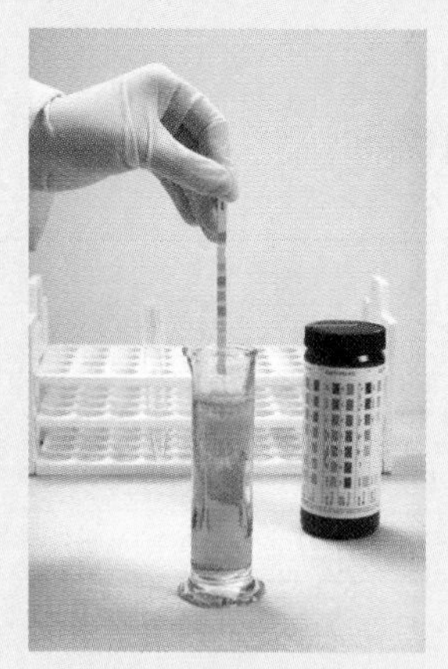

11. Tap edge of strip on container to remove excess urine.
12. Compare reagent side of test areas with color chart on bottle. Use time intervals that are given on bottle.

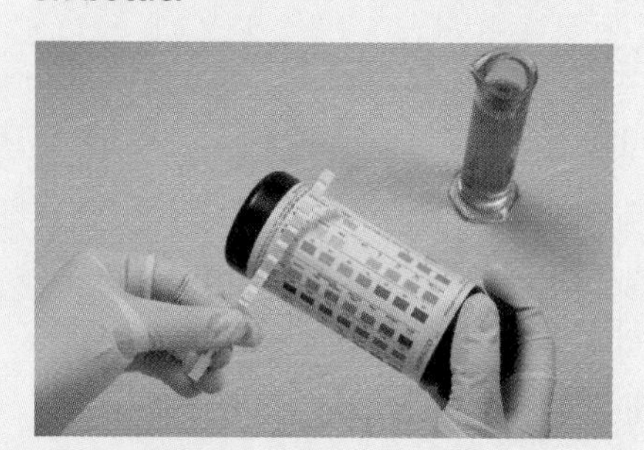

NOTE: Do not touch reagent strip to bottle.

13. Remove gloves and discard both strip and urine specimen according to facility policy and procedure. Need to discard specimen and then take off gloves.

POSTPROCEDURE

14. Replace equipment.
15. Wash hands.
16. Record results.
    a. Date and time
    b. Name of procedure used
    c. Results

10/04/11	1800
	Urine specimen tested with a
	hemacombistix
	Results negative for blood
	R. Johnson CNA

PROCEDURE 18.79 Straining Urine

BACKGROUND: Pouring urine through a strainer allows calculi (kidney stones) to be collected.

ALERT: Follow Standard Precautions.

PREPROCEDURE

1. Wash hands.
2. Assemble equipment:
   a. Paper strainers or gauze
   b. Specimen container and label
   c. Bedpan or urinal and cover
   d. Laboratory request for analysis of specimen
   e. Sign for patient's room or bathroom explaining that all urine must be strained
   f. Nonsterile gloves
3. Identify patient.

PROCEDURE

4. Tell the patient to urinate into a urinal or bedpan and that the nurse assistant must be called to filter each specimen. Tell patient not to put paper in specimen.
5. Put on gloves.
6. Pour voided specimen through a paper strainer or gauze into a measuring container.
7. Place paper or gauze strainer into a dry specimen container if stones or particles are present after pouring urine through.

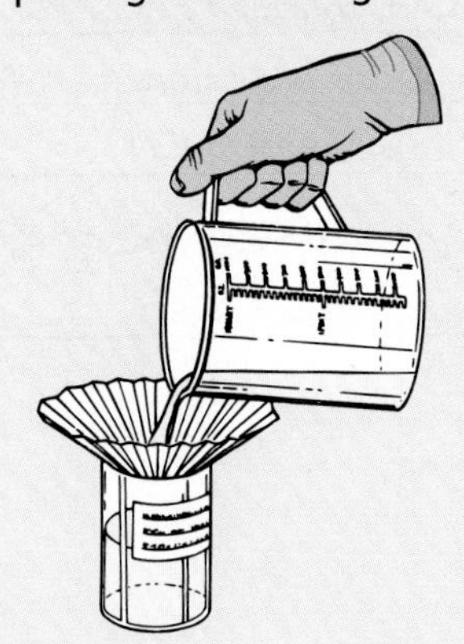

NOTE: Do not attempt to remove the particles from strainer.

8. Measure the amount voided and record on intake and output record.
9. Discard urine and container according to facility policy and procedure.
10. Clean urinal or bedpan and put away. Flush toilet and turn faucet on with a paper towel.
11. Remove gloves and discard according to facility policy and procedure.
12. Wash hands.
13. Label specimen:
    a. Patient's name
    b. Date
    c. Room number
    d. Time
14. Return patient to comfortable position.
15. Place call button within reach of patient.
16. Provide for patient safety by raising side rails when indicated or using postural supports as ordered.

POSTPROCEDURE

17. Wash hands.
18. Report collection of specimen to supervisor immediately.
19. Record specimen collection.

6/20/12	1400
	300 cc strained
	Two small stones collected
	Given to team leader
	S. Gomez CNA

PROCEDURE 18.80 Stool Specimen Collection

BACKGROUND: Stool specimens are collected most frequently to determine if blood or parasites are present in the stool.

ALERT: Follow Standard Precautions.

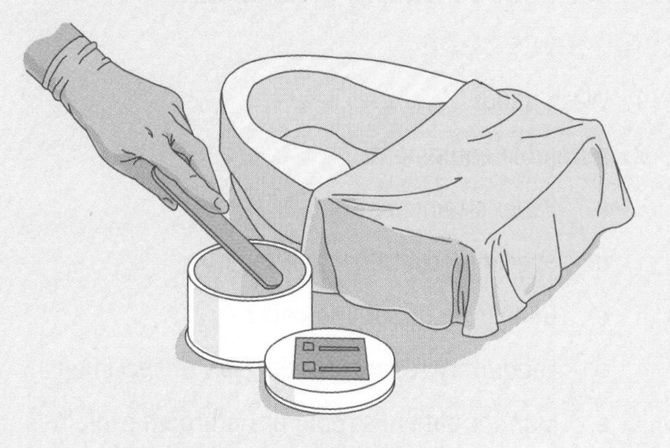

PREPROCEDURE

1. Wash hands.
2. Assemble equipment:
   a. Stool specimen container with label
   b. Wooden tongue depressor
   c. Disposable gloves
   d. Bedpan and cover
3. Identify patient.
4. Explain what you are going to do.

PROCEDURE

5. Be certain container is properly labeled with
   a. Patient's name
   b. Time
   c. Date
   d. Room number
6. Provide privacy by pulling privacy curtains.
7. Put on gloves.
8. Take bedpan into bathroom after patient has had bowel movement.
9. Use tongue depressor to remove about 1 to 2 tablespoons of feces from bedpan.
10. Place specimen in specimen container.
11. Cover container immediately.
12. Wrap tongue depressor in paper towel and discard as per facility rules.
13. Remove gloves and dispose of according to facility policy.

POSTPROCEDURE

14. Wash hands.
15. Follow instruction for storage of specimen for collection by lab.
16. Position patient comfortably with call bell in place.
17. Report and record procedure.

12/14/11	1000
	Soft, brown stool collected,
	labeled, and sent to laboratory
	R. Johnson CNA

PROCEDURE 18.81 Occult Blood Hematest

BACKGROUND: Occult blood Hematest reveals the presence of blood in a stool specimen.

ALERT: Follow Standard Precautions.

PREPROCEDURE

1. Wash hands.
2. Assemble equipment:
   a. Hematest Reagent filter paper
   b. Hematest Reagent tablet
   c. Distilled water
   d. Tongue blade
   e. Disposable gloves
3. Identify patient.
4. Explain what you are going to do.
5. Put on gloves.

PROCEDURE

6. Secure stool specimen from patient.
7. Place filter paper on glass or porcelain plate.
8. Use tongue blade to smear a thin streak of fecal material on filter paper.
9. Place Hematest Reagent tablet on smear.
10. Place 1 drop distilled water on tablet.
11. Allow 5 to 10 seconds for water to penetrate tablet.
12. Add second drop, allowing water to run down side of tablet onto filter paper and specimen.
13. Gently tap side of plate to knock water droplets from top of tablet.
14. Observe filter paper for color change (2 minutes). Positive is indicated by blue halo on paper.
15. Dispose of specimen and equipment according to your facility's policy.
16. Remove gloves and dispose of according to your facility's policy.

POSTPROCEDURE

17. Wash hands.
18. Report and record results (e.g., date, time, procedure, and results).

PROCEDURE **18.82** **24-Hour Urine Test**

BACKGROUND: Routine urine tests were performed as early at 1821. Analysis of the patient's urine is useful for diagnosing renal disease or metabolic disease not related to the kidneys. For some laboratory studies, 24-hour urine specimens are required.

ALERT: Follow Standard Precautions.

PREPROCEDURE

1. Determine the laboratory test and any special requirements associated with the test.

   This could include altering the dietary intake, special collection containers, adding preservatives to the designated container, icing the container, etc.
2. The nurse should determine if any drugs affect the results of this test. Obtain a history of any drugs the patient is currently taking and advise the laboratory as necessary.
3. Obtain the appropriate container to be used for urine collection. Label the container with the patient's name, hospital number, date, and time of the urine collection.

PROCEDURE

4. Explain the procedure to the patient. Provide a means for the patient to collect their urinary output, if the patient is able to participate in the procedure.
5. Post a sign that all urine is to be collected for a specified time. Assure that all staff providing care for this patient during this period of time are aware of the need to save all urine output.
6. When initiating the collection the patient will empty his bladder, and this specimen will be discarded. All urine produced after this time will be saved. At the end of the time period, the patient will again empty his bladder and this last specimen will be added to the specimen container.
7. If any urine is inadvertently discarded during the 24-hour collection, the test must be restarted.

POSTPROCEDURE

8. At the end of the test period, transport the labeled specimen to the laboratory.

PROCEDURE 19.1 Preparing Moist Hot Soaks

BACKGROUND: You can prevent injury by using the correct temperature for the hot moist pads. Make sure you carefully observe the treated area to watch for irritation or excessive redness.

ALERT: Follow Standard Precautions.

PREPROCEDURE

1. Check physician's orders.
2. Wash hands.
3. Assemble equipment:
   a. **Hydroculator pad**
   b. Towel
4. Identify patient.
5. Explain what you will be doing and reassure patient that procedure is painless.
6. Provide privacy.
7. Cover warm hydroculator pad with towel.
8. Expose site to be treated.
9. Position patient for comfort.

PROCEDURE

10. Apply covered warm hydroculator pad to appropriate site. (Never put warm hydroculator pad directly on the skin, unless it is covered.)
11. Make sure call bell is in reach.
12. Wash hands.
13. Recheck patient frequently—every 5 minutes when heating device is on skin. Look for:
    a. Severely reddened areas
    b. Irritated areas
    c. Painful areas
14. Remove soaks as ordered.

POSTPROCEDURE

15. Position patient for comfort and make sure call bell is in reach.
16. Wash hands.
17. Report and record patient's tolerance of treatment and any changes in condition you observed.

PROCEDURE **19.2** **Moist Cryotherapy (Cold) Compresses**

BACKGROUND: You can prevent injury by using the correct temperature for moist cryotherapy. Make sure you carefully observe the treated area to watch for any pain or irregularities. Using correct temperature for moist cryotherapy and careful observation of the treated area prevents injury.

ALERT: Follow Standard Precautions.

PREPROCEDURE

1. Check doctor's orders.
2. Wash hands.
3. Assemble equipment:
   a. Cool, wet cloth
   b. Plastic cover
   c. Dry towel

PROCEDURE

4. Explain procedure to client/patient.
5. Apply cool, wet cloth to patient as ordered.*

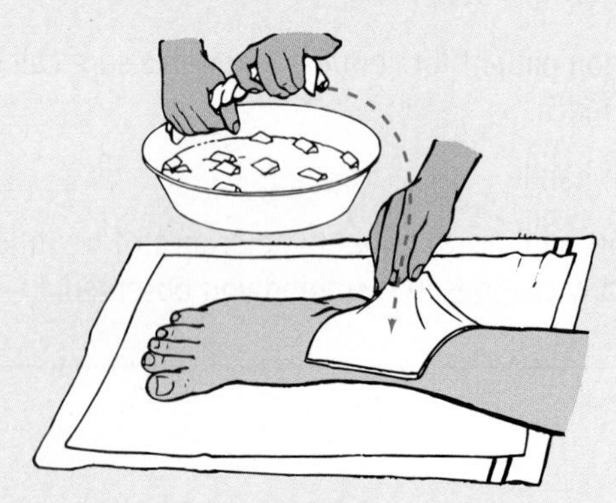

6. Cover wet area with plastic cover.
7. Cover plastic with dry towel.

* Wear gloves if there are broken areas on the skin.

8. Wash hands.
9. Recheck frequently for:
   a. Coolness of cloth
   b. Position
   c. Patient's comfort needs (reapply PRN)
10. Remove as ordered.

POSTPROCEDURE

11. Dry skin.
12. Dispose of supplies and clean area.
13. Wash hands.
14. Report and document effects of treatment.

11/20/11 1100
No skin reddened or irritated areas
Moist, cold towels applied times 15 minutes
Recheck skin at site
No reddened or irritated areas
Patient states: Pain is better after treatment but returns in about an hour
________ A. Cantina student

PROCEDURE 19.3 Dry Cryotherapy: Ice Bags/Ice Collars

BACKGROUND: Using the correct temperature for dry cryotherapy and careful observation of the treated area prevents injury.

ALERT: Follow Standard Precautions.

PREPROCEDURE

1. Check physician's orders.
2. Wash hands.
3. Assemble equipment:
   a. Ice bag or commercial cold compress
   b. Ice
   c. Cover for ice bag
4. Fill bag with ice. (Run water over cubes to soften sharp edges.)
5. Remove air from bag by pressing sides together.
6. Close end and check for leaks.
7. Cover bag with cloth or towel. (Never apply bag directly to skin; it may stick, burn, and tear skin when removed.)

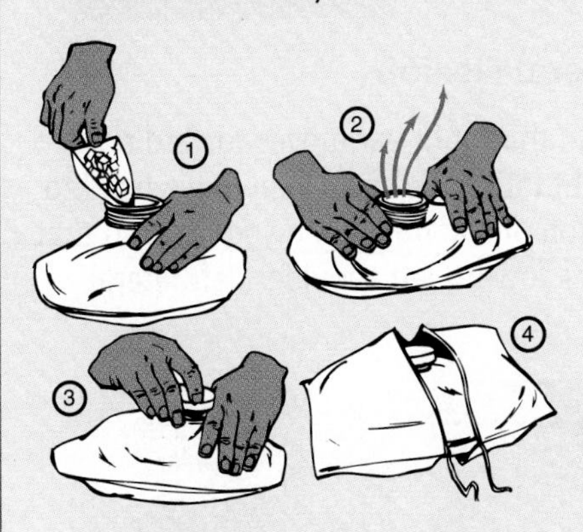

8. Identify patient by checking order and name with patient's armband or patient chart.

PROCEDURE

9. Explain procedure to patient.
10. Gently position ice bag as ordered. (The metal cap cannot touch the skin.)*
11. Secure bag so that it does not move away from affected area.
12. Provide needed comfort measures for patient. Make sure call bell is in reach.
13. Wash hands.
14. Return frequently to check for:
    a. Coolness of ice bag
    b. Position of ice bag
    c. Color of skin (remove ice if skin is white or bluish in color or if patient reports numbness and report)
15. Remove ice bag at ordered time.
16. Make sure patient is comfortable and call bell is in reach.

POSTPROCEDURE

17. Wash hands.
18. Recheck skin, and report and document effects of treatment.
19. Wash hands.
20. Empty bag, dry, and return to appropriate area for cleaning.

11/20/11	1100
	No skin reddened or irritated areas Dry
	cold compress applied times 15 minutes
	Recheck skin at site
	No reddened or irritated areas
	Patient states: Pain is better after
	treatment but returns in about an hour
	________ A. Cantina student

* Wear gloves if there are broken areas on the skin.

PROCEDURE 19.4 **Range of Motion**

BACKGROUND: Correct ROM provides exercise to the joints and muscles, preventing contractures and immobility.

NOTE: The use of passive and active range of motion (ROM) is related to resident's ability level.

- **Active ROM**—Resident is able to perform all movements without assistance.
- **Passive ROM**—Health care worker moves body parts for resident.

ALERT: Follow Standard Precautions.

PREPROCEDURE

1. Wash hands.
2. Assemble equipment:
   a. Sheet or bath blanket
   b. Treatment table or bed
   c. Good lighting
3. Identify resident.
4. Explain what you are going to do.
5. Ask visitors to wait outside, and provide privacy.

PROCEDURE

6. Place resident in a supine position on bed or treatment table and cover with sheet or bath blanket. Only expose affected area. Instruct resident to do the following movements at least five times each or to tolerance.

Head Flexion and Extension

7. Bend head until chin touches chest (flexion), then gently bend backward (extension).

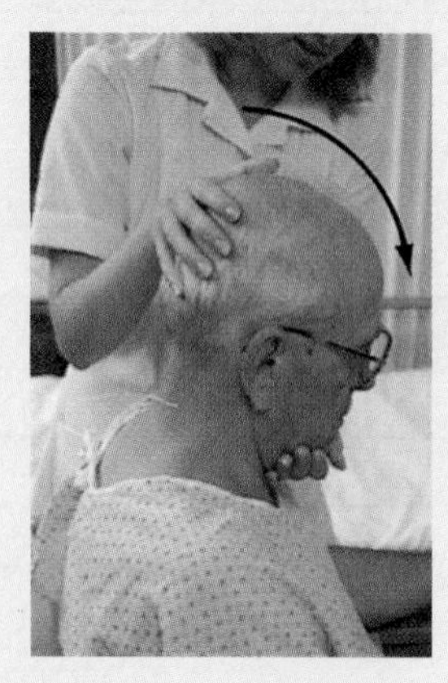

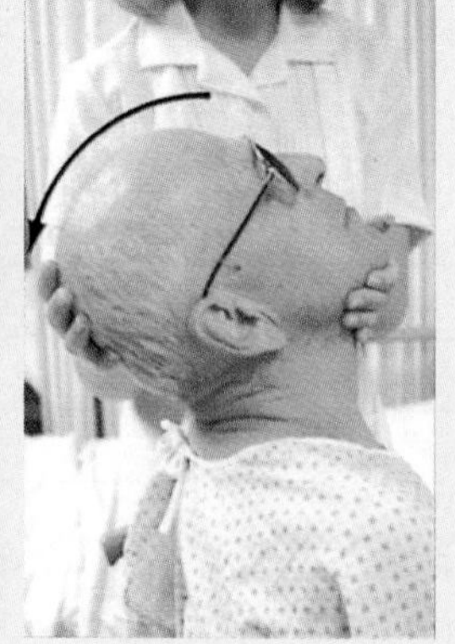

Right/Left Rotation

8. Turn head to right (right rotation), then turn head to left (left rotation).

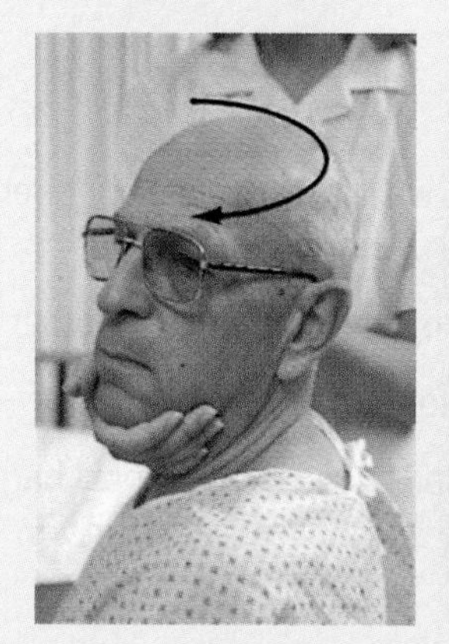

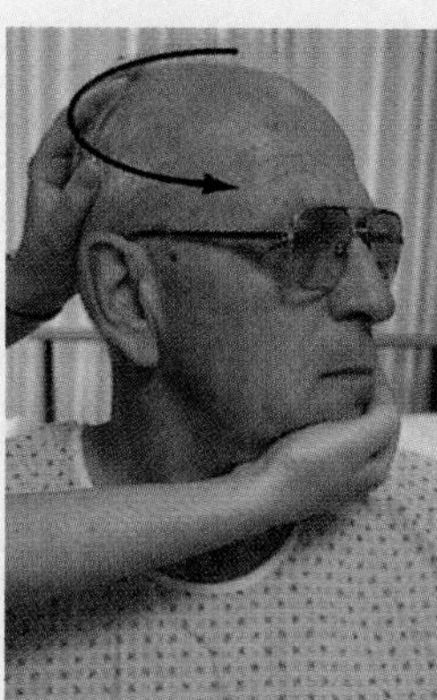

Right/Left Lateral Flexion

9. Move head so that right ear moves toward right shoulder (right lateral flexion), then move head to central position and continue moving head so that left ear moves toward left shoulder (left lateral flexion).

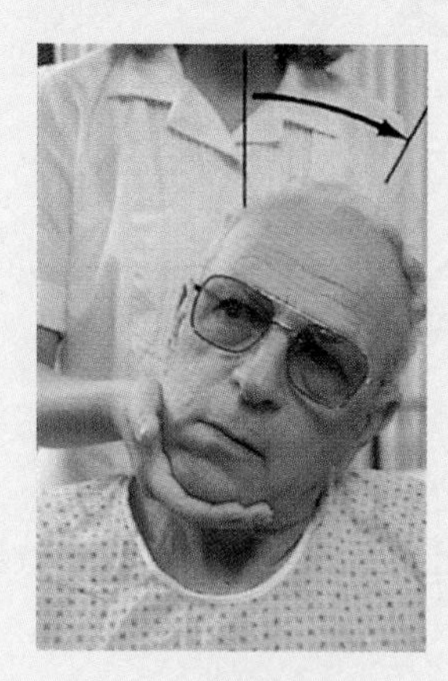

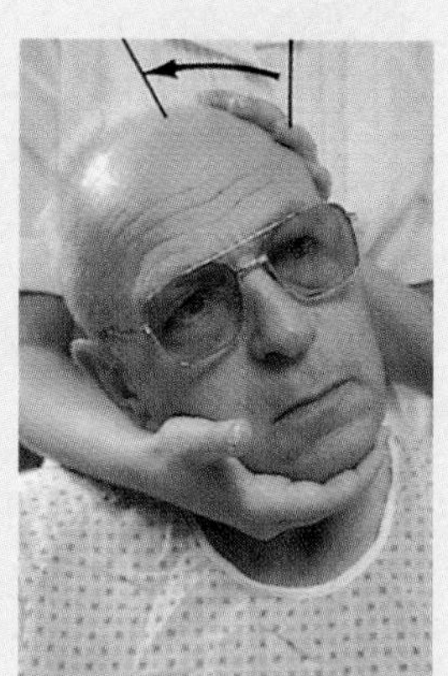

(continued)

PROCEDURE 19.4 Range of Motion (continued)

Hyperextension and Extension

10. Place the pillow under the shoulders and gently support the head in a backward tilt and return to straight position. Readjust pillow under head when finished.

Shoulder Flexion and Extension

11. Raise one arm overhead keeping elbow straight. Return to side position. Repeat with other arm.

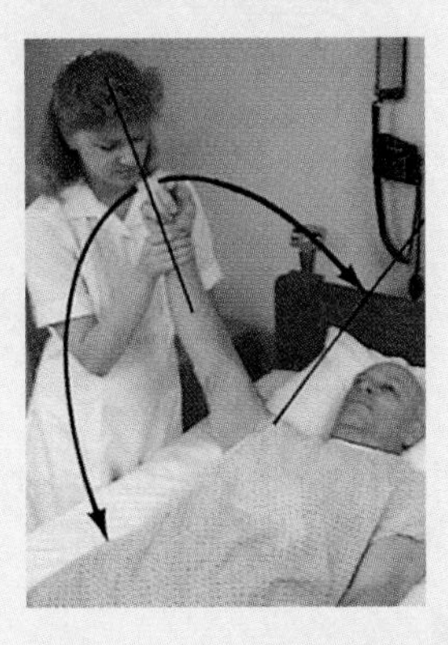

12. With the shoulder in abduction, flex the elbow and raise the entire arm over the head.

Shoulder Abduction and Adduction

13. Raise arm overhead, then lower, keep arm out to side. Repeat with other arm.

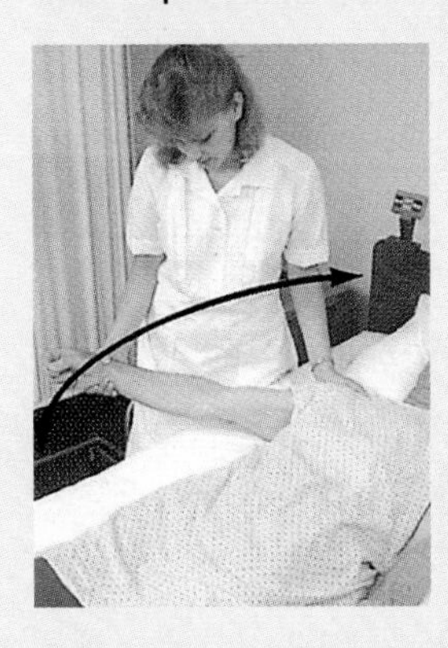

14. With the shoulder in abduction, flex the elbow and raise the arm over the head.

Internal and External Rotation of Shoulder

15. Roll entire arm toward body and away.

Elbow Flexion and Extension

16. Bend one hand and forearm toward shoulder (flexion) and straighten (extension). Repeat with other arm.

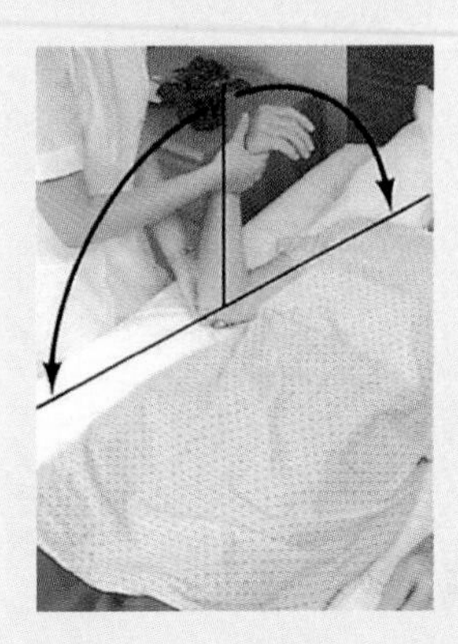

Forearm Pronation and Supination

17. Bend arm at elbow and rotate hand toward body (pronation), then rotate away from body (supination). Repeat with other arm.

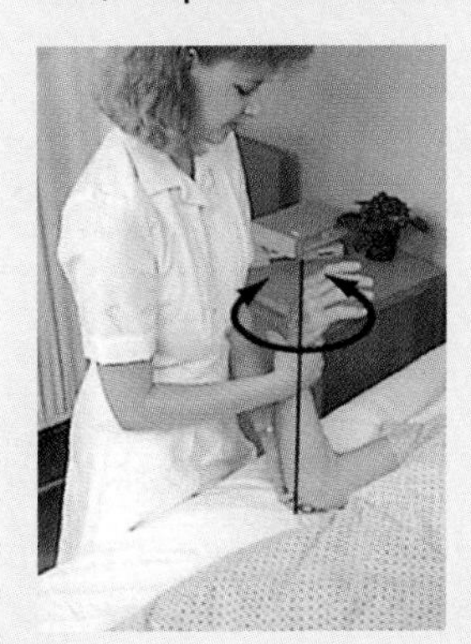

Wrist Flexion and Extension

18. Bend hand at wrist toward shoulder (flex), then gently force backward past a level position with arm (extension) to below arm level (hyperextension). Repeat with other hand.

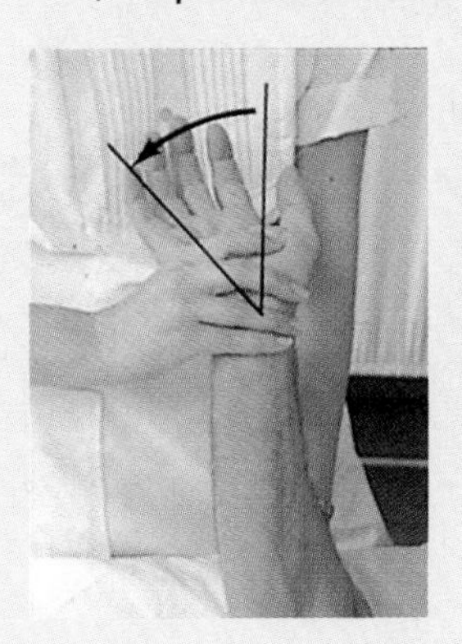

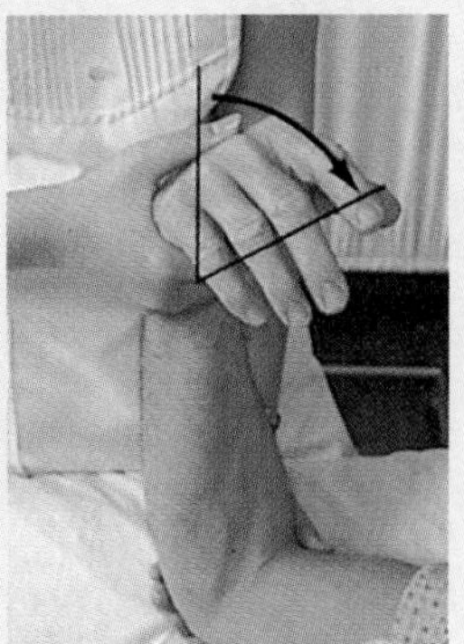

(continued)

Ulnar and Radial Deviation

19. Holding hand straight, move toward thumb (radial deviation), then move hand toward little finger (ulnar deviation). Repeat with other hand.

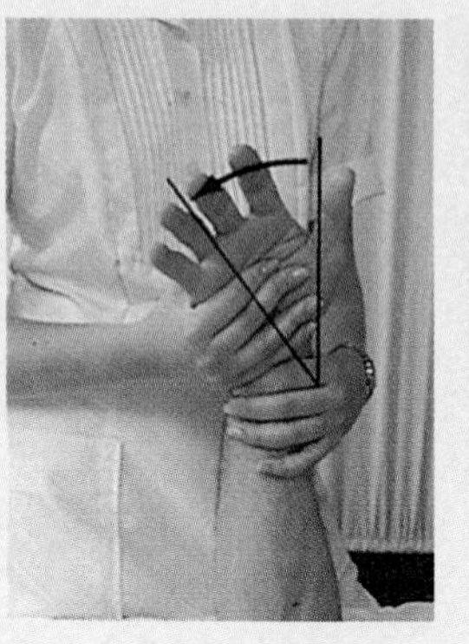
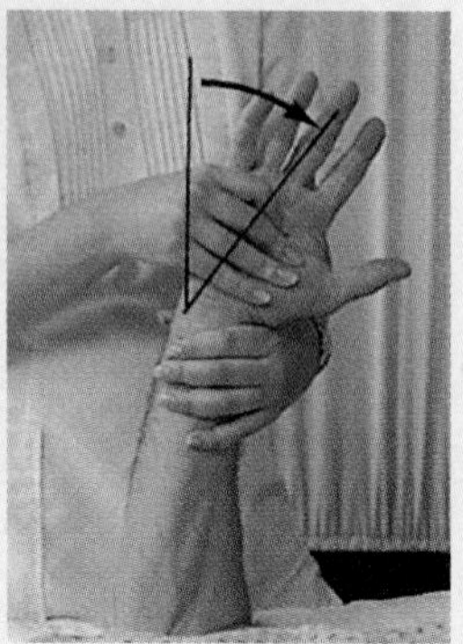

Finger Flexion and Extension

20. Bend thumb and fingers into hand making a fist (flexion), then open hand by straightening fingers and thumb (extension). Repeat with other hand.

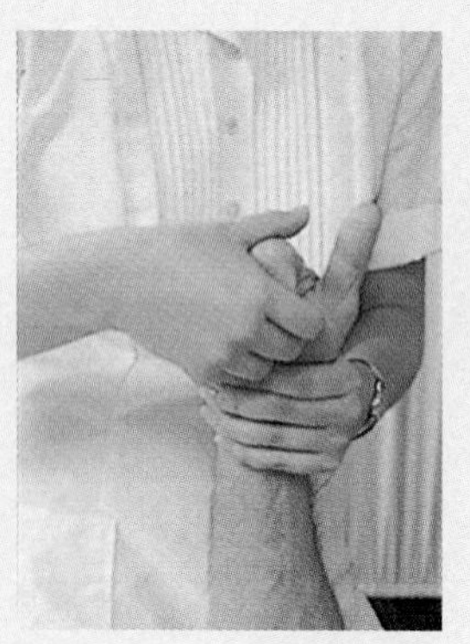
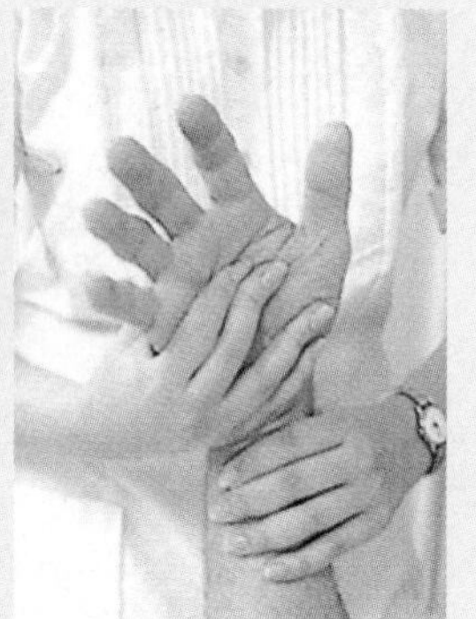

21. Move thumb away from hand (abduct), then toward hand (adduct). Repeat with other hand.

Finger/Thumb Opposition

22. Move thumb toward little finger, touch tips. Touch tip of thumb to each finger. Open hand each time. Repeat with other hand.

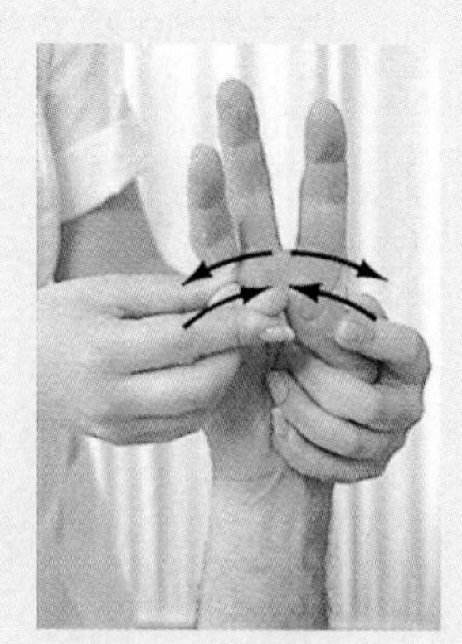

Finger Adduction and Abduction

23. Keeping fingers straight, separate them (abduction), then bring them together (adduction). Repeat with other hand.

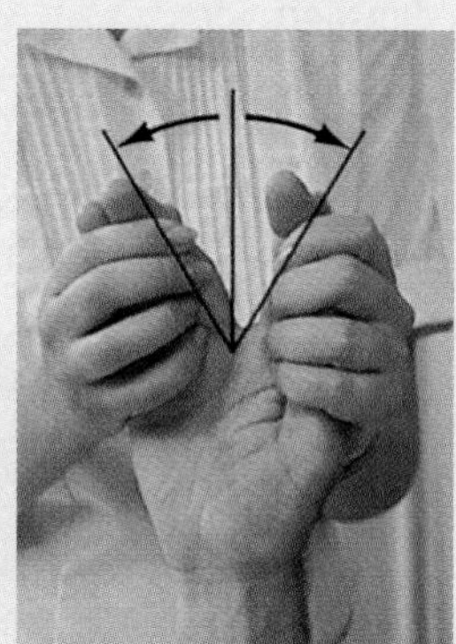

Hip/Knee Flexion and Extension

24. Raise leg, bend knee, then return to bed straightening knee. Repeat with other leg.

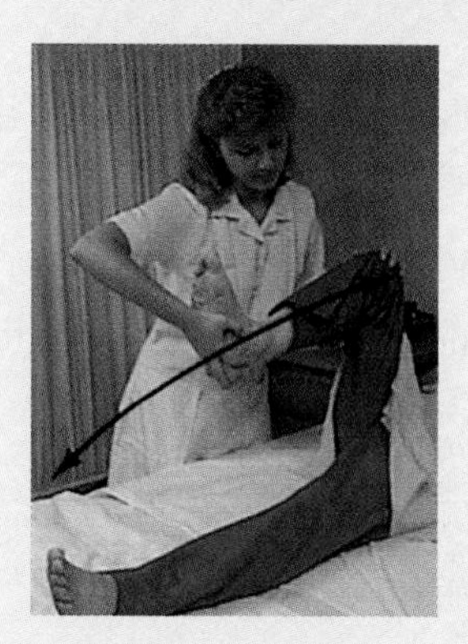

Straight Leg Raising

25. Keep knee straight. Slowly raise and lower leg. Repeat with other leg.

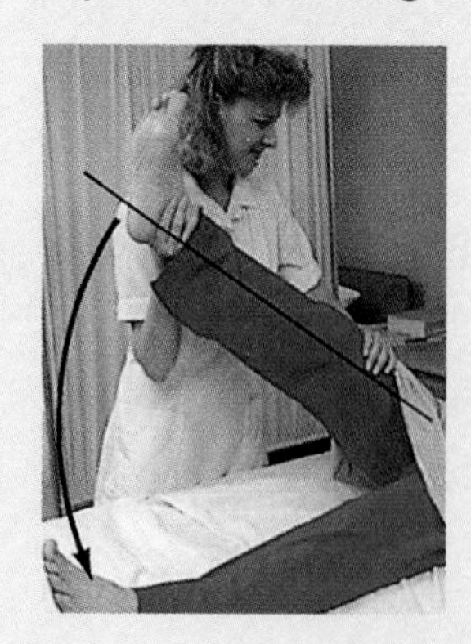

(continued)

Hip Abduction and Adduction

26. Supporting the knee and ankle, separate legs (abduction), then bring back together (adduction). Then turn both legs so knees face outward. Turn legs so knees face inward.

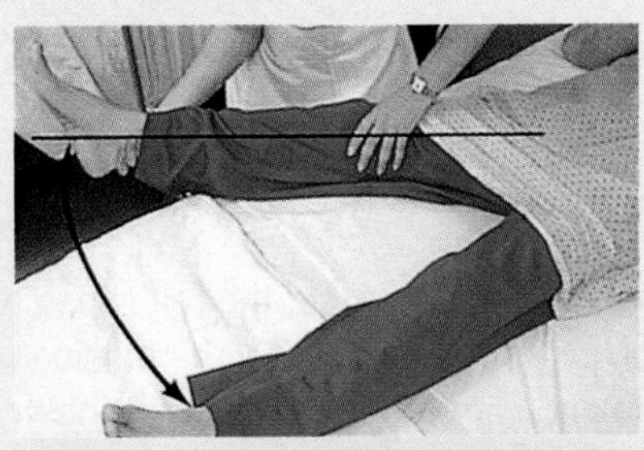

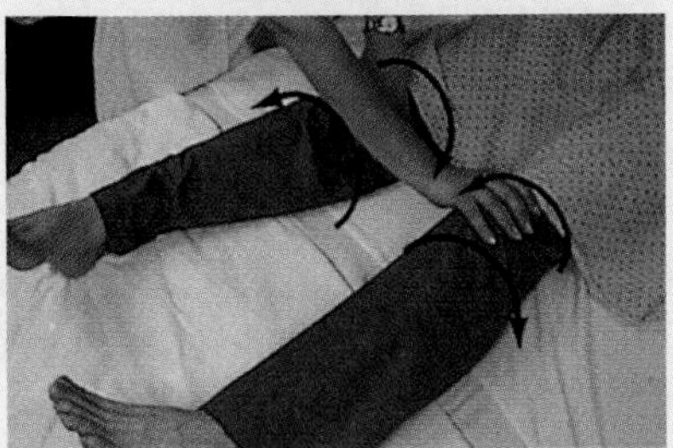

Lateral and Medial Hip Rotation

27. Roll leg in a circular fashion away from body and then toward body.
28. Rotate one foot toward other foot (internal rotation), then rotate away from other foot (external rotation). Repeat with other foot.

Ankle Dorsiflexion and Plantar Flexion

29. Grasp toes while supporting ankle. Move foot so that toes move toward knee (dorsi flexion), then move foot so that toes point away from head (plantar flexion). Repeat with other foot.

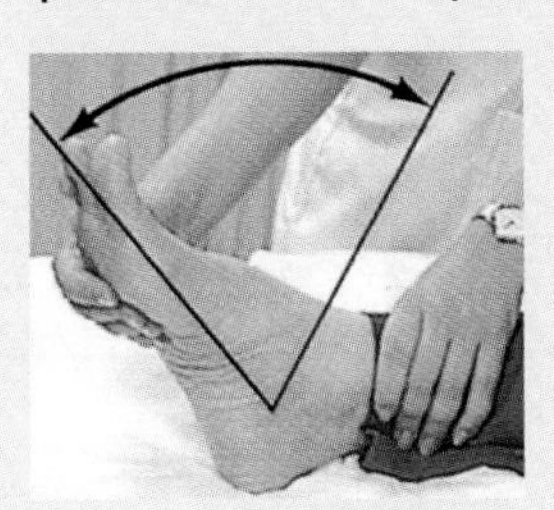

Toe Flexion and Extension

30. Spread toes apart (abduction) on one foot, then bring toes together (adduction). Repeat on other foot.

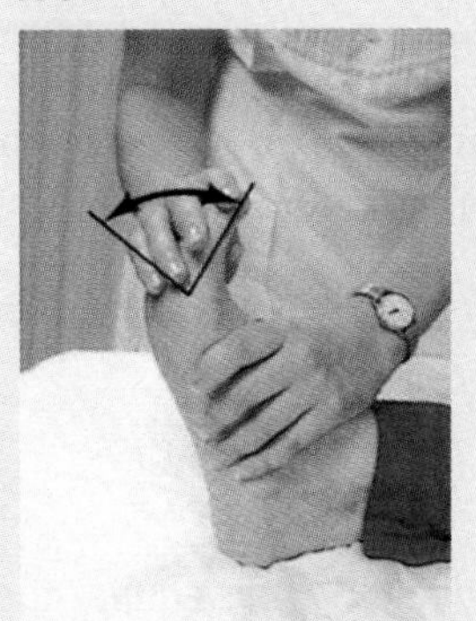

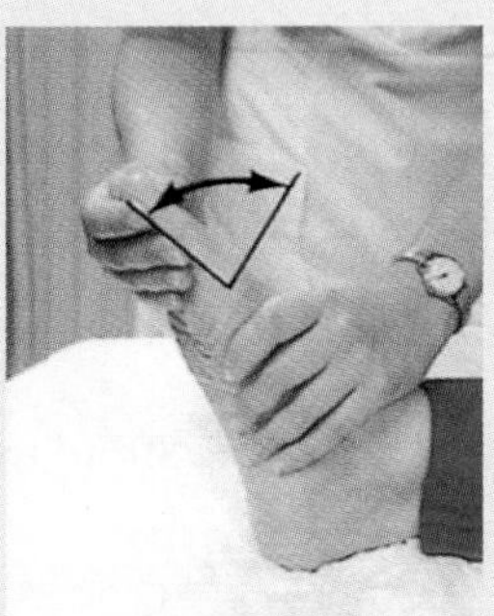

31. Turn resident in a prone position.

Arm Abduction and Adduction

32. Move arm toward ceiling; do not bend elbows (hyperextension), then return to bed. Repeat with other arm.

Leg Flexion and Extension

33. Bend leg so that foot moves toward resident's back (flexion), then straighten leg (extension). Repeat with other leg.
34. Position resident for comfort.

POSTPROCEDURE

35. Place bath blanket or sheet in laundry basket.
36. Wash your hands.
37. Report and document resident's tolerance of procedure.

12/06/11	1510
	Passive ROM to all joints
	Complained of some discomfort
	in left elbow
	Noted some increased stiffness
	in fingers of the right hand
	Reported to charge nurse
	ROM tolerated well
	________ *S. Gomez CNA*

PROCEDURE 19.5 Wrapping/Taping an Ankle

BACKGROUND: Tape and elastic bandages are used to provide support and strength for a joint such as the ankle, elbow, wrist, or shoulder. Tape may be used for support in an athletic setting but caution must be used to avoid constriction of the circulatory system or worsening of any swelling that might be present in an injured joint.

The bandage is a continuous strip of elasticized material that is wound on itself to form a cylinder or roll. The common name used for these bandages is **Ace**. These bandages vary in width from 1 to 6 inches.

ALERT: Follow Standard Precautions.

PREPROCEDURE

1. Identify the patient and joint which requires the use of a supportive bandage. Check the physician's order for any special instructions. Gather the appropriate bandage.
2. Wash hands. Put on gloves.
3. Explain the procedure to the patient. Assist the patient to a comfortable position that provides easy access to the affected joint.

PROCEDURE

4. Remove any old bandage and discard. If the bandage is to be reused, it may be unwound by keeping the loose end together and passing it as a ball from one hand to the other while unwinding it. Assess the joint for mobility and pain.
5. Clean the area before reapplying bandage. Make sure skin is dry before re-wrapping.
6. To begin, the free end of the bandage roll is held in place with one hand while the other hand passes the roll around the top middle of the ankle and then around the back of the Achilles tendon. After the bandage is anchored, the roll is passed or tolled around the ankle.
7. After the bandage is anchored, the roll is passed or rolled under the foot and back up the outside of the ankle, taking care to exert equal tension in all turns. There should be even overlapping of one-half to two-thirds the width of each bandage, except for the circular turn.
8. The figure-of-eight turn is most effective for use around joints such as the ankle. The figure-of-eight turns consists of making oblique overlapping turns that ascend and descend alternatively.

POSTPROCEDURE

9. Assure that the patient is comfortable and has no other needs before leaving the area.
10. Wash hands.
11. Document the appearance of the joint, any discomfort present and the application of the new bandage.

PROCEDURE 19.6 Elastic Hose (Antiembolism Hose)

BACKGROUND: Elastic hose help prevent blood from pooling in the legs, thus reducing the possibility of developing phlebitis.

ALERT: Follow Standard Precautions as needed.

PREPROCEDURE

1. Wash hands.
2. Select elastic hose. Check to be sure that they are the correct size and length.

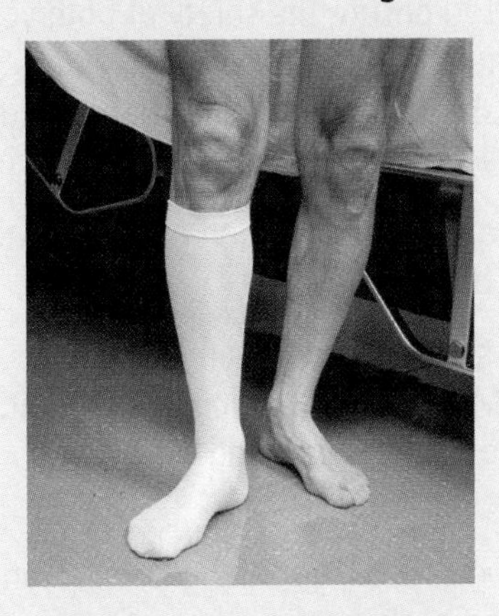

3. Identify resident and explain procedure to patient.
4. Provide for patient 's privacy.
5. Have resident lie down; expose one leg at a time.

PROCEDURE

6. Hold the hose with both hands at top and roll toward toe end. Turn stockings inside-out, at least to heel area.
7. Place hose over toes, positioning opening at base of toes unless toes are to be covered. The raised seams should be on outside.
8. Pull top of stocking over foot, heel, and leg. Move patient's foot and leg gently and naturally. Avoid forcing and overextending limbs and joints.
9. Check to be sure that the stocking is applied evenly and smoothly. There must be no wrinkles.
10. Repeat on opposite leg.

POSTPROCEDURE

11. Make patient comfortable, lower bed and raise side rails. Make sure call bell is within reach of patient.
12. Wash hands.
13. Record the following in the medical record:
    a. Date and time applied
    b. Any skin changes, temperature change, or swelling
14. Remove and reapply at least once every 8 hours, or more often if necessary.

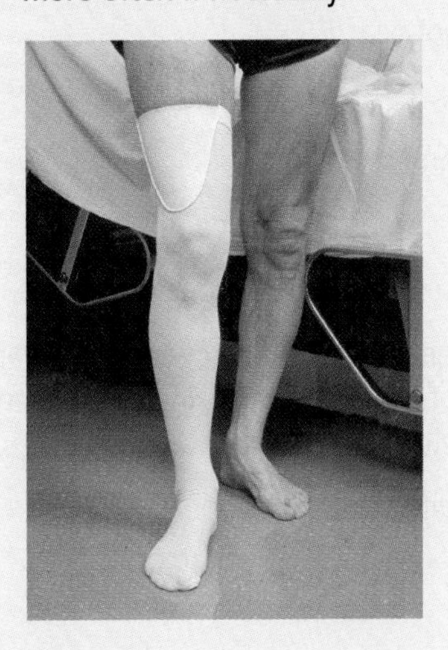

PROCEDURE 19.7 Ambulating with a Gait Belt

BACKGROUND: Using a **gait belt** protects the patient from falling when ambulating. It ensures the safety and security of the patient. Gait belts also decrease caregiver injuries and enable the caregiver to assist heavy patients they would not be able to assist otherwise.

NOTE: Caregivers are sometimes seen assisting a patient by holding them at the axillary area and without a gait belt. This type of assistance could result in the subluxation of the shoulder joint. If a patient cannot ambulate independently a gait belt should always be used.

ALERT: Follow Standard Precautions.

PREPROCEDURE

1. Wash hands.
2. Assemble equipment:
   a. Gait belt/walking belt (correct size)
   b. Patient's robe
   c. Patient's footwear
3. Identify patient.
4. Explain what you are going to do.
5. Provide for privacy and lower side rail.
6. Assist patient to sitting position on side of bed.
7. Encourage patient to take a few deep breaths and ask if he or she feels dizzy. (If dizziness is present, let the patient sit a while before walking.)
8. Assist patient with robe and slippers.
9. Secure gait belt around patient's waist over clothing.
10. Tighten belt and buckle securely. Position buckle/clasp slightly off center. Check to see if patient can breathe easily and that breasts are above the belt.*

PROCEDURE

11. Stand in front of patient with broad base of support.
12. Instruct patient to put hands on your shoulder. Position yourself to ensure the safety of both yourself and the patient during transfer (e.g., knees bent, feet apart, back straight). Place hands under side of belt. Give signal for patient to stand.
13. Ease patient to a standing position and hold handgrip securely at back of belt.
14. Keep your back straight /straighten knees as patient stands. Move to position behind patient. Keep one hand on side of belt and other hand should grasp the back of the belt.

    TIP: If patient is confused, grip the gait belt from underneath in the back, holding the patient's arm nearest the caregiver, and pointing the patient's arm in the direction you want to move. This helps the patient move with you instead of against you.
15. Ambulate patient as ordered.
16. Observe patient for weakness or discomfort.
17. Return patient to room and make comfortable.
18. Remove belt, help take off robe and slippers, position patient in bed, raise siderails, and make sure call bell is in place.

POSTPROCEDURE

19. Document and report patient's tolerance of procedure.
20. Return gait belt to storage area so that it will be available for the next procedure.
21. Wash hands.

* Belt is too tight if you cannot put two fingers under it.

PROCEDURE 19.8 Walking with a Cane

BACKGROUND: Safe canes, if correctly sized, and careful safety instruction protect the patient from falls or injuries.

ALERT: Follow Standard Precautions.

PREPROCEDURE

1. Wash hands.
2. Assemble equipment:
   a. Cane in good repair and with rubber tip
   b. Patient's/client's footwear
   c. Patient's/client's robe
3. Identify patient.
4. Assist patient with shoes and robe.
5. Explain what you are going to do.
6. Provide privacy as appropriate.
7. Assist to sitting position, feet resting on floor. Secure gait belt snug enough to provide support and loose enough to provide comfort. Place cane in reach.
8. Position patient in a standing position (have a co-worker help you if necessary).
9. Check height of cane. Top of cane should be at the patient's hip joint.

PROCEDURE

10. Check arm position at side of body and hold top of cane. Arm should be bent at a 25 to 30° angle.
11. Have patient hold cane in hand on strongest side of body (unaffected side). Walk mostly beside, but slightly to the rear of the patient, while grasping gait belt to provide support. Observe for discomfort or weakness.
12. Assist patient as needed while ambulating. Most physicians order a standard gait procedure.
    a. With cane in hand on strongest side, move cane and weakest foot forward.
    b. Place body weight forward on cane and move strongest foot forward. (Patient will have cane's maximum support when this procedure is used when walking on flat surface, hill, or stairs. Remember: Weak leg and cane move together.)
13. When you have completed ordered ambulation, return patient to the starting place.

POSTPROCEDURE

14. Provide for patient's comfort.
15. Place cane in proper location. If patient is capable and physician permits ambulation without assistance, leave cane in a convenient place for patient.
16. Wash hands.
17. Report/document patient's tolerance of procedure.
    a. Date
    b. Time
    c. Ambulated with cane (e.g., 15 minutes in hall)
    d. How tolerated
    e. Signature and classification

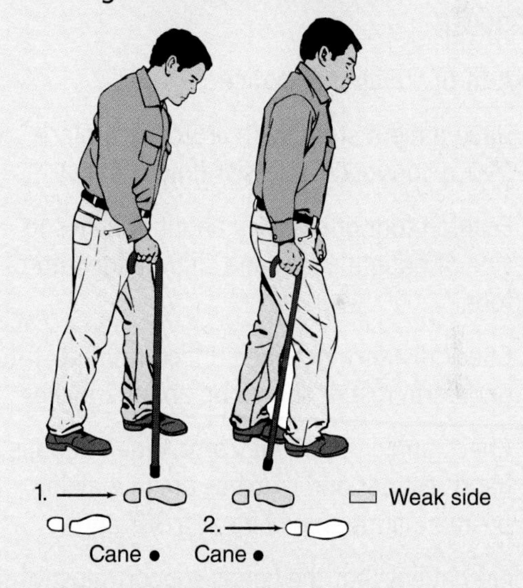

11/03/11	2100
	Height of cane correct
	Checked for safety
	Instructions given with emphasis
	on using the cane on the
	affected side
	Ambulated without difficulty 15
	minutes in hall
	Tolerated well
	________ *J. Munoz student*

PROCEDURE 19.9 Walking with Crutches

BACKGROUND: Measuring crutches to fit properly and careful instruction in how to use crutches safely prevents injury.

ALERT: Follow Standard Precautions.

PREPROCEDURE

1. Wash hands.
2. Assemble equipment:
   a. Crutches in good repair with rubber tips
   b. Patient's footwear
   c. Patient's robe, if necessary
3. Identify patient.
4. Explain what you are going to do.
5. Help patient with shoes and robe. Provide privacy if needed.

PROCEDURE

6. Check fit of crutches to patient.
   a. Have patient stand with crutches in place. (Ask a co-worker to assist if necessary.)
   b. Position foot of crutches about 4 inches to side of patient's foot and slightly forward of foot.
   c. Check distance between underarm and crutch underarm rest. It should be about 2 inches.
   d. Check angle of patient's arm. When hand is on hand rest bar and crutches are in walking position, arms should be at a 30° angle.
7. Remind patient that the hands support most of the body weight, not the underarms (axilla).
8. Assist patient to ambulate following gait method ordered. There are a variety of crutch walking gaits. The following will provide guidelines to the most commonly used:
   a. Three-point gait (beginners):
      (1) One leg is weight-bearing.
      (2) Place both crutches forward along with non-weight-bearing foot. Weight will be supported primarily by weight-bearing foot.
      (3) Shift weight to hands on crutches and move weight-bearing foot forward.
   b. Four-point gait (beginners) (see figure below):
      (1) Both legs are weight-bearing.
      (2) Place one crutch forward.
      (3) Move foot on opposite side of body forward, parallel with forward crutch.
      (4) Place other crutch forward and parallel with first crutch.
      (5) Move other foot forward so that it rests next to first foot.

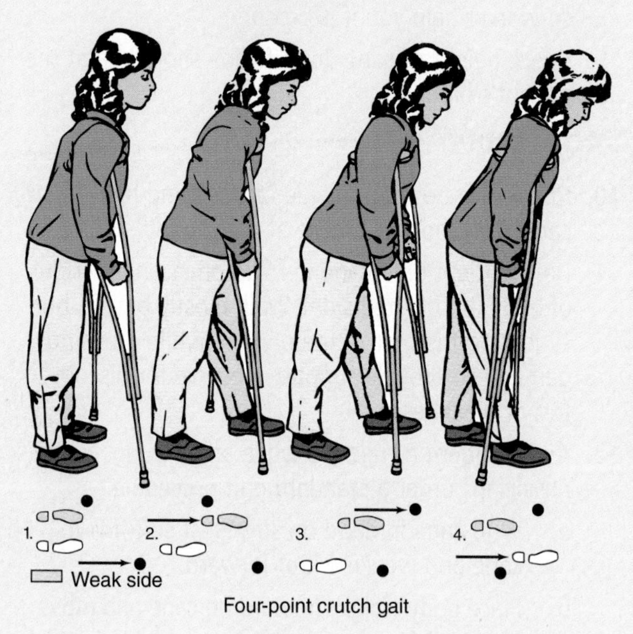

Four-point crutch gait

(continued)

c. Two-point gait (advanced) (see figure below):

(1) Both legs are weight-bearing.

(2) Place one crutch forward and move opposite foot forward with it.

(3) Place other crutch forward and parallel with first crutch. Then move opposite foot forward so that it is even with other foot.

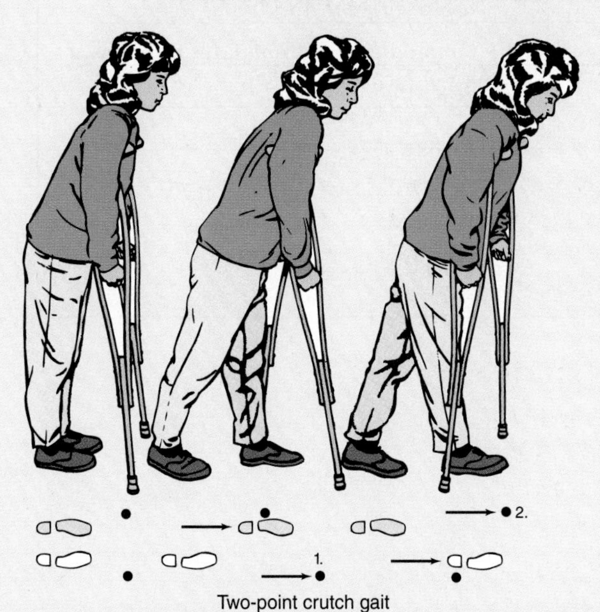

Two-point crutch gait

d. Swing-to gait (arm and shoulder strength are needed) (see figure below):

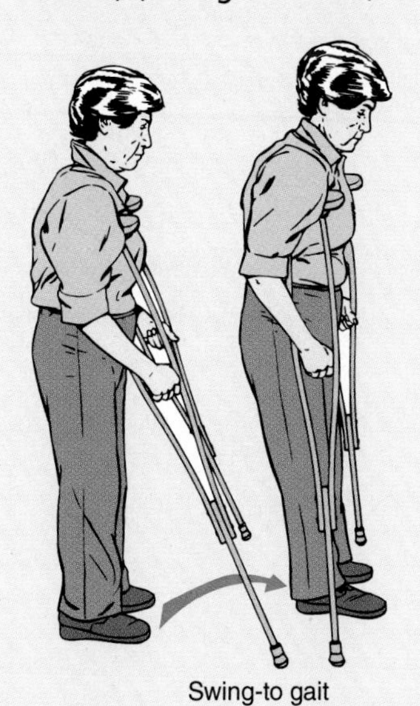
Swing-to gait

(1) One or both legs are weight-bearing.

(2) Balance weight on weight-bearing limb.

(3) Place both crutches forward.

(4) Shift weight to hands on crutches.

(5) Swing both feet forward until parallel with crutches.

CAUTION: Placing crutches too far forward can result in a fall!

e. Swing-through gait (advanced: arm and shoulder strength are needed) (see figure below):

(1) One or both legs are weight-bearing.

(2) Balance weight on weight-bearing limb(s).

(3) Place both crutches forward.

(4) Shift weight to hands on crutches.

(5) Swing both feet forward just ahead of crutches.

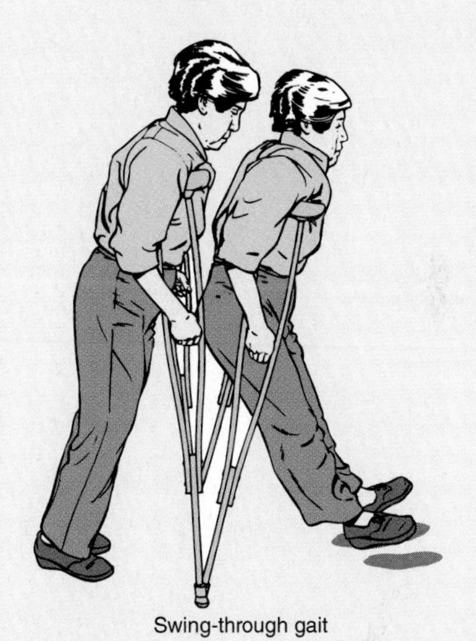
Swing-through gait

9. Return to room.

(continued)

PROCEDURE 19.9 Walking with Crutches (continued)

POSTPROCEDURE

10. Ensure that patient is comfortable.
11. Wash hands.
12. Record the following:
    a. Date
    b. Time
    c. Distance ambulated
    d. How tolerated
    e. Signature and classification

NOTE: Patients with memory loss (dementia) are not good candidates for education in the use of canes, crutches, or walkers as they can not retain information and may be endangered using this type of equipment.

12/10/11	2000
	Measured crutches for
	correct size and safety
	Instructed patient in safe
	use to prevent additional injury
	Ambulated for 15 minutes in hallway
	Tolerated well
	________ J. Munoz student

PROCEDURE 19.10 Walking with a Walker

BACKGROUND: It is important to measure a walker to fit properly and give the patient careful safety instruction in order to prevent injury.

ALERT: Follow Standard Precautions.

PREPROCEDURE

1. Wash hands.
2. Assemble equipment:
   a. Walker in good condition
   b. Patient's footwear
   c. Patient's robe if necessary
3. Identify patient.
4. Tell patient what you are going to do.
5. Check walker for safety.
6. Help put on proper and safe footwear and robe if necessary.
7. Assist to sitting position with feet resting on the floor.
8. Secure gait belt snug enough to provide support and loose enough to provide comfort. Place walker within reach.

PROCEDURE

9. Stand patient up with walker. (Ask a co-worker to help if necessary.) Remind patient to stand as straight as possible.
10. Check to see if walker fits patient properly.
    a. Walker's handgrips should be at top of patient's leg or bend of leg at hip joint.
    b. Arm should be at a 25 to 30° angle.
11. Gripping gait belt from behind,assist patient to ambulate as ordered. Basic guidelines for walking with a walker are as follows:
    a. Patient begins by standing inside walker frame.
    b. Patient lifts walker (never slides) and places back legs of walker parallel with toes (never ahead of toes).
    c. Patient shifts weight onto hands and walker (for balance and support).
    d. Patient then walks into walker.
    e. Place yourself just to side and slightly behind patient. This position will allow you to observe and be close enough to assist if necessary.
    f. Ambulate as ordered, observing for correct use of walker.
12. When you have completed the ordered ambulation, return patient to his or her starting place.

POSTPROCEDURE

13. Provide for patient's comfort with call signal in reach.
14. Place walker in proper location. If patient is capable and physician permits ambulation without assistance, leave walker in a convenient place for patient.
15. Wash hands.
16. Report/document patient's tolerance of procedure.
17. Record the following:
    a. Date
    b. Time
    c. Distance and amount of time ambulated
    d. How tolerated
    e. Signature and classification

12/04/11	0800
	Checked walker for safety measures
	Instructed patient in correct use
	of walker
	Ambulated in hallway for 10 minutes
	Patient complained of dizziness
	initially
	Dangled from bed until dizziness subsided
	Tolerated with some difficulty with fatigue
	Patient stated "I feel really tired
	after using the walker."
	__________ J. Munoz P.T. Aide

PROCEDURE 19.11 Respiratory Therapy

BACKGROUND: Respiratory therapy is the provision of care dedicated to improving the pulmonary function of the patient. The provision of respiratory therapy has developed into a stand-alone discipline because of the specialized learning required to provide this care.

A respiratory therapist is trained in techniques that improve pulmonary function and oxygenation. Respiratory therapists may also be responsible for administering a variety of tests that measure lung function and for educating the patient about the use of various devices and machines prescribed by the physician.

The health care professional must have knowledge of respiratory physiology, the variables, and diseases that affect respiratory function. In some cases, the health care professional will be responsible for using specific equipment and protocols necessary to diagnose and treat respiratory problems.

ALERT: Follow Standard Precautions.

PREPROCEDURE

1. Determine the baseline function of the patient's respiratory system.
2. Consult the physician's orders to determine any specific respiratory treatment prescribed for the patient.
3. Determine the health care professional's responsibility for administering/supporting the treatment.

PROCEDURE

4. Assess the patient's current respiratory status.
5. Review available documentation to determine when specific respiratory treatments were last delivered, and when they will be due again.
6. Determine what the health care professional's role is to be in assisting/promoting respiratory therapy.
7. Consult with the respiratory therapist for any necessary instructions on the use of equipment or procedures.
8. Encourage the patient to use good pulmonary toileting techniques such as deep breathing, coughing, incentive spirometry.

   NOTE: Incentive spirometry works to mimic natural sighing or yawning by encouraging the patient to take long, slow, deep breaths.
9. Provide continuous monitoring of the patient's respiratory status so that any decline in function can be addressed early and successfully.

POSTPROCEDURE

10. Collaborate with the physician and the respiratory therapist if there is a decline in the patient's respiratory status.
11. Document the respiratory assessment and any ongoing problems and their resolution in the medical chart.

PROCEDURE 20.1 Admitting a Patient

BACKGROUND: Carefully following the admitting procedure gives the patient a sense of well-being and security. It also protects the facility from errors in identification and loss of patients' belongings.

ALERT: Follow Standard Precautions.

PREPROCEDURE

1. Wash hands.
2. Assemble equipment.
   a. Admission checklist
   b. Admission pack (may be all disposable depending on facility)
      (1) Bedpan
      (2) Urinal
      (3) Emesis basin
      (4) Wash basin
      (5) Tissues
   c. Gown or pajamas
   d. Portable scale
   e. Thermometer
   f. Blood pressure cuff
   g. Stethoscope
   h. Clothing list
   i. Envelope for valuables

PROCEDURE

3. Fan-fold bed covers to foot of bed. (See the procedure "Making an Open Bed.")
4. Put away patient's equipment.
5. Put gown or pajamas on foot of bed.
6. Greet patient and introduce yourself.
7. Identify patient by looking at arm band and asking name (see figure at top right). Ask what they like to be called.
8. Introduce patient to roommates, if appropriate.

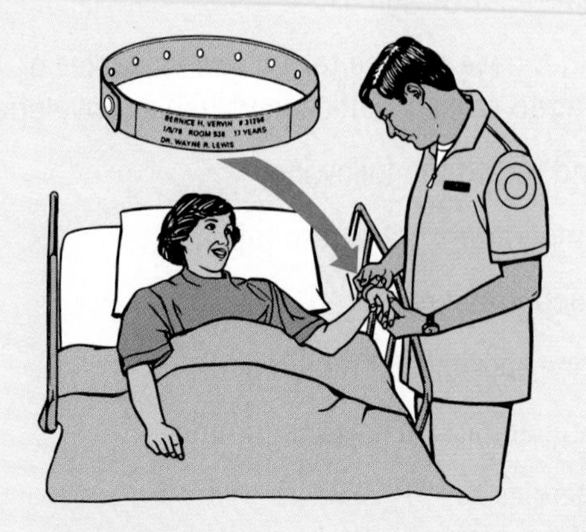

9. Explain:
   a. How call signal works
   b. How bed controls work (see figure below)
   c. Hospital regulations
   d. What you will be doing to admit him or her
   e. How telephone and television work

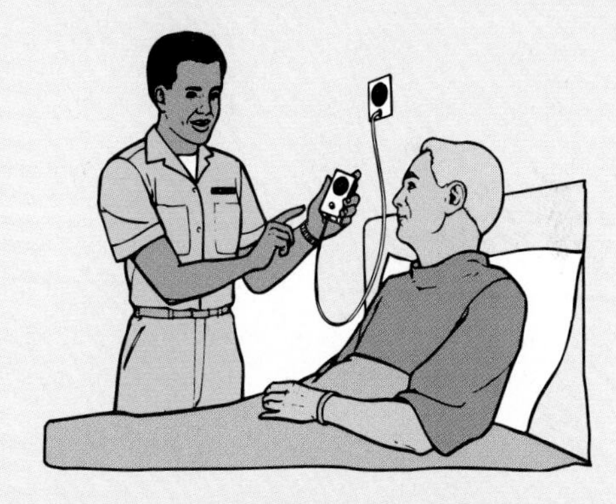

10. Provide privacy by pulling privacy curtains.
11. Ask patient to put on gown or pajamas.
12. Check weight and height. (You will find this skill later in this chapter.)
13. Help to bed if ordered. (Check with nurse.)
14. Put up side rails if required.

(continued)

PROCEDURE 20.1 Admitting a Patient (continued)

15. If patient has valuables:
    a. Make a list of jewelry, money, wallet, etc.
    b. Have patient sign list
    c. Have relative sign list
    d. Either have relative take home valuables or send to cashier's office in valuables envelope
16. Take and record the following:
    a. Temperature, pulse, respiration
    b. Blood pressure
    c. Urine specimen, if required
17. Complete admission checklist noting:
    a. Allergies
    b. Medications being taken
    c. Food preferences and dislikes
    d. Any prosthesis
    e. Skin condition
    f. Handicaps (e.g., deafness, sight, movement)

NOTE: This is usually done by a registered nurse.

18. Orient patient to meal times, visiting hours, use of television and telephone.
19. Ask if patient has any questions regarding the information given.

POSTPROCEDURE

20. Wash hands.
21. Record information according to your facility's policy.

10/04/12	1500
	VS 98=76=18 120/80
	Admitted and oriented to facility.
	Admission checklist completed.
	Sitting in chair.
	States "Wish I could stay at home."
	________ S. Gomez CNA

PROCEDURE **20.2**

Measuring Weight on a Standing Balance Scale or Digital Scale

BACKGROUND: Weighing the patient provides a weight baseline. This baseline is used to compare decreases or increases in the patient's weight. Changes in body weight may indicate a change in the patient's health.

ALERT: Follow Standard Precautions.

PREPROCEDURE

1. Wash hands.
2. Assemble equipment.
   a. Portable balance or digital scale
   b. Paper towel
   c. Paper and pencil/pen
   d. Knock before entering the patient's room
3. Identify patient.
4. Explain what you are going to do and ask patient if they need to void before you weigh them.
5. Provide privacy with curtain, screen, or door.

PROCEDURE

6. Take patient to scale or bring scale to patient's room.
7. Place paper towel on platform of scale (with standing scale).
8. Put both weights to the very left on zero.

   When using a digital scale, turn the scale on and wait for the display to show a reading; make sure the display reads "zero" before you begin weighing the patient.
9. Balance beam pointer must stay steady in middle of balance area. (If pointer does not center, turn balance screw until it remains centered.)

   The manufacturer's instructions for a digital scale will provide instructions on how to calibrate the scale, or bring the display to zero. There usually is a button to push for calibration.
10. Have patient remove shoes and assist to stand on scale.

NOTE: The balance bar raises to top of bar guide and pointer is not centered.

11. While keeping one hand near the patient's back, use other hand to move large weight to estimated weight of patient.
12. Move small weight to right until balance bar hangs free halfway between upper and lower bar guide.
13. The largest (lower) weight is marked in increments of 50 pounds; the smaller (upper weight) is marked in single pounds. The even-numbered pounds are marked with numbers (e.g., 2, 4, 6). The uneven pounds are unmarked long lines and the short line is one-fourth of a pound.
14. Write down weight on a notepad. Record weight displayed on a digital scale.
15. Help patient with shoes and make him or her comfortable.

POSTPROCEDURE

16. Discard towel.
17. Replace scale. With a digital scale, make sure the power is off.
18. Wash hands.
19. Chart weight. Report any unusual increases or decreases in weight.

10/05/12	0900
	Standing scale weight 125; 10
	pounds less than last weight.
	No complaints of loss of appetite,
	pain, or other problems. Weight
	change reported to head nurse.
	________ S. Gomez CNA

PROCEDURE 20.3 Measuring Weight on a Chair Scale

BACKGROUND: The chair scale provides a safe way to weigh a nonambulatory patient. Weighing the patient provides a weight baseline. This baseline is used to compare decreases or increases in the patient's weight. Changes in body weight may indicate a change in the patient's health.

ALERT: Follow Standard Precautions.

PREPROCEDURE

1. Wash hands.
2. Assemble equipment.
   a. Balance scale
   b. Paper towel
   c. Paper and pencil/pen
   d. Knock before entering the patient's room

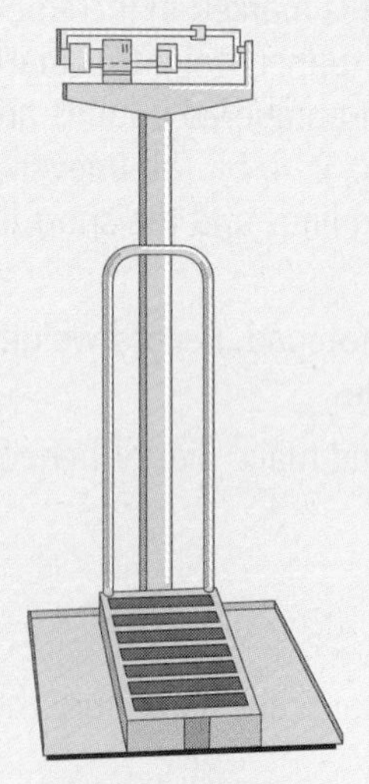

Wheelchair scale

3. Identify patient.
4. Explain what you are going to do and ask patient if they need to void before you weigh them.
5. Provide privacy with curtain, screen, or door.

PROCEDURE

6. Take patient to scale or bring scale to patient's room.
7. Put both weights to the very left on zero. If you are using a digital scale, make sure the display reads zero.
8. Balance beam pointer must stay steady in middle of balance area. (If pointer does not center, turn balance screw until it remains centered.) Calibrate a digital scale according to the manufacturer's instructions.
9. Have patient remove shoes and move patient to chair at the side of the scale. .
10. Place wheelchair on scale and weigh it.
11. Assist patient back into wheelchair. Weigh wheelchair with patient in it.

NOTE: To determine weights, see previous procedure: "Measuring Weight on a Standing Balance or Digital Scale."

12. Determine patient weight by subtracting the weight in #10 above from the weight in #11.
13. Write down weight on a notepad. Record weight displayed on a digital scale.
14. Help patient with shoes and make him or her comfortable.

POSTPROCEDURE

15. Replace scale. With a digital scale, make sure the power is off before replacing it.
16. Wash hands.
17. Chart weight. Report any unusual increases or decreases in weight.

05/03/11	0800
	Chair scale weight 125;
	no weight change.
	S. Gomez CNA

PROCEDURE 20.4 Measuring Weight on a Mechanical Lift

BACKGROUND: The mechanical lift provides a safe method for weighing a bedridden patient. Weighing the patient provides a weight baseline. This baseline is used to compare decreases or increases in the patient's weight. Changes in body weight may indicate a change in the patient's health.

ALERT: Follow Standard Precautions.

PREPROCEDURE

1. Wash hands.
2. Assemble equipment.
   a. Mechanical lift
   b. Sling
   c. Clean sheet
3. Identify patient.
4. Explain what you are going to do.
5. Pull privacy curtain.

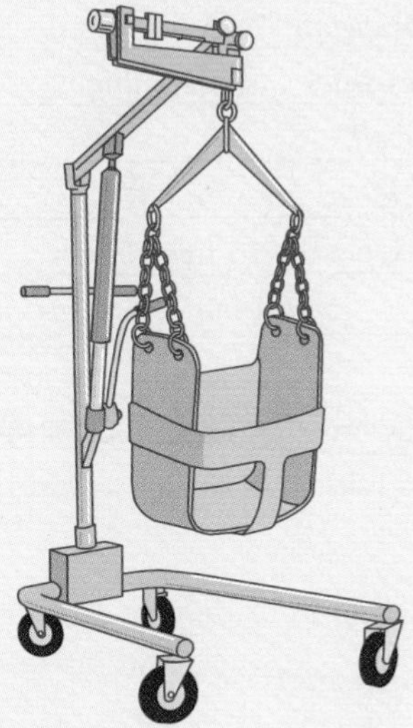

Scale with mechanical lift

PROCEDURE

6. Lower side rail on side you are working on.
7. Cover sling with clean sheet.
8. Help patient roll on side and place sling with top at shoulders and bottom at knees.
9. Fan-fold remaining sling.
10. Help patient roll to other side onto one half of sling and pull other half of sling through.
11. Broaden base of lift.
12. Wheel lift to side of bed with base beneath bed.
13. Position lift over patient.
14. Attach sling using chains and hooks provided. *Keep open end of hook away from patient to avoid injury.*
15. Use hand crank or pump handle to raise patient from bed. Make certain that buttocks are not touching bed.
16. Check to be certain that patient is in center of sling and is safely suspended.
17. To weigh patient:
    a. Swing feet and legs over edge of bed; move lift away from bed so that no body part contacts bed.

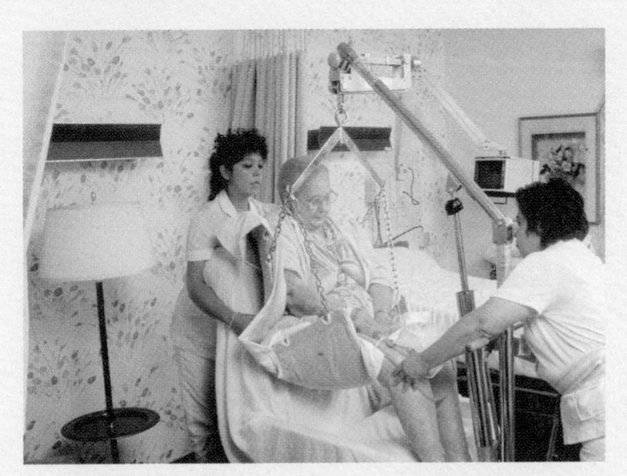

    b. If bed is low enough, raise patient above bed so that no body part contacts bed.

(continued)

PROCEDURE 20.4 Measuring Weight on a Mechanical Lift (continued)

18. Adjust weights until scale is balanced. (See the procedure "Measuring Weight on a Standing Balance Scale.") Remember, that most mechanical lift scales these days are electric. You just make sure it is on zero before you weigh them.

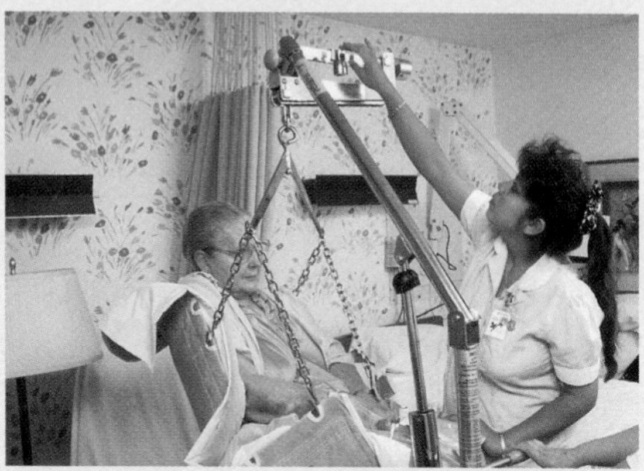

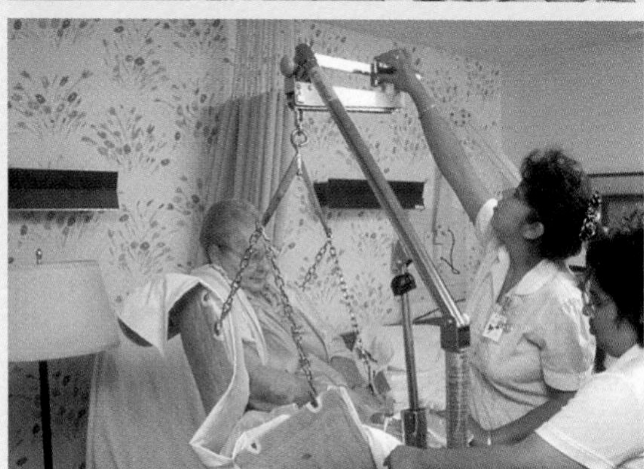

19. Return patient to bed by reversing steps.

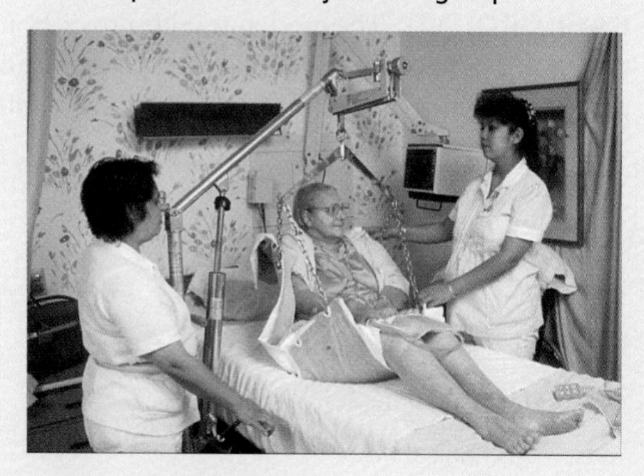

POSTPROCEDURE

20. Replace mechanical lift.
21. Wash hands.
22. Note weight.

02/26/12	1000
	Chair scale weight 250
	No changes since last weighing
	Tolerated well.
	Noted reddened area on left
	shoulder. Reported to head nurse
	________ S. Gomez CNA

PROCEDURE 20.5 Measuring Height

BACKGROUND: Accurately measuring height provides a baseline to help determine the patient's ideal weight. A loss in height over a period of time may indicate osteoporosis.

ALERT: Follow Standard Precautions.

PREPROCEDURE

1. Wash hands.
2. Assemble equipment.
    a. Balance scale with height rod
    b. Paper towels
3. Identify patient and explain procedure.
4. Put paper towel on platform of scale.
5. Explain what you are going to do.
6. Have patient remove shoes.

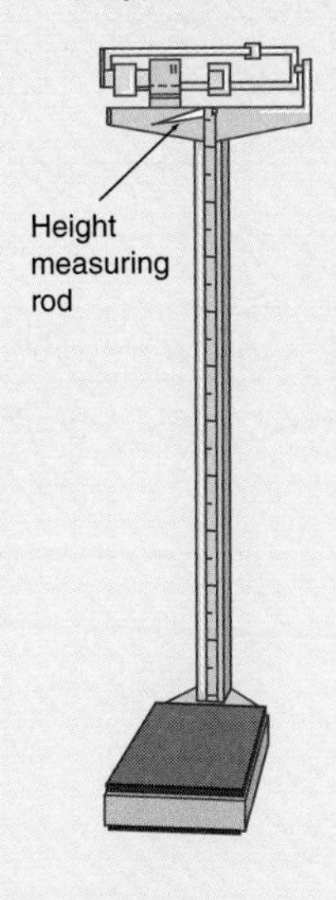

PROCEDURE

7. Raise measuring rod above head.
8. Assist patient onto the scale. Have patient stand with back against measuring rod.
9. Instruct patient to stand straight, with heels touching measuring rod.
10. Lower measuring rod to rest on patient's head.
11. Check number of inches indicated on rod. This number is found where the sliding rod enters the hollow post.
12. Assist patient off of the scale.
13. Record in meters, centimeters, or feet and inches according to hospital policy.

POSTPROCEDURE

14. Help patient with shoes.
15. Chart height.
16. Discard paper towel and wash hands.

02/09/11 0700
Height 55 inches on admission.
________ S. Gomez CNA

PROCEDURE 20.6 Measuring Height of Adult/Child (Over 3 Years of Age)

BACKGROUND: Height measurement is an indicator of normal or abnormal growth and development. Accurate measurement helps determine whether the child is developing normally.

ALERT: Follow Standard Precautions.

PREPROCEDURE

1. Wash hands.
2. Put paper towel on platform of scale.
3. Explain procedure and provide privacy.

PROCEDURE

4. Raise height-measuring rod on back of scale so that tip of height-measuring rod is above patient's head.
5. Instruct patient to remove shoes.
6. Ask patient to step onto scale and turn around to face away from balance bar.
7. Instruct patient to place heels against back of scale and stand straight.
8. Lift up measuring rod so that it points out above patient's head.
9. Lower rod gently until it rests on patient's head.
10. Assist patient in stepping off scales.
11. Read numbers just above edge of hollow bar of rod at back of scale.
12. Record height on medical record in feet and inches, centimeters, or inches only, according to your provider's policy.

POSTPROCEDURE

13. Discard paper towel.
14. Wash hands.

12/09/11	*1500*	
	Height 33 in.	
	________	*M. Gonzales CMA*
	or	
04/02/11	*1500*	
	Height 82.5 cm.	
	________	*M. Gonzales CMA*

PROCEDURE 20.7

Measuring the Head Circumference of an Infant/Toddler (Under 3 Years of Age)

BACKGROUND: Head circumference is an indicator of normal or abnormal growth development. Accurate measurement helps determine whether the infant/toddler is developing normally.

ALERT: Follow Standard Precautions.

PREPROCEDURE

1. Wash hands.
2. Obtain measuring tape.
3. Identify the patient.
4. Explain procedure to parent.

PROCEDURE

5. Place infant in supine position.
6. Position measuring tape over occipital bone and wrap toward forehead. Bring tape just above ears to the center of the forehead.
7. Record measurement.

POSTPROCEDURE

8. Wash hands.

04/02/11	*1000*
	Head circumference measures 15 in.
	________ M. Gonzales CMA
	or
04/26/12	*1000*
	Head circumference measures 37.5 cm
	________ M. Gonzales CMA

PROCEDURE 20.8 Measuring the Height of an Infant/Toddler

BACKGROUND: Height is an indicator of normal or abnormal growth development. Accurate measurement helps determine whether the infant/toddler is developing normally.

ALERT: Follow Standard Precautions.

PREPROCEDURE

1. Wash hands.
2. Obtain tape measure or measuring bar.

PROCEDURE

3. Place infant on flat surface.
4. Place zero mark of tape or measuring bar level with top of infant's head.
5. Ask parent or co-worker to hold top of head gently at zero mark.
6. Gently straighten legs.
7. Read measurement that is level with infant's heel.

NOTE: An alternative is to lay the infant on exam paper or sheet. Draw a line at the top of the infant's head. Have the parent hold on to the infant and stretch out the infant's leg. Draw another line at the infant's heel. Have parent pick up the infant, and then measure between the two lines.

POSTPROCEDURE

8. Wash hands.

02/23/11	1000	
	Height 21 in.	
	________	M. Gonzales CMA
	or	
03/30/12	1000	
	Height 52.5 cm	
	________	M. Gonzales CMA

PROCEDURE 20.9 Measuring the Weight of an Infant/Toddler

BACKGROUND: Infant weight is an indicator of normal or abnormal growth development. Accurate measurement helps determine whether the infant/toddler is developing normally.

ALERT: Follow Standard Precautions.

PREPROCEDURE

1. Wash hands.
2. Assemble equipment.
    a. Infant scale, either balance or digital
    b. Towel
    c. Growth chart
3. Ask parent to remove infant's clothing.
4. Place clean towel on scale cradle to decrease shock of cold metal against infant or to prevent friction on a plastic cradle.
5. Balance the scale at zero with towel in place. Calibrate a digital scale to zero with towel in place.

PROCEDURE

6. Place infant face up on scale. Keep diaper or towel over infant's genital area in case of elimination.

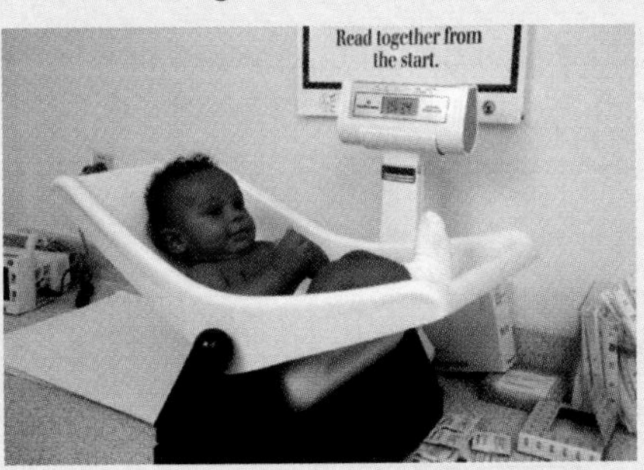

7. Place one hand over infant (almost touching) to give a sense of security.
8. Slide weight easily until scale balances or take measurement from digital reading.
9. Read scale in pounds and ounces or in kilograms.
10. Return infant to parent.

POSTPROCEDURE

11. Balance the scale at zero mark or power off a digital scale.
12. Discard towel.
13. Wash hands.
14. Record weight on growth chart and in patient's chart.

04/29/12	*0800*
	Measured on balance scale, wt. 25 lb.
	M. Gonzales CMA
	or
04/29/12	*0800*
	Weighed mother and then mother
	and child to determine weight
	Infant too distressed to weigh
	on infant balance scale
	Wt. 25 lb.
	M. Gonzales CMA

PROCEDURE 20.10 Moving Patient and Belongings to Another Room

BACKGROUND: Following the transfer procedure provides a sense of security for the patient and ensures that personal belongings are not lost. Introduction to the new area, roommate, and caregiver reduces the stress and provides continuing care.

ALERT: Follow Standard Precautions.

PREPROCEDURE

1. Wash hands.
2. Assemble equipment.
   a. Patient's chart
   b. Nursing care plan
   c. Medications (Remember: Nursing assistants cannot transfer medications.)
   d. Paper bag
3. Identify patient.
4. Explain what you are going to do.

PROCEDURE

5. Determine location to which patient is being transferred and see if new room is ready.
6. Gather patient belongings. (Check admission list.)

7. Determine how patient is to be transported.
   a. Wheelchair
   b. Stretcher
   c. Entire bed
   d. Ambulation
8. Transport patient to new unit.
9. Introduce to staff on new unit.
10. Introduce to new roommate.
11. Make patient comfortable.
12. Put away belongings.
13. Notify family members listed on patient's admission record of the move.

POSTPROCEDURE

14. Wash hands.
15. Give transferred medications, care plan, and chart to nurse. (Remember: Nursing assistants cannot transfer medication.)
16. Before leaving unit, record the following:
    a. Date and time of transfer
    b. How transported (e.g., wheelchair)
    c. How transfer was tolerated by patient.
17. Return to original unit and report completion of transfer.

07/14/11	1430
	Transferred in bed to room 20
	Introduced to roommate and
	caregiver. Resting quietly in bed.
	S. Gomez CNA

PROCEDURE 20.11 Discharging a Patient

BACKGROUND: Carefully following the discharge procedure ensures that the patient takes all medications and personal belongings and that final arrangements are completed.

ALERT: Follow Standard Precautions.

PREPROCEDURE

1. Check chart for discharge order.
2. Wash hands.
3. Identify patient.
4. Explain what you are going to do.
5. Provide privacy by pulling the privacy curtain.

PROCEDURE

6. Check with the patient's nurse regarding discharge status prior to continuing process. The nurse will need to:
   a. Remove any tethers such as IV lines or indwelling catheters.
   b. Review the patient's medication list, especially new medications and their use.
   c. Notify the patient of any follow up appointments to be scheduled or already scheduled with the physician, or for follow up lab or diagnostics.
   d. Inform the patient of any restriction of activity or diet.
7. Help patient dress.
8. Collect patient's belongings. Check room carefully. Remember to check for hearing aids and dentures.
9. Check belongings against admission list.
10. Secure and return valuables.
    a. Verify with patient that all valuables are there.
    b. Have patient sign for them.
11. Check to see if patient has prescriptions and/or medications and discharge instructions to take home.
12. Check to see if any equipment is to be taken home.
13. Help patient into wheelchair.

NOTE: Patients may have to go by the financial office before leaving.

14. Help patient into car.

POSTPROCEDURE

15. Return to unit.
    a. Remove all items left in unit (e.g., basins, disposable items).
    b. Clean unit according to your facility's policy.
16. Wash hands.
17. Record discharge.
    a. Date and time
    b. Method of transport
    c. Whom patient left with

08/31/12	1100
	Discharged by wheelchair with son,
	personal belongings,
	medications, and instructions
	________ S. Gomez CNA

PROCEDURE 20.12 Horizontal Recumbent (Supine) Position

BACKGROUND: Placing the patient in the correct position for treatment, examinations, and for comfort measures is essential for safe and accurate care of the patient.

ALERT: Follow Standard Precautions.

PREPROCEDURE

1. Wash hands.
2. Explain to patient what you are going to do.

PROCEDURE

3. Assist patient with gown.
4. Determine any problems associated with placing the patient in this position, such as increased respiratory distress, etc..
5. Assist patient to a position lying flat on his or her back with arms at side in good alignment, with a small pillow under the head.
6. Drape cover so that he or she is not exposed, leaving all edges of drape loose.

POSTPROCEDURE

7. After exam, assist patient off the table and with dressing if needed.
8. Wash hands.

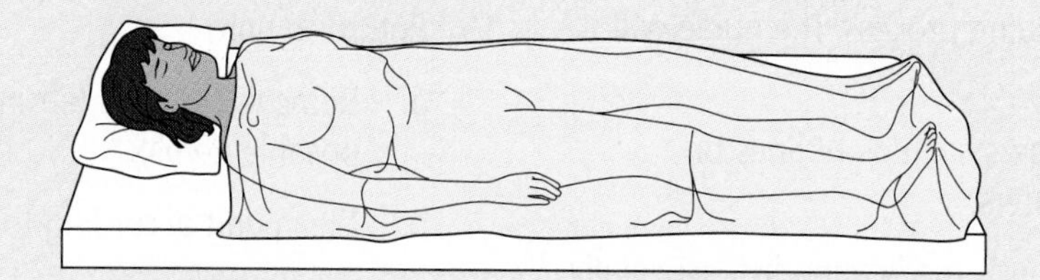

PROCEDURE 20.13 Fowler's Position

BACKGROUND: Placing the patient in the correct position for treatment, examinations, and for comfort measures is essential for safe and accurate care of the patient.

ALERT: Follow Standard Precautions.

PREPROCEDURE

1. Wash hands.
2. Explain to patient what you are going to do.
3. Assist patient with gown.

PROCEDURE

4. Determine any problems associated with placing the patient in this position, such as increase in back pain, etc.
5. Assist patient to a position lying flat on his or her back in good alignment with small pillow under their head.
6. Keep patient covered so that he or she is not exposed.
7. Flex knees slightly and support them with a pillow.
8. Adjust backrest to one of the following positions according to patient's or physician's needs: Low Fowlers 25°; Semi-Fowlers 45°; High Fowlers 90°. (See figure at top right.)

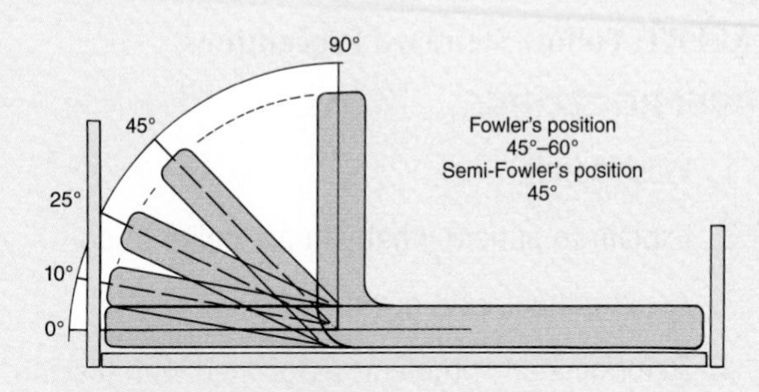

9. Drape cover so that patient is not exposed, leaving all edges of drape free.

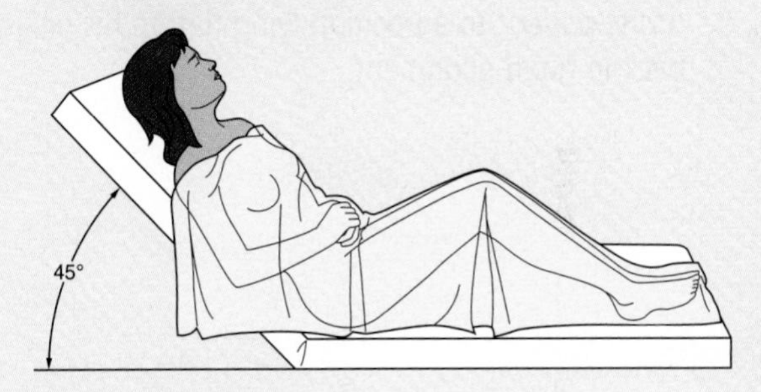

POSTPROCEDURE

10. After exam, assist patient off and table and with dressing.
11. Wash hands.

PROCEDURE 20.14 Trendelenburg Position

BACKGROUND: Placing the patient in the correct position for treatment, examinations, and for comfort measures is essential for safe and accurate care of the patient.

ALERT: Follow Standard Precautions.

PREPROCEDURE

1. Wash hands.
2. Explain to patient what you are going to do.
3. Assist patient with gown.
4. Determine any problems associated with placing patient in this position, such as increased respiratory distress, etc.
5. Assist patient to a position lying flat on his or her back in good alignment.

PROCEDURE

6. Drape cover so that he or she is not exposed, leaving all edges of drape loose.
7. Lower the head of the table until the body is at a 45° angle. Legs may be bent or extended.
8. Reassure patient that he or she will not slide off table. Remain with patient at all times.

POSTPROCEDURE

9. After exam, assist patient off the table and with dressing.
10. Wash hands.

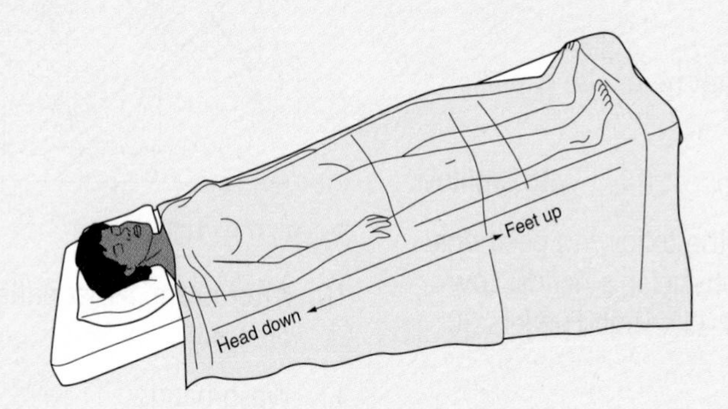

PROCEDURE 20.15 Dorsal Lithotomy Position

BACKGROUND: Placing the patient in the correct position for treatment, examinations, and for comfort measures is essential for safe and accurate care of the patient.

ALERT: Follow Standard Precautions.

PREPROCEDURE

1. Wash hands.
2. Explain to patient what you are going to do
3. Assist patient with gown.

PROCEDURE

4. Determine any problems associated with placing patient in this position, such as increased pain, etc.
5. Assist patient to a position lying flat on his or her back with arms at side.
6 Place pillow under head.
7. Cover patient so that he or she is not exposed.
8. Gently assist patient to bend knees.
9. Separate legs by placing each foot flat on bed about 2 feet apart or in stirrups attached to examination table.
10. Move patient's hips to edge of end of table when stirrups are available.
11. Drape with half-size sheet positioned with one corner toward head and opposite corners between legs. Secure side corner around legs.
12. Remain with the patient.

POSTPROCEDURE

13. After exam, assist patient off the table and with dressing.
14. Wash hands.

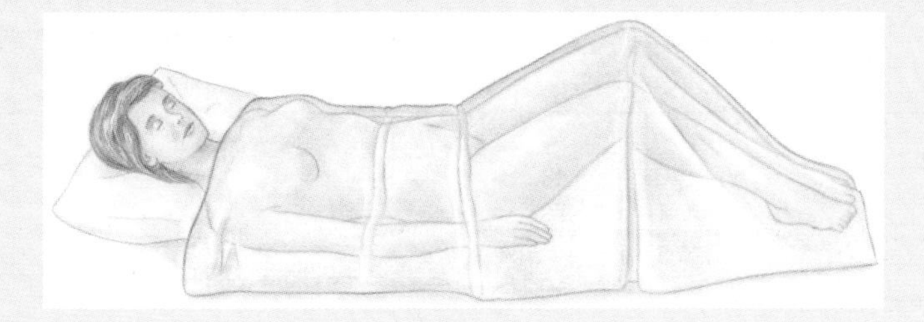

PROCEDURE 20.16 Prone Position

BACKGROUND: Placing the patient in the correct position for treatment, examinations, and for comfort measures is essential for safe and accurate care of the patient.

ALERT: Follow Standard Precautions.

PREPROCEDURE

1. Wash hands.
2. Explain to patient what you are going to do.
3. Assist patient with gown.

PROCEDURE

4. Determine any problems associated with placing patient in this position, such as increased pain or respiratory distress.
5. Turn patient toward self.
6. Position patient on the abdomen with arms flexed by head.
7. Position head to side on small pillow.
8. Cover patient so that he or she is not exposed and let drape hang loosely.

POSTPROCEDURE

9. After exam, assist patient off the table and with dressing.
10. Wash hands.

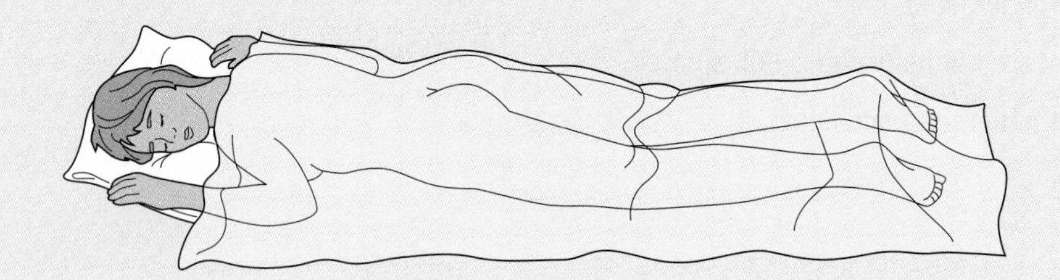

PROCEDURE 20.17 Left Lateral Position and Left Sims' Position

BACKGROUND: Placing the patient in the correct position for treatment, examinations, and for comfort measures is essential for safe and accurate care of the patient.

ALERT: Follow Standard Precautions.

PREPROCEDURE

1. Wash hands.
2. Explain to patient what you are going to do.
3. Assist patient with gown.

PROCEDURE

4. Determine any problems associated with placing patient in this position, such as increased pain, respiratory distress, etc.
5. Assist patient to a position lying flat on his or her back.
6. Cover patient so that he or she is not exposed.
7. Assist patient to turn onto left side.
8. Position patient's left arm slightly behind him or her on bed and bend right arm in front of the body.
9. Turn head to side on small pillow.
10. Gently bend both knees.
11. Place right leg slightly forward of left leg for lateral position.
12. Bend right knee toward chest for Sims' position.
13. Drape with one sheet; make sure drape is hung loosely.

POSTPROCEDURE

14. After exam, assist patient off table and with dressing.
15. Wash hands.

PROCEDURE 20.18 Knee-Chest Position

BACKGROUND: Placing the patient in the correct position for treatment, examinations, and for comfort measures is essential for safe and accurate care of the patient.

ALERT: Follow Standard Precautions.

PREPROCEDURE

1. Wash hands.
2. Explain to patient what you are going to do.
3. Determine any problems associated with placing patient in this position such as increased pain, etc.
4. Assist patient to a position lying flat on his or her back.

PROCEDURE

5. Cover patient so that he or she is not exposed.
6. Assist patient to turn onto his or her stomach, keeping patient covered.
7. Instruct patient to raise hips upward by kneeling on both knees.

NOTE: It is hard for the patient to stay in this position, so put them in it immediately prior to the procedure and stay with them.

8. Rest patient's head and shoulders on a pillow.
9. Flex arms slightly and have them at the side of their head.
10. Drape with a large sheet, allowing edges to hang free.

POSTPROCEDURE

11. After exam, assist patient off table and with dressing.
12. Wash hands.

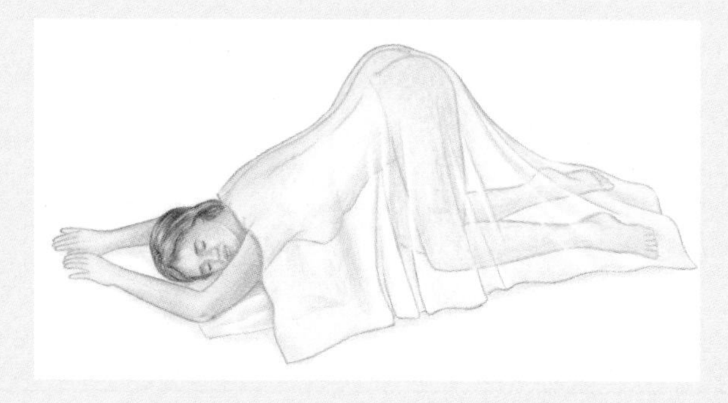

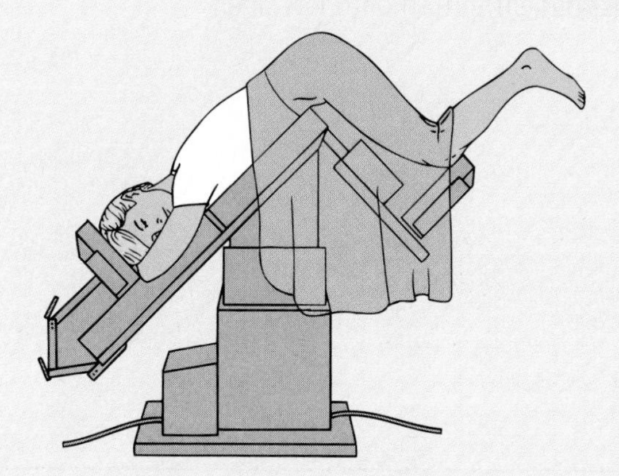

PROCEDURE 20.19 Testing Visual Acuity: Snellen Chart

BACKGROUND: Vision affects all activities of daily living. Correct measurement of visual acuity is essential to determine whether patient has normal or abnormal eyesight.

ALERT: Follow Standard Precautions.

PREPROCEDURE

1. Wash hands.
2. Assure that the Snellen Chart is at patient's eye level and that the tape for them to stand on is 20 feet from the chart.
3. Identify patient.
4. Explain procedure to patient.

PROCEDURE

5. Position patient 20 feet (6 meters) from Snellen chart. Have patient stand with heel on 20 foot mark.
6. Instruct patient to keep both eyes open during testing. Ask them to remove corrective lenses.
7. Ask patient to cover left eye with an occluder and read smallest line of letters that he or she can see.
8. Use a pointer and point to letters in the row in random order. Do not cover the letter or symbol with the pointer.
9. Record the distance patient is from the chart compared to the size of letters patient can see clearly (e.g., 20/20, 20/30, 20/40).
10. Repeat test with right eye covered.
11. Repeat test, allowing patient to use both eyes.
12. Repeat each test with patient wearing glasses (if he or she has prescription lenses).

POSTPROCEDURE

13. Wash hands.

PROCEDURE 20.20 Using the *Physicians' Desk Reference* (*PDR*)

BACKGROUND: It is important for the health care worker to know details about medications. The PDR is an essential tool that provides information about medications the health care worker gives. Understanding how to use the PDR helps in finding information in a timely manner.

PROCEDURE

1. Identify the name of the manufacturer by going to Section 5; compare the tablet with pictures to identify the medication.
   a. Wallace is the manufacturer.
   b. Turn to the page where Wallace pills are displayed.
   c. Match the pill with pictures of pills displayed.
   d. A yellow oval pill marked "Wallace 200" matches "Soma Compound with Codeine 200 mg" in the display.
2. Turn to Section 2, the pink pages. Find "Soma Compound with Codeine 200 mg." Two page numbers are listed.
   a. The first page number refers to Section 5, the picture of the medication.
   b. The second page number refers to Section 6 and provides product information.
3. Turn to the page number indicated in Section 6 to find specific drug information.
   a. Description of drug
   b. Clinical pharmacology
   c. Indications and usage (describes the reasons for using the drug)
   d. Contraindications (reasons not to give this drug)
   e. Warnings
   f. Precautions
   g. Dosage and administration
   h. How supplied
   i. Storage recommendations
4. Go to Section 1 for more information about a drug. Find the manufacturer:
   a. Wallace Laboratories is listed with the W's in the alphabetical list.
   b. Write requests for information using the address supplied.
   c. Call for assistance using the professional services telephone number or night and weekend emergency number if available.

PROCEDURE 20.21 Using a Microscope

BACKGROUND: Proper care and use of the microscope prevents errors.

ALERT: Follow Standard Precautions.

PREPROCEDURE

1. Assemble equipment.
   a. Microscope
   b. Lens paper
   c. Slides and slide cover
   d. Specimen
   e. Oil if using oil immersion
   f. Gloves if specimens have been contaminated by blood or body fluids.
2. Wash hands.
3. Place specimen (e.g., hair, scraping from under nails, scraping from tooth) on clean slide (one drop only if liquid specimen).
4. Add required solution.
5. Drop clean slide cover over specimen. Hold cover at an angle and let it drop. Make sure there are no air bubbles between the slide and cover slip. If there are bubbles, must do again.
6. Clean eyepiece with lens paper.
7. Clean objectives with lens paper.
8. Turn on illuminating light.
9. Open iris diaphragm.
10. Turn revolving nosepiece to low-power objective.

PROCEDURE

11. Place slide on stage under slide clips. Avoid getting finger prints on the slide.
12. Turn coarse adjustment knob to move objective close to slide. Do not look into eyepieces while doing this, as you could crack the slide.
13. Look into eyepiece and slowly turn coarse adjustment to move tube upward until you focus specimen.
14. Turn fine-adjustment knob until specimen is clear and focused.
15. Continue steps 12 through 14 using higher objectives until you have best possible focus for specimen.
16. Observe specimen. If setup is for technician or physician, tell that person that slide is ready.

POSTPROCEDURE

17. Remove slide after it is read.
18. Discard slide according to procedure in your facility.
19. Clean lens and objective with lens paper.
20. Turn off illuminating light.
21. Put cover back on microsope
22. Wash hands

21\. Fill out lab slips according to your facility's policies.

PROCEDURE 20.22 Using Reagent Strips to Test Urine

BACKGROUND: Careful testing with reagent strips and accurate reporting of information are essential to reach a correct diagnosis. Always use the proper techniques to prevent contamination of the specimen.

ALERT: Follow Standard Precautions.

PREPROCEDURE

1. Wash hands.
2. Assemble equipment.
   a. Reagent strips and bottle
   b. Laboratory report slip
   c. Watch
   d. Urine specimen
   e. Disposable nonsterile gloves
3. Complete laboratory slip.
   a. Name
   b. Sex
   c. Age
   d. Physician
   e. Date
   f. Type of test
4. Put on gloves.

PROCEDURE

5. Hold specimen to light and observe:
   a. Color (colorless, yellow, light yellow, brown, orange, etc.)
   b. Clarity (clear, hazy, cloudy)
6. Write color and clarity on lab slip.
7. Open reagent jar and remove one strip .
   a. Note expiration date. *Do not use if expired.*
   b. Replace jar cover immediately.
8. Hold strip by clear end and immerse in urine (see figure top right).

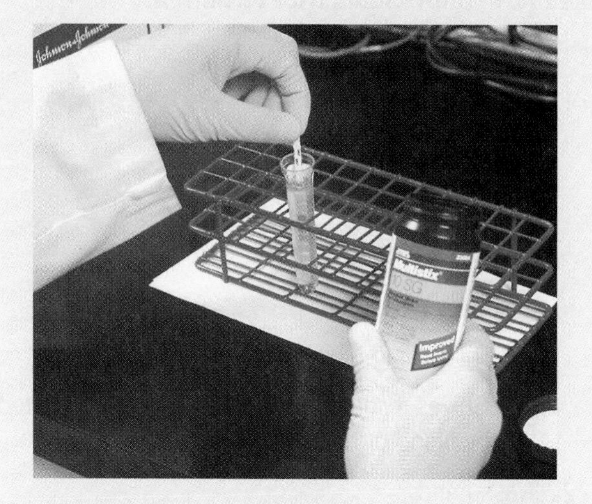

9. Remove strip immediately by pulling gently over lip of tube to remove excess urine.
10. Hold strip in horizontal position to prevent mixing of chemicals.
11. Hold strip close to color blocks on bottle label and match carefully. Note time.
12. Read strip at time indicated and record results.

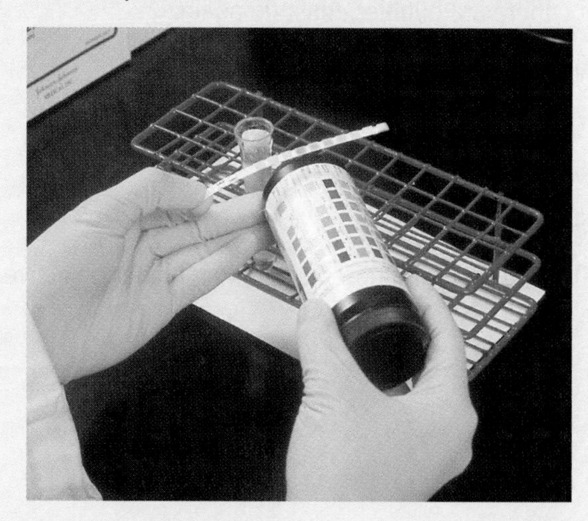

13. Discard reagent strip in biohazard waste.

(continued)

PROCEDURE 20.22 Using Reagent Strips to Test Urine (continued)

POSTPROCEDURE

14. Clean and replace equipment.
15. Remove gloves.
16. Wash hands.
17. Record required information.
18. Report any abnormal results to supervisor immediately.

1/03/12	0700
	Reagent strip test, pH 7,
	Protein: Pos., Glucose: 1%, Ketones: Tr.,
	Blood: Neg. Positive protein and
	trace blood reported to health care
	provider
	G. Jones Lab Asst.

PROCEDURE 20.23 Measuring Specific Gravity with Urinometer

BACKGROUND: Careful testing of specific gravity and accurate reporting of information are essential to reach a correct diagnosis. Always use proper techniques to prevent contamination of the specimen.

ALERT: Follow Standard Precautions.

PREPROCEDURE

1. Wash hands.
2. Assemble equipment.
   a. Disposable gloves
   b. Glass cylinder (5 inches high)
   c. Urinometer (This is a float with a stem that is calibrated in thousands: 1.000, 1.001, 1.002, etc.)
   d. Fresh urine specimen. Do not refrigerate.
3. Put on gloves.

PROCEDURE

4. Pour urine into cylinder to about one inch from the top.
5. Place urinometer in urine.
6. Spin urinometer gently. You must not touch side or bottom.
7. Place cylinder with lower line of meniscus at eye level.

NOTE: In glass containers, which curve at the edges, the curvature is called the meniscus. You measure the level at the horizontal center or inside part of the meniscus. With water in glass, the meniscus will curve up at the edges and down in the center so we say you read the bottom of the meniscus.

8. Read specific gravity:
   a. Look at point where lowest part of meniscus crosses urinometer scale.
   b. Read gauge on nearest line.
9. Record reading to enter in computer or on lab slip.
10. Discard urine according to facility's contaminated waste policy.
11. Rinse urinometer with water and dry.
12. Rinse cylinder with water and dry.
13. Remove gloves and discard in contaminated waste.

POSTPROCEDURE

14. Wash hands.
15. Record specific gravity in computer or on lab list.
16. Document according to facility procedure.

1/01/12	0800
	Sp Gr 1.011
	______ S. Jones MA

PROCEDURE 20.24

Measuring Specific Gravity with Refractometer

BACKGROUND: Careful testing of specific gravity and accurate reporting of information are essential to reach a correct diagnosis. Always use proper techniques to prevent contamination of the specimen.

ALERT: Follow Standard Precautions.

PREPROCEDURE

1. Wash hands.
2. Assemble equipment
   a. Disposable gloves
   b. Refractometer
   c. Distilled water
   d. Fresh urine sample Do not refrigerate.
   e. Will need eye dropper or pipette to get drop of water and/or urine
3. Put on gloves.

PROCEDURE

4. Place one drop of distilled water on the glass plate.
5. Close lid.
6. Look through eyepiece to read specific gravity.

NOTE: Make sure it reads 1.000. If reading is not 1.000, follow manufacturer's directions to recalibrate refractometer.

7. Transfer one drop of well-mixed urine onto glass plate of refractometer.
8. Close lid.
9. Look through eyepiece to read specific gravity.
10. Record reading to enter in computer or on lab slip.
11. Discard urine according to facility's contaminated waste policy.

POSTPROCEDURE

12. Clean refractometer according to manufacturer's directions.
13. Remove gloves and discard in contaminated waste.
14. Wash hands.
15. Record specific gravity in computer or on lab list.

10/10/11 0800
Sp. gravity 1.040, reported to lab tech
S. Jones Lab Asst.

PROCEDURE 20.25 Centrifuging a Urine Specimen

BACKGROUND: Careful centrifuging ensures that urine is properly concentrated for testing. Specimens must be properly prepared in order to achieve accurate results.

ALERT: Follow Standard Precautions.

PREPROCEDURE

1. Wash hands.
2. Assemble equipment.
   a. Centrifuge
   b. Two centrifuge tubes
   c. Microscope slide (number slide)
   d. Coverslip
   e. Pipette
   f. Disposable nonsterile gloves
   g. Urine specimen. It's best to use the first voiding in AM , as it is more concentrated.
3. Fill in lab slip:
   a. Name
   b. Date
   c. Time
4. Put on gloves.

PROCEDURE

5. Mix urine to suspend sediment by rolling specimen container gently between your hands.
6. Pour 10 mL of urine into centrifuge tube.
7. Put tube with urine into centrifuge.

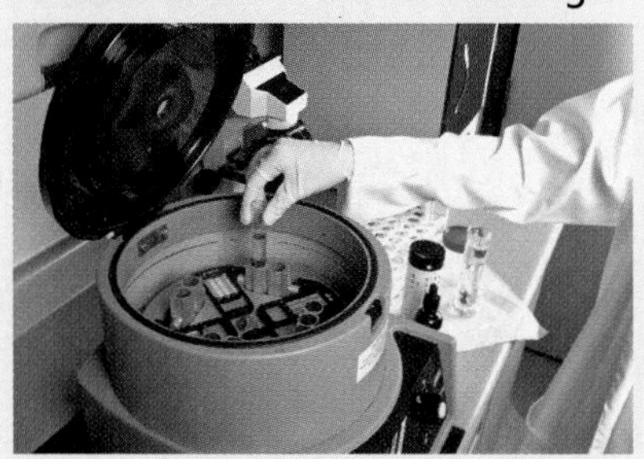

8. Pour 10 mL of water into second centrifuge tube.
9. Place in centrifuge opposite the tube with urine. This is very important for balance.
10. Secure centrifuge lid.
11. Set centrifuge timer for 4 to 5 minutes. (Allow it to stop on its own.)
12. Remove tube with urine.
13. Carefully invert urine centrifuge tube quickly over sink to pour 9 mL of urine into sink.
14. Turn tube right side up immediately. (About 1.0 cc will remain in tube.)
15. Mix sediment by snapping end of centrifuge tube with finger or gently shaking.
16. Pipette 1 drop of urine on numbered slide. A pipette works by creating a vacuum above the liquid-holding chamber and then selectively releasing this vacuum to draw up and dispense liquid.
17. Put on coverslip. (Redo if air bubbles appear under coverslip.)
18. Put slide on microscope stage.
19. Use 10× objective with coarse adjustment to focus on slide. Watch while moving course adjustment, so that slide does not break.
20. Adjust light source.
21. Follow your facility's policy for reading slide. (If setup is for technician, tell him or her that slide is ready.)
22. Remove slide after it is read.
23. Discard slide according to facility procedure.
24. Clean lens and objective with lens paper.
25. Cover microscope.

POSTPROCEDURE

26. Clean equipment and replace equipment.
27. Remove gloves, and dispose of according to facility policy.
28. Wash hands.
29. Record results if you read the specimen.
30. Document according to facility procedure.

1/20/12	0745
	Microscopic Exam: epithelial:
	few/1pf, WBCs: 2-3, /hpf,
	RBCs: few/hpf, casts: neg.,
	crystals: few/hpf
	________ *B Smith MA*

PROCEDURE 20.26 Midstream Clean-Catch Urine, Female

BACKGROUND: Careful instruction of the patient helps prevent contaminating the specimen. A clean-catch specimen is essential to accurately diagnose and treat the patient.

ALERT: Follow Standard Precautions.

PREPROCEDURE

1. Wash hands.
2. Assemble equipment.
    a. Sterile urine container for clean catch
    b. Label
    c. Disposable antiseptic towelettes
    d. Disposable nonsterile gloves: wear if you handle cup with specimen.

PROCEDURE

3. Label container.
4. Instruct patient to:
    a. Wash hands.
    b. Remove container lid and place on counter with inside of lid facing up.
    c. Separate labia to expose meatus.
    d. Take towelette and wipe on side of urinary meatus from front to back.
    e. Dispose of towelette.
    f. Repeat with new towelette on other side.
    g. Wipe directly over meatus with new towelette.
    h. Continue to hold labia open.
    i. Urinate small amount into toilet.
    j. Stop stream.
    k. Place sterile container under meatus and void into container (60 cc).
    l. Stop stream.
    m. Remove container carefully.
    n. Empty bladder.
    o. Carefully replace lid.
    p. Wipe outside of container with paper towel.
    q. Transport the specimen to the laboratory within 30 minutes of collection or else refrigerate.
5. Put on gloves.
6. Finish testing as ordered (e.g., dipstick, set up microscopic exam, drug test).

POSTPROCEDURE

7. Document procedure according to facility procedure.
8. Wash hands.

03/26/12	*0800*
	Instructed in correct procedure
	for collecting clean catch
	S. Jones CNA

PROCEDURE 20.27 Midstream Clean-Catch Urine, Male

BACKGROUND: Careful instruction of the patient helps prevent contaminating the specimen. A clean-catch specimen is essential to accurately diagnose and treat the patient.

ALERT: Follow Standard Precautions.

PREPROCEDURE

1. Wash hands.
2. Assemble equipment.
   a. Sterile container for clean catch
   b. Label
   c. Disposable antiseptic towelettes
   d. Disposable nonsterile gloves: wear if handling container with specimen

PROCEDURE

3. Label container.
4. Instruct patient to:
   a. Wash hands.
   b. Remove container lid and place on counter with inside of lid facing up.
   c. Cleanse head of penis in a circular motion with towelette. (If uncircumcised, pull back foreskin before cleaning.)
   d. Urinate into toilet. (If uncircumcised, pull back foreskin while urinating.)
   e. Allow stream to begin.
   f. Stop stream and place specimen container to collect midstream. (Fill about half way full or 60 mL.)
   g. Remove container before bladder is empty.
   h. Empty bladder into toilet.
   i. Carefully replace lid.
   j. Wipe outside of container with paper towel.
   k. Transport the specimen to the laboratory within 30 minutes of collection or else refrigerate.
5. Put on gloves.
6. Finish testing as ordered (e.g., dip stick, set up microscopic exam, drug test).

POSTPROCEDURE

7. Document procedure according to facility procedure.
8. Wash hands.

06/17/12 0800
Instructed in correct procedure
for collecting clean catch
S. Jones CNA

PROCEDURE 20.28 Collecting Urine from an Infant

BACKGROUND: Using the proper technique prevents leakage around the bag and thus prevents contamination of the specimen.

ALERT: Follow Standard Precautions.

PREPROCEDURE

1. Wash hands.
2. Assemble equipment.
   a. Specimen container
   b. Disposable urine collector (small plastic bag with opening and sticky area)
   c. Disposable nonsterile gloves
3. Identify patient.
4. Explain to parents what you are going to do.
5. Tell child what you are going to do even if you think that he or she is too young to understand. Children often understand.

PROCEDURE

6. Put on gloves.
7. Remove diaper.
8. Make certain that skin is clean and dry in genital area.
9. Remove outside cover that is around opening of bag. This has a sticky area that is applied to vulva or around penis. Place over vulva or penis (see figures at top right).
10. Replace diaper.
11. Remove gloves and dispose of according to facility procedure.
12. Check every half hour to see if bag has urine in it.
13. Remove bag when specimen is collected.
14. Rinse, clean, and dry genital area.
15. Replace diaper.
16. Put specimen in specimen container for lab.

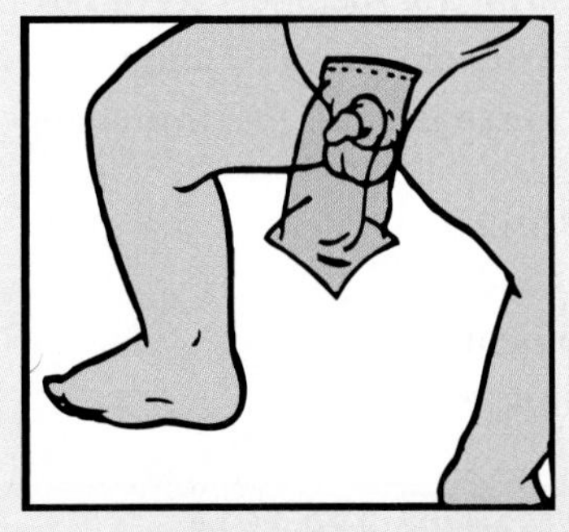

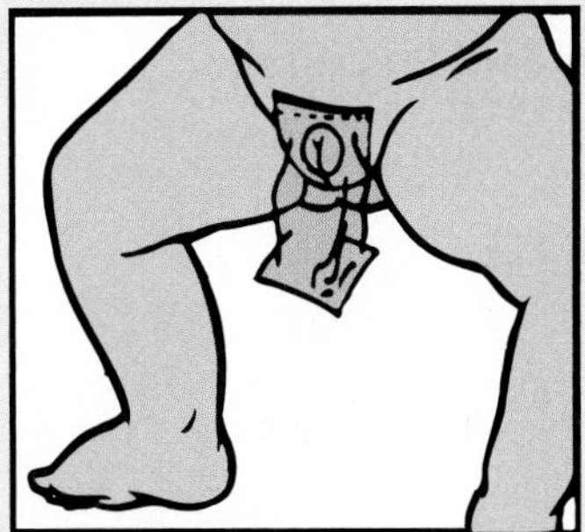

POSTPROCEDURE

17. Label with:
    a. Patient's name
    b. Time of collection
    c. Date
    d. Room number
18. Record collection of specimen.
19. Wash hands.

10/25/11	1030
	Urine bag applied
	Specimen successfully collected
	for testing
	Sent to lab
	________ *H. Martinez CNA*

PROCEDURE 21.1 How to Operate a Fire Extinguisher

BACKGROUND: Health care facilities are required by law to establish safety boards and to inspect the facility regularly for any type of potential fire hazard. Equipment must be checked regularly and escape routes must be kept open.

Fire drills are performed at specific intervals to assure that the facility and its staff are equipped to handle any fire emergency. Nurses are educated and tested annually on their knowledge of the procedures for response to a fire and how to remove patients from danger. Fire extinguishers can be used for types A, B, or C fires.

A Trash, wood, or paper
B Liquids
C Electrical equipment
ABC Use on all fires

ALERT: Follow Standard Precautions.

PREPROCEDURE

1. First Response: **RACE**

   Rescue

   Alert appropriate facility officials

   Contain Fire

   Extinguish Fire

PROCEDURE

2. Locate fire extinguisher and check type.

NOTE: Every nurse should know the location of the closest fire extinguisher to his/her work station.

3. Hold fire extinguisher upright. Pull ring pin.
4. Stand back six to ten feet and direct flow towards base of the fire.
5. Squeeze lever, sweeping side to side.

POSTPROCEDURE

6. Replace or have extinguisher recharged after use.

PROCEDURE 21.2 **Rescue Breathing—Adult**

BACKGROUND: Rescue breathing is used when a victim is no longer breathing on his or her own. Rescue breathing delivers essential oxygen to the brain cells of the victim. This procedure explains how to administer rescue breathing to an adult.

ALERT: Follow Standard Precautions.

PREPROCEDURE

1. Put on disposable gloves.
2. Check for consciousness by shaking victim's shoulder gently and asking if he or she is OK. If there is no response, activate EMS system.

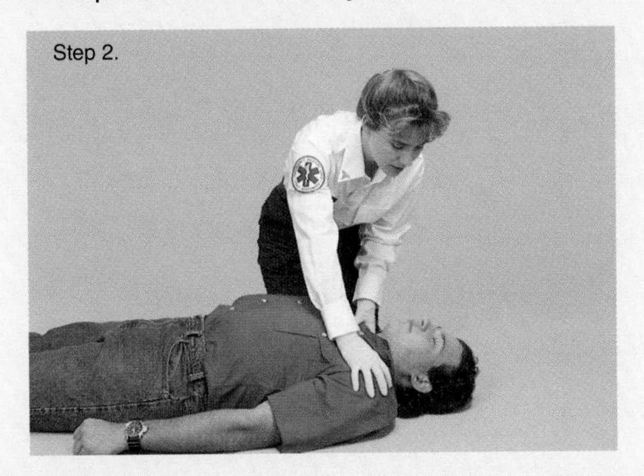

Step 2.

PROCEDURE

3. Open airway by placing one hand at victim's chin and the other hand on victim's forehead; gently lift chin by supporting jawbone with fingertips and lifting upward to open mouth. (Do not put pressure on throat; this may block airway.) This is called the *head tilt/chin lift.*

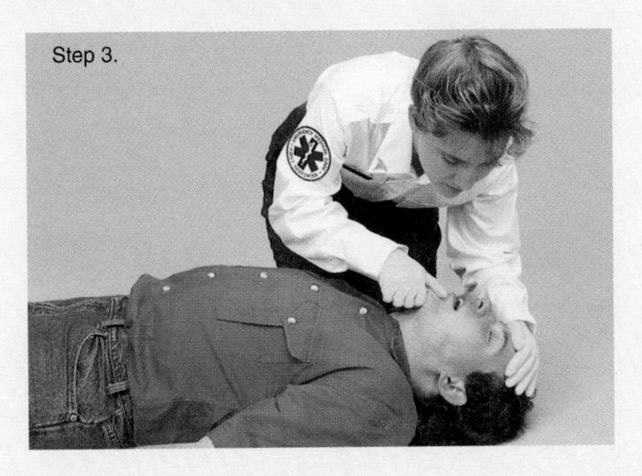

Step 3.

4. Check for breathing by placing your ear near victim's mouth and nose. Turn your head so that you can see his or her chest. Look to see if chest is rising or falling. Listen for breathing. Feel for air from victim's mouth or nose on your cheek. If breathing is *not* present go to step 5.

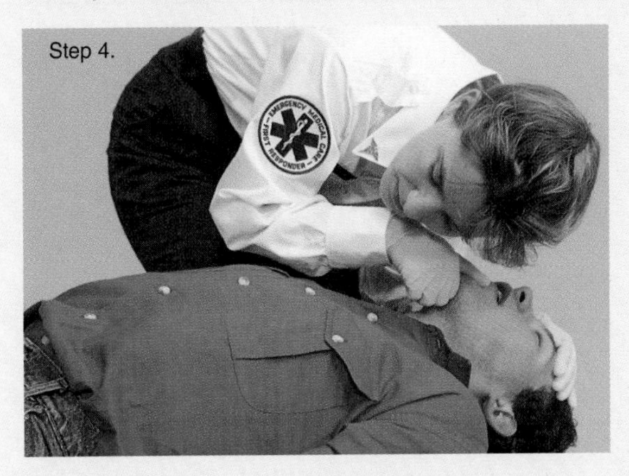

Step 4.

5. Ventilate. Place a pocket mask over mouth and nose. Put apex (point) over bridge of nose and base between lip and chin. Give two breaths ($1\frac{1}{2}$ to 2 seconds per breath) through the one-way valve. Allow lungs to empty between each breath. (If dentures obstruct the airway, remove them.) If air does *not* inflate lungs: retilt head to ensure an open airway and repeat the two breaths. Watch for chest to rise, allow for exhalation between breaths. (If lungs still do not inflate, treat victim for an obstructed airway; see the Obstructed Airway procedures.)

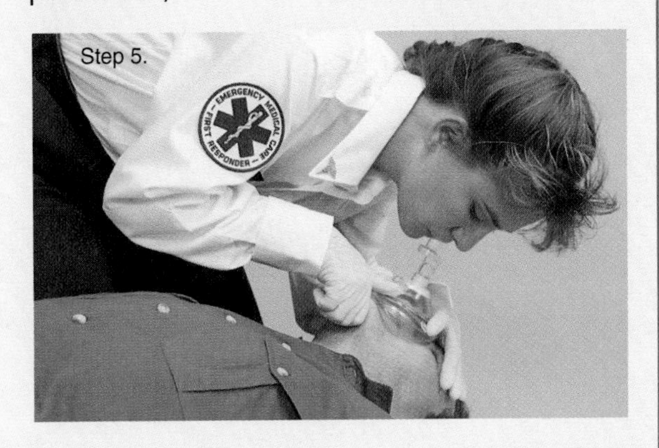

Step 5.

(continued)

PROCEDURE 21.2 Rescue Breathing—Adult (continued)

6. Check carotid pulse.
7. If breathing is absent and pulse is present, keep the airway open and give one breath to victim every 5 seconds. If there is no pulse, cardiopulmonary resuscitation (CPR) is needed to circulate oxygenated blood through body.

   See Section 21.6 for CPR procedures. CPR should be learned by taking a course given by a qualified instructor approved by the American Heart Association or American Red Cross.

POSTPROCEDURE

8. Ensure that victim has follow-up treatment or assessment by Emergency Medical Technicians or hospital personnel.
9. Discard gloves and wash hands (follow handwashing guidelines).

PROCEDURE 21.3

Obstructed Airway in a Conscious Victim—Adult

BACKGROUND: An obstructed airway may occur if a victim inhales food or drink. This procedure explains how to apply pressure from an abdominal thrust (also called the Heimlich maneuver) to force an obstruction out of an adult victim's airway.

ALERT: Follow Standard Precautions.

PREPROCEDURE

When signs of choking are present:

1. Ask "Are you choking?" Observe victim for coughing or wheezing. Do *not interfere* if good air exchange is present.

PROCEDURE

2. Give **abdominal thrust**, sometimes called the **Heimlich maneuver**. Stand in back of victim; put your arms around victim's waist. Make a fist with one hand and put the thumb side of the fist slightly above the navel and well below the breast bone.

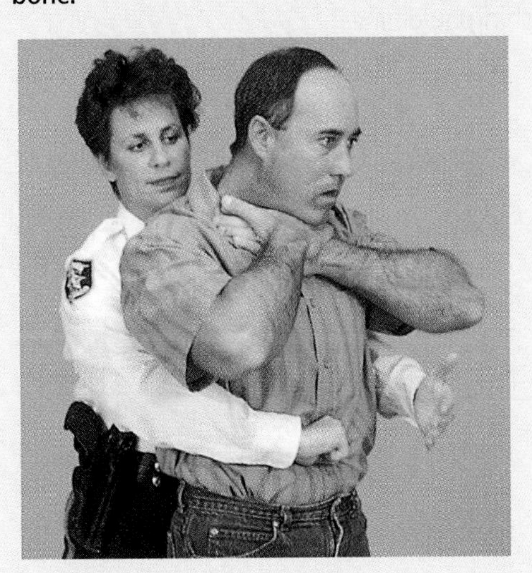

Take your other hand and grasp fist; pull into victim's abdomen with quick upward thrust. Repeat separate, rapid inward and upward thrusts until airway is cleared or patient becomes unconscious. (Use chest thrusts for a pregnant or obese victim.)

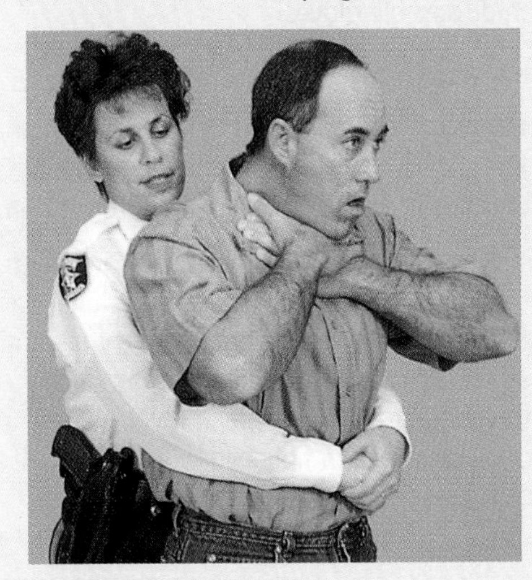

POSTPROCEDURE

3. Ensure that victim has follow-up treatment or assessment by Emergency Medical Technicians or hospital personnel, if needed.
4. Wash hands (follow hand-washing guidelines).

PROCEDURE 21.4 Obstructed Airway in an Unconscious Victim—Adult

BACKGROUND: An airway obstruction can cause the victim to become unconscious due to lack of oxygen. This procedure explains how to clear an obstructed airway in an adult.

ALERT: Follow Standard Precautions.

PREPROCEDURE

If the victim becomes unconscious:

1. Activate the EMS system.
2. Put on disposable gloves.

PROCEDURE

3. Open airway. Place one hand at victim's chin and the other hand on victim's forehead; gently tip head back. Lift chin in head tilt/chin lift position.
4. Attempt to ventilate. Open the airway and ventilate through a pocket face mask with a one-way valve. If no air enters, retilt head and try to ventilate again. Every time you give a breath, open mouth wide and look for object. If you see an object, remove it with fingers. If you do not see an object, proceed with CPR.

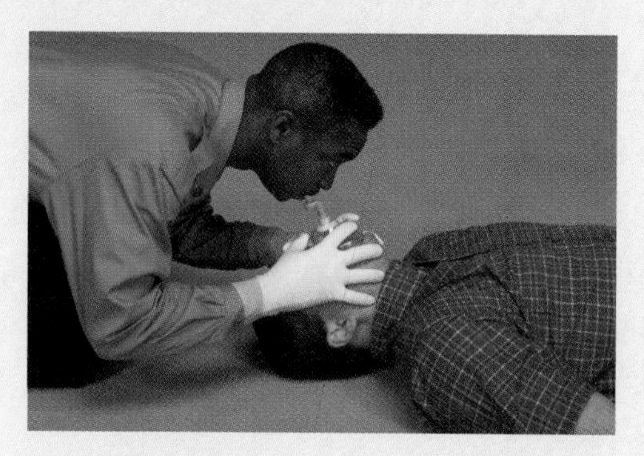

POSTPROCEDURE

5. Ensure that victim has follow-up treatment or assessment by Emergency Medical Technicians or hospital personnel.
6. Discard gloves and wash hands (follow handwashing guidelines).

PROCEDURE 21.5 Stopped Breathing in an Infant

BACKGROUND: It is important to quickly deliver oxygen to an infant who has stopped breathing. An infant's brain is actively developing and may become damaged if it lacks oxygen. This procedure explains how to deliver rescue breaths to an infant who has stopped breathing.

ALERT: Follow Standard Precautions.

PREPROCEDURE

1. Put on disposable gloves.
2. **Check for consciousness.** Shake baby's shoulders gently and speak baby's name. If no response, shout for help.

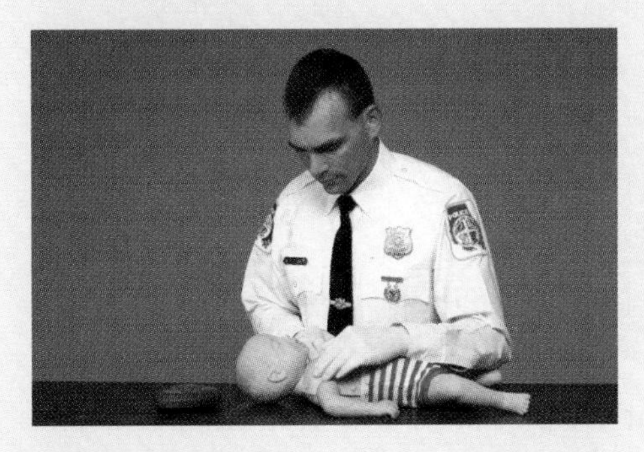

PROCEDURE

3. **Open airway.** Use head tilt/chin lift method. Do not overtilt head or neck.

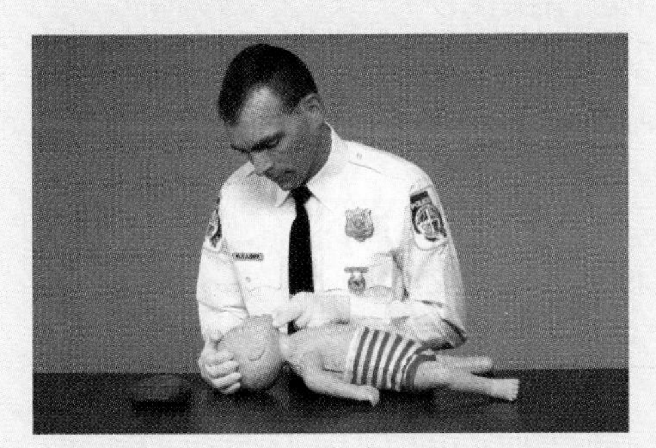

4. **Check for breathing.** Look, listen, and feel.

If not breathing:

5. Place an infant-sized barrier device on the infant's face.* Ventilate through the one-way valve and give rescue breathing. Give two slow breaths using only air in your cheeks. (Too much air may overinflate an infant's lungs.)

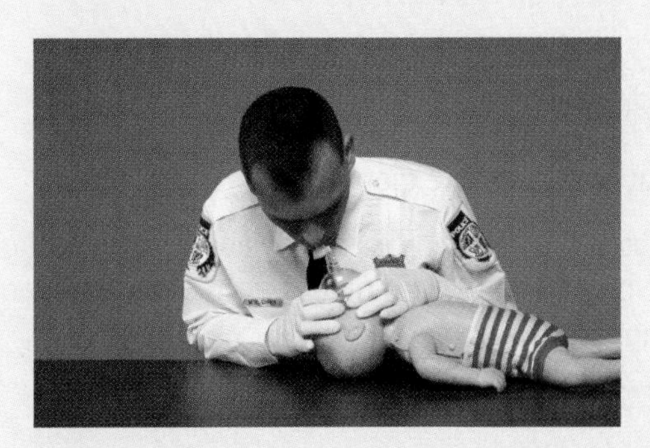

Watch for chest to rise and allow chest to fall or deflate between each breath. If air does not inflate lungs:

6. Retilt head to ensure open airway. Repeat the two breaths. If lungs still do not inflate, treat infant for an obstructed airway.

If lungs do inflate:

7. **Keep airway open**, and give one breath to infant every 3 seconds. After 1 minute activate EMS.
8. **Check pulse.** Place three fingers over brachial artery/pulse. The baby's heart may have stopped. In this event, only cardiopulmonary resuscitation (CPR) will help to circulate oxygenated blood throughout the body. See Procedures 21.22, 21.23 and 21.24 for CPR procedures. CPR should be learned by taking a course offered by an instructor who is certified by the American Heart Association or the American Red Cross. We strongly recommend you complete such a program.

POSTPROCEDURE

9. Ensure that victim has follow-up treatment or assessment by Emergency Medical Technicians or hospital personnel.
10. Discard gloves and wash hands (follow handwashing guidelines).

* Adult-sized pocket face masks can be adapted by inverting (reversing) them. See manufacturer's guidelines.

PROCEDURE 21.6 Obstructed Airway in a Conscious Infant

BACKGROUND: The procedures for clearing an obstructed airway in an infant are different from the procedures for an adult. Care must be taken to protect the smaller, more delicate organs and bones of the infant. This procedure explains how to clear an obstructed airway in a conscious infant.

ALERT: Follow Standard Precautions.

PREPROCEDURE

1. Put on disposable gloves
2. Observe to determine infant's ability to cry, cough, or breathe. If there is no evidence of air exchange, shout for help.

PROCEDURE

3. Give five back blows. Place infant face down, supporting head and neck and tilting infant so that the head is lower than rest of body. Give five firm hits with heel of your hand over backbone and between shoulder blades.

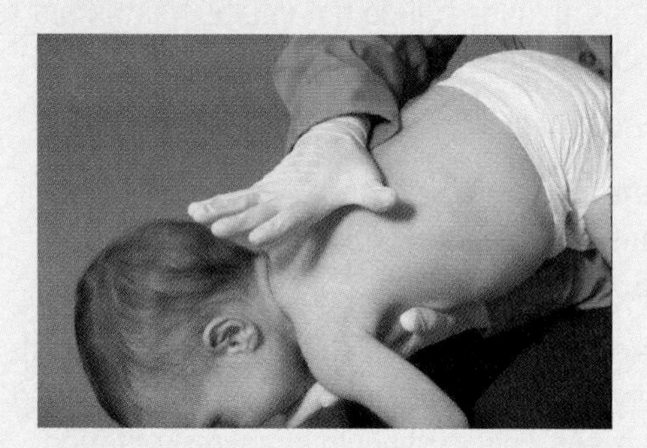

4. Give five chest thrusts by turning infant on its back with head lower than rest of body. Using two to three fingers, push five times on midsternum, which is about one finger's width below nipple line at midchest at a rate of about one per second.

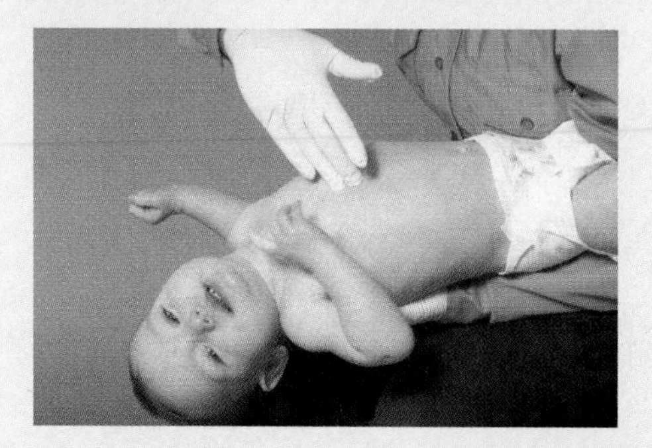

5. Continue procedure until obstruction is clear or infant becomes unconscious. If infant becomes unconscious, stop giving black blows and start CPR.

POSTPROCEDURE

6. Ensure that victim has follow-up treatment or assessment by Emergency Medical Technicians or hospital personnel.
7. Discard gloves and wash hands (follow handwashing guidelines).

PROCEDURE 21.7 Obstructed Airway in an Unconscious Infant

BACKGROUND: It is important to deliver oxygen to an infant who is not breathing as soon as possible to prevent brain damage. This procedure explains how to clear an obstructed airway in an unconscious infant.

ALERT: Follow Standard Precautions.

PREPROCEDURE

1. Put on disposable gloves
2. Observe to determine infant's ability to cry, cough, or breathe. If there is no evidence of air exchange, shout for help.

PROCEDURE

3. Place infant on a firm flat surface.
4. Open infant's airway and look for an object in the pharynx. If an object is visible, remove it. Do not perform a blind finger sweep.

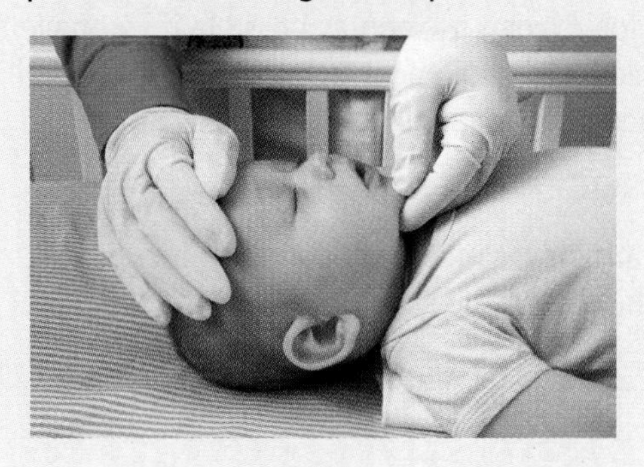

5. Begin CPR with one extra step–each time you open the airway, look for the obstructing object in the back of the throat. If you see an object, remove it. After about 2 minutes, activate the EMS.
6. Once the airway is clear, ventilate once every 3 seconds.

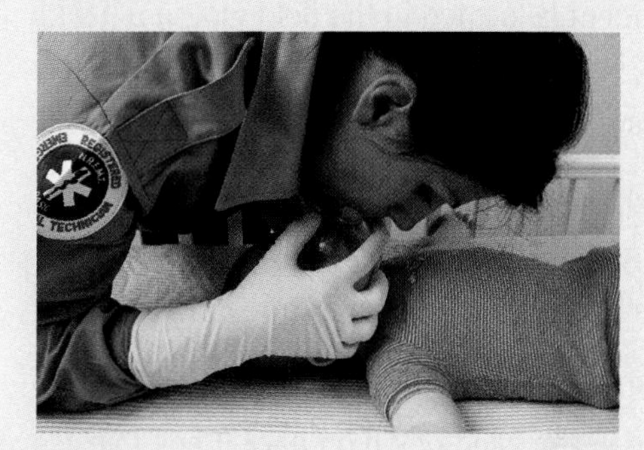

POSTPROCEDURE

7. Ensure that victim has follow-up treatment or assessment by Emergency Medical Technicians or hospital personnel.
8. Discard gloves and wash hands (follow hand-washing guidelines).

PROCEDURE 21.8 Preventing Shock

BACKGROUND: Shock is a life-threatening condition that must be treated immediately. A victim who remains in shock could die. The most common symptoms of shock include an extremely low blood pressure; fast but weak pulse; dizziness, faintness or light-headedness; feeling weak or nauseous ; moist, clammy skin; profuse sweating; unconsciousness; rapid, shallow breathing; feeling anxious, agitated or confused; chest pain; and/or blue lips and fingernails. This procedure explains how to stabilize a victim and prevent shock.

ALERT: Follow Standard Precautions.

PREPROCEDURE

1. If patient is located in the field (not in a health care facility), contact EMS.

PROCEDURE

2. Provide comfort, quiet, and warmth.
3. Maintain normal body temperature by covering with blanket.
4. Keep victim calm.
5. Keep victim lying down on back if possible. Elevate feet and arms. Do not elevate an unsplinted arm or leg that is fractured.
6. If victim is vomiting, bleeding from mouth, or feels like vomiting, position victim on side. Do not move the victim if there is any possibility of a spinal injury or if the victim complains of numbness, tingling, lack of sensation, or inability to move limbs.
7. If person has a head injury, neck injury, or breathing problem, feet should not be elevated and the victim should not be turned on his or her side.
8. Do not give the victim anything to eat or drink.
9. Provide oxygen as soon as possible if you have the training and equipment to do so; otherwise, call immediately for someone who does.

POSTPROCEDURE

10. Discard gloves and wash hands (follow handwashing guidelines).

PROCEDURE 21.9 Treating a Conscious Poison Victim

BACKGROUND: A poison victim should get emergency treatment as soon as possible. A person who has ingested poison may experience organ damage, shock, or death. This procedure explains how to treat a conscious poison victim.

ALERT: Follow Standard Precautions.

PREPROCEDURE

1. Put on disposable gloves.
2. Try to locate poison container (try to identify source of poisoning); do not waste time. Check victim's body and clothes for signs of poisoning.
3. Position victim on his side to let mouth drain.

PROCEDURE

4. Call 911 to get an ambulance as soon as possible; then call the nearest poison center, hospital, or physician.* (Directions on poison containers and for ingested substances are *not* always correct.) When you call, state that you have a poisoning emergency. If you have the container, be prepared to read ingredients. Follow the directions from the poison center.
5. If poison on skin, wash with water.
6. If poison is from a snakebite: Cover and wrap the affected snakebite area. Continue wrapping the entire affected limb and apply a splint. This is called the pressure immobilization technique. Remember to make sure the wound does not swell enough to make the splint a tourniquet, cutting off the blood flow. Get person to an emergency care center as soon as possible.
7. If poison is from an insect bite: Apply cold compresses. A doctor may prescribe calcium gluconate for muscle pain and an anti-anxiety drug for spasms. For any poisonous insect bite, be sure your tetanus immunization is current.
8. Be alert for breathing problems. If breathing stops, you will perform mouth-to-mask (rescue breathing) resuscitation as discussed at beginning of section.
9. Follow procedure for preventing shock.

POSTPROCEDURE

10. Ensure that victim has follow-up treatment or assessment by Emergency Medical Technicians or hospital personnel.
11. Discard gloves and wash hands (follow handwashing guidelines).

* Ambulance personnel can communicate directly with the hospital and the poison control center. They can start lifesaving procedures with special equipment and poison treatment medications.

PROCEDURE 21.10 Treating an Unconscious Poison Victim

BACKGROUND: An unconscious poison victim must receive emergency medical treatment as quickly as possible, to prevent damage to organs, shock, or death. This procedure explains how to treat an unconscious poison victim.

ALERT: Follow Standard Precautions.

PREPROCEDURE

1. Put on disposable gloves.
2. Do *not* give any fluids.

PROCEDURE

3. Position victim on his or her side in a safe place.
4. Try to identify the poison source; do not waste time.
5. Call 911 to get an ambulance as soon as possible; then call the nearest poison center, hospital, or physician. Follow their directions.*
6. If chemicals have gotten on skin, wash with water. Remove clothes and jewelry that are contaminated.
7. Be alert for breathing problems.
8. Follow procedure for preventing shock.

POSTPROCEDURE

9. Ensure that victim has follow-up treatment or assessment by Emergency Medical Technicians or hospital personnel.
10. Discard gloves and wash hands (follow hand-washing guidelines).

* Ambulance personnel can communicate directly with the hospital and the poison control center. They can start lifesaving procedures with special equipment and poison treatment medications.

PROCEDURE 21.11 Treating Burns

BACKGROUND: A burn destroys tissue and may send a victim into shock. This procedure explains how to treat victims of first-degree, second-degree, or third-degree burns. You must identify the degree of the burn:

- *First-Degree Burn* (superficial partial-thickness burn): Appears pink or red; sensitive to touch
- *Second-Degree Burn* (deep partial-thickness burn): Appears pink or red with a mottled appearance; blisters and edema; touching causes severe pain
- *Third-Degree Burn* (full-thickness burn): Appears red, waxy white, brown or black; insensitive to touch; loss of hair in area

ALERT: Follow Standard Precautions.

PREPROCEDURE

1. Put on disposable gloves.

PROCEDURE

First-Degree Burn

2. Apply cool water to burn area, submerge burn site in cool water, or cover the are with cool damp cloths; this will reduce pain.
3. Large surface burns should never be wet as this causes shock. Large burns may be dried with sterile dressing. Apply a cold pack over dressing to reduce discomfort. Partial thickness or deeper burns (full thickness) require the following procedure.

PROCEDURE

Second- and Third-Degree Burns

1. Stop the burning process by smothering or dousing with water and removing smoldering or hot clothing. Remove any sources of heat such as metal jewelry, belts, etc.
2. Cover burned area with dry, sterile, nonstick dressing to help prevent infection. Do not pull away clothing that is stuck to burn site.
3. Check the patient's:

   Airway
   Breathing
   Circulation

   Perform CPR if necessary
4. Contact emergency medical service.
5. Cover with a dry sterile dressing if available. A non-fuzzy clean sheet or tablecloth could be substituted if sterile dressing is not available.
6. If you can elevate the burned area to decrease swelling, especially if head is involved and victim is having trouble breathing.
7. Follow procedure to prevent shock.

POSTPROCEDURE

8. Ensure that victim has follow-up treatment or assessment by Emergency Medical Technicians or hospital personnel.
9. Discard gloves and wash hands (follow handwashing guidelines).

PROCEDURE 21.12 Applying a Splint

BACKGROUND: A splint helps to stabilize a broken bone and prevent further injury to tissues. This procedure explains how to make a splint out of a variety of materials.

ALERT: Follow Standard Precautions.

PREPROCEDURE

1. Put on disposable gloves.
2. Move fractured area as little as possible.

PROCEDURE

3. Splint area with a firm object, such as newspapers, magazines folded flat, wood, or a commercially made **splint**. The splint should extend from the fingertips to the elbow. Need to immobilize joints above and below injury. Pad splint with clothing or towels if possible. Place padding or roller gauze in the hand for support and comfort.
4. Secure splint in place using roller gauze, wrapping it snugly and overlapping about two-thirds each wrap, or secure splint to extremity with strips of cloth at distal and proximal ends of the arm. You can wrap roller gauze over the fracture site. Do not exert any pressure over the injury.

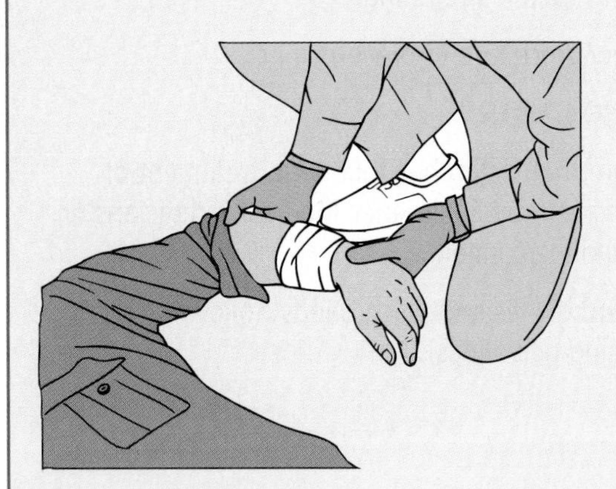

5. If it is an open fracture, apply dressing over wound and secure in place with tape or with roller gauze that holds splint in place.

POSTPROCEDURE

7. Ensure that victim has follow-up treatment or assessment by Emergency Medical Technicians or hospital personnel.
8. Discard gloves and wash hands (follow hand-washing guidelines)

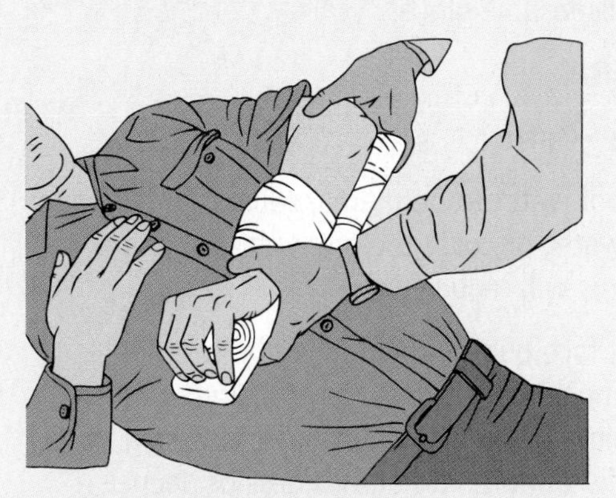

PROCEDURE 21.13 Applying a Triangular Sling

ALERT: Follow Standard Precautions.

PREPROCEDURE

1. Put on disposable gloves.
2. Make a sling from a piece of cloth, clothing, towel, or sheet; fold or cut this material into shape of a triangle. The ideal sling is about 50 to 60 inches long at its base and 36 to 40 inches long on each side.

PROCEDURE

3. Position triangular material over top of patient's chest opposite the injured arm, as shown in Figure A. Fold patient's arm across chest. If patient cannot hold his or her own arm, have someone assist you, or provide support for patient's arm until you are ready to tie sling. Note that one point of triangle should extend beyond patient's elbow on injured side.
4. Take bottom point of triangle and bring this end up over patient's arm. When you are finished, take this bottom point over top of patient's shoulder on the side of injured arm. (See Figure B.)
5. Draw up on ends of sling so that patient's hand is about 4 inches above elbow. Tie the two ends of the sling together, making sure that the knot does not press against back of patient's neck. Place a flat pad of dressing or a handkerchief under the knot. (Figure C.) Leave patient's fingertips exposed so that you can see any color changes that indicate lack of circulation. Check for radial pulse. If pulse is absent, take off sling and attempt to reposition arm to regain pulse, then repeat procedure.
6. Take point of material at patient's elbow and fold it forward. Pin it to front of sling. This forms a pocket for the elbow. If you do not have pin, twist excess material and tie knot in point. This will provide a shallow pocket for patient's elbow. (Figure D.)

A

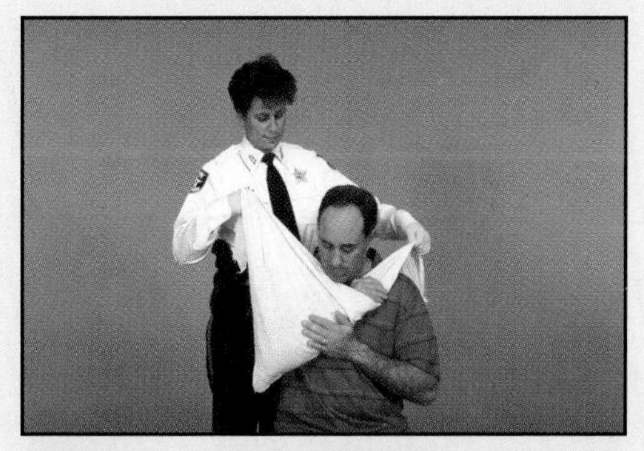
B

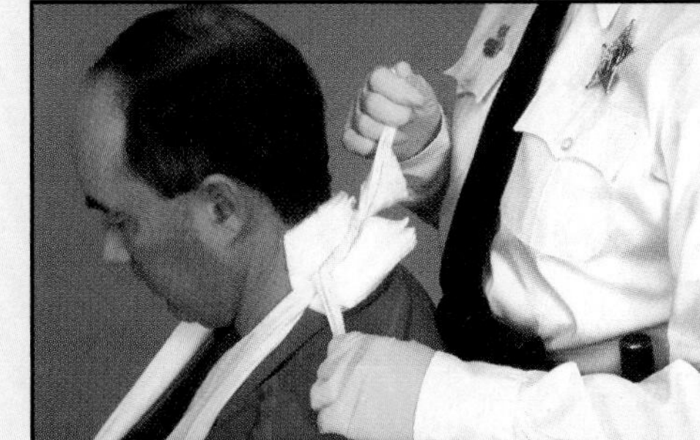
C

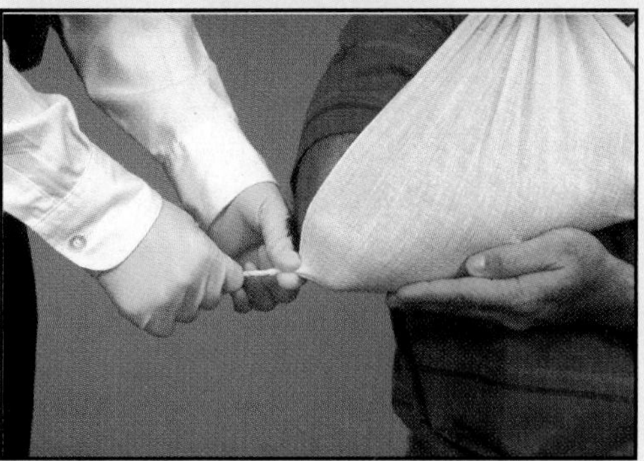
D

(continued)

PROCEDURE 21.13 Applying a Triangular Sling (continued)

7. Create a swathe by folding a triangular bandage in half and then folding it to a 4-inch width. This swathe is tied around chest and injured arm, over sling. Do not place this swathe over patient's arm on uninjured side. (See Figure E.)

POSTPROCEDURE

8. Ensure that victim has follow-up treatment or assessment by Emergency Medical Technicians or hospital personnel.
9. Discard gloves and wash hands (follow hand-washing guidelines).

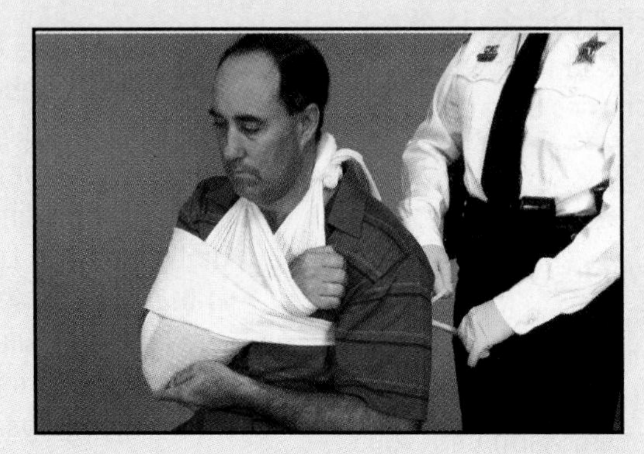

E

PROCEDURE 21.14

Triangular Bandaging of an Open Head Wound

BACKGROUND: A triangular bandage can be used to hold a dressing on a wound. This procedure explains how to fold a triangular bandage to bandage an open head wound.

ALERT: Follow Standard Precautions.

PREPROCEDURE

1. Put on disposable gloves.
2. Fold triangular bandage to make 2-inch hem along base.

PROCEDURE

3. Apply gauze pad over wound. With folded edge face out, position bandage on patient's forehead, just above eyes. Make certain that point of bandage hangs down behind patient's head.
4. Draw ends of bandage behind patient's head and tie them.
5. Next, pull ends to front of patient's head and tie them together.
6. Tuck in the tail at back.

POSTPROCEDURE

7. Ensure that victim has follow-up treatment or assessment by Emergency Medical Technicians or hospital personnel.
8. Discard gloves and wash hands (follow handwashing guidelines).

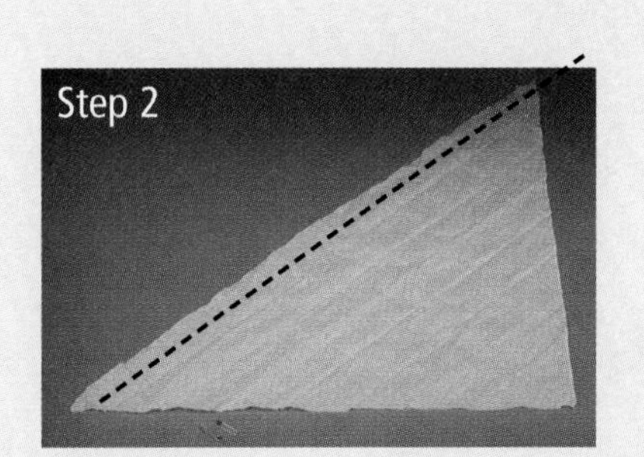

Step 3

Courtesy of Dorling Kindersley.

Step 4

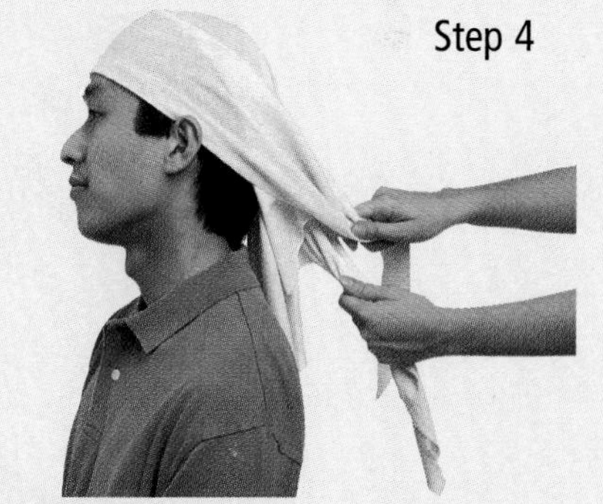

Courtesy of Dorling Kindersley.

Step 5

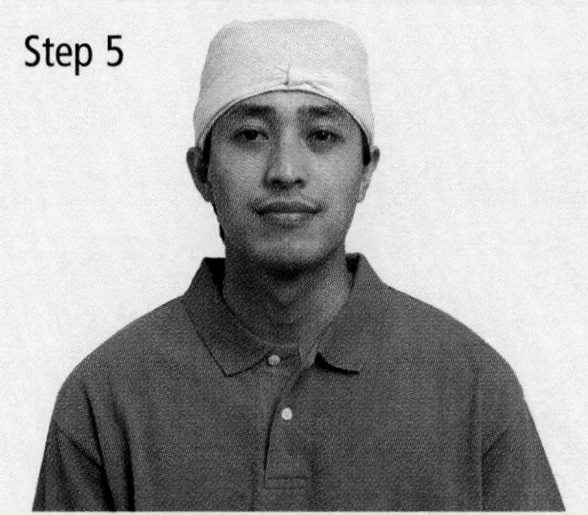

Courtesy of Dorling Kindersley.

Step 6

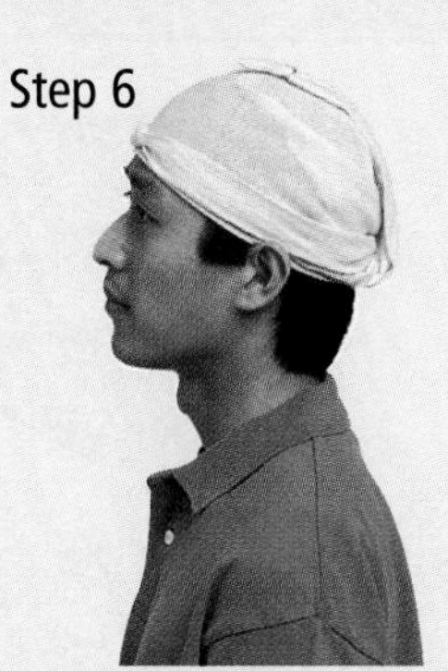

Courtesy of Dorling Kindersley.

PROCEDURE 21.15 Circular Bandaging of a Small Leg or Arm Wound

BACKGROUND: Circular bandaging holds a dressing in place over a wound and applies pressure to the wound. This procedure explains how to apply a circular bandage to a small leg or arm wound.

ALERT: Follow Standard Precautions.

PREPROCEDURE

1. Put on disposable gloves.

PROCEDURE

2. Apply dressing to wound and elevate extremity.
3. Place end of gauze roll (1 to 2 inches wide) on dressing. Anchor end of gauze roll over dressing with two initial wraps. (Place end of gauze over the dressing. Wrap gauze around the area once. Fold angled corner of gauze back over wrapped gauze.) Continue to wrap from distal (far) end of extremity to proximal (near the torso) end until entire dressing is covered. Bandage will overlap dressing on both sides. Pull bandage snug as you wrap. Overlap each wrap by about two-thirds. Cut gauze and tape end or tie gauze to secure in place.

POSTPROCEDURE

4. Ensure that victim has follow-up treatment or assessment by Emergency Medical Technicians or hospital personnel.
5. Discard gloves and wash hands (follow hand-washing guidelines).

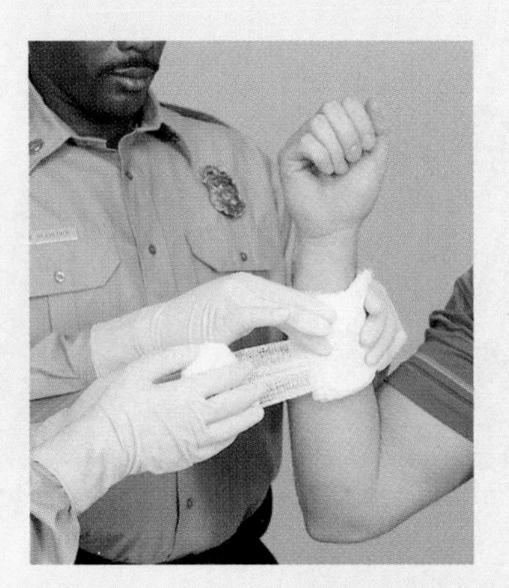

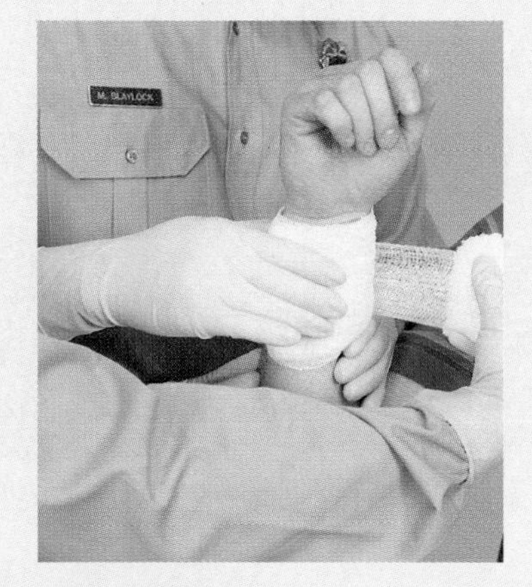

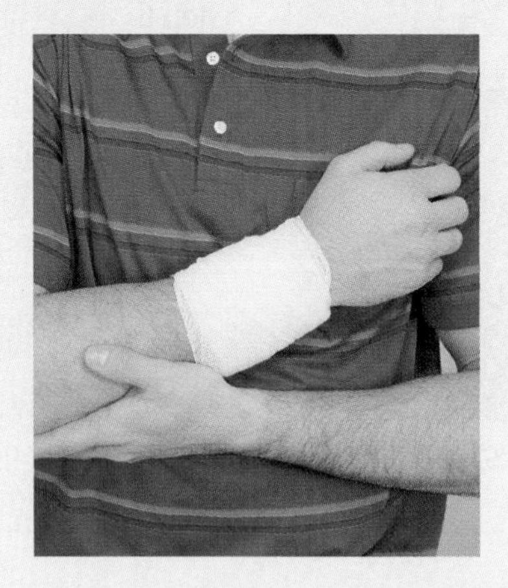

PROCEDURE 21.16 Spiral Bandaging of a Large Wound

BACKGROUND: Spiral bandaging can be used to hold on a dressing and apply pressure to a large wound of the arm or leg. This procedure explains how to use spiral bandaging on a large wound.

ALERT: Follow Standard Precautions.

PREPROCEDURE

1. Put on disposable gloves.

PROCEDURE

2. Apply dressing to wound.
3. Place end of gauze roll (3 to 6 inches wide) on lower edge of dressing.
4. Anchor end.
5. Wrap gauze around arm or leg at an angle and overlap the edges.
6. If you use up the gauze, continue the wrap with another roll.
7. Secure end by taping or tying off.

POSTPROCEDURE

8. Ensure that victim has follow-up treatment or assessment by Emergency Medical Technicians or hospital personnel.
9. Discard gloves and wash hands (follow hand-washing guidelines).

PROCEDURE 21.17 Bandaging of an Ankle or Foot Wound

BACKGROUND: A bandage can be wrapped around the ankle or foot, to secure a dressing and apply pressure to a wound. This procedure explains how to bandage an ankle or foot wound.

ALERT: Follow Standard Precautions.

PREPROCEDURE

1. Put on disposable gloves.

PROCEDURE

2. Apply dressing to wound.
3. Place end of gauze roll (1 to 2 inches wide) on top of foot just above toes, and anchor ends.
4. On second wrap around foot, bring gauze around back of ankle and over top of foot. Bring gauze under foot and over top of foot again. Wrap around ankle and over top of foot, then under foot. Continue these steps until dressing is covered, and secure gauze by tying off or taping.

POSTPROCEDURE

5. Ensure that victim has follow-up treatment or assessment by Emergency Medical Technicians or hospital personnel.
6. Discard gloves and wash hands (follow handwashing guidelines).

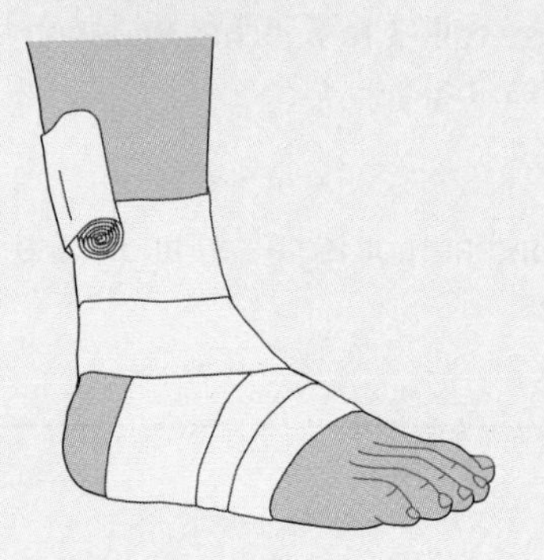

PROCEDURE 21.18 How to Care for a Dislocation

BACKGROUND: A dislocation occurs when excessive stress in an abnormal direction on one or more bones near a joint disrupts the continuity of joint configuration and articulation. When this occurs the bones' articulating surfaces no longer contact each other. Most dislocations result from trauma. Damage to ligaments and soft tissue may complicate these injuries.

ALERT: Follow Standard Precautions.

PREPROCEDURE

Expect the patient to complain of pain and decreased range of motion around the affected joint. Dislocations generally occur during a traumatic event so expect that the patient may have other injuries which could include a fracture of the joint. Depending on the nature of the injury the patient may require closed reduction of the injured joint or a surgical intervention to properly realign the affected joint. Expect that an x-ray of the affected joint will be necessary.

1. Determine the traumatic event leading to the injury.
2. Inspect the patient's affected joint for swelling, bruising, odd configuration of joint anatomy, and altered mobility.
3. Gently palpate the joint noting any tenderness. Palpate nearby pulses to assess the circulatory status. Obtain medical assistance right away.

PROCEDURE

Closed Reduction

NOTE: Closed Reduction and Surgical Correction will occur in a hospital or other care facility and will be done by physicians.

4. Provide support for the patient during the examination and any procedure that may be indicated.
5. Assist with the application of an external immobilization device.
6. Apply ice for at least the first 24 hours.
7. Monitor the patient's neurovascular status by checking for pulses, warmth, color, and sensory function of the region around the injury site. Also note any increased swelling.

NOTE: The patient will be medicated with prescribed pain medication only by licensed individuals.

8. Use a pain rating scale, such as a scale of 1 to 10, to evaluate the effectiveness of the pain medication.
9. Provide education to the patient/family regarding any ongoing care necessary and any rehabilitative exercise program prescribed for after the immobilizing device is removed.

Surgical Correction

10. Monitor the patient closely in the immediate postoperative period for:
    - neurovascular status
    - pain
    - alteration in vital signs
11. Expect the patient to have either a cast or an external immobilizer.
12. Provide pain medication as directed by the physician.
13. Apply ice as directed by the physician.
14. Use a pain rating scale, such as a scale of 1 to 10, to evaluate the effectiveness of the pain medication and other interventions provided to relieve discomfort.
15. Prepare the patient for the rehabilitation period.

Note: Possible complications of a joint dislocation and its treatment include:

- vascular impairment
- nerve injury
- residual joint laxity with chronic joint instability.
- degenerative arthritis
- thromboembolic complications
- neurovascular compromise
- skin breakdown from extended wearing of an immobilization device

PROCEDURE 21.19 How to Care for a Strain

BACKGROUND: A strain occurs when partial, microscopic muscle tears result from overuse or overstretching of a single muscle, muscle group, or tendon. A strain can be acute or chronic. An acute strain arises from a sudden forced movement that overstretches a muscle; a chronic strain results from the cumulative effects of repeated muscle overuse.

Strains commonly result from injury suffered while playing active sports or from poor body mechanics, such as improper lifting and carrying techniques. Strains are classified into three grades of injury:

- *Grade I* (mild): microscopic muscle and/or tendon tear with no strength loss.
- *Grade II* (moderate): incomplete muscle and/or tendon tear with bleeding into muscle tissue and some strength loss.
- *Grade III* (severe): complete muscle and/or tendon tear usually resulting from separation of muscle from muscle, muscle from tendon, or tendon from bone.

It is worth remembering RICE when it comes to the treatment of uncomplicated soft tissue, such as strains and sprains. This stand for:

R (rest)
I (ice)
C (compression)
E (elevate)

ALERT: Follow Standard Precautions.

PREPROCEDURE

Expect the patient to complain of pain, decreased mobility, and strength loss at the site of injury. Important points to remember when assessing the patient are:

1. Ask how the injury occurred.
2. Ask about prior joint injuries.
3. Inspect the injured joint for swelling, bruising.
4. Palpate the joint, noting any tenderness. Palpate nearby pulses to assess the circulatory status.
5. To rule out a fracture, the physician will order x-rays.

PROCEDURE

6. Consult with the physician for any specific instructions related to the injury.
7. Apply a compression bandage as ordered by the physician.
8. Elevate the affected joint.
9. Check with the physician. Apply ice or heat as directed. If injury is several days old the physician may order heat rather than ice to reduce pain.
10. Elevate the affected extremity.
11. Monitor the patient's neurovascular status by checking for pulses, warmth, color, and sensory function of the region around the injury site. Also note any increased swelling.
12. Medicate as directed by the physician. In most cases, analgesics, anti-inflammatory drugs, or a muscle relaxant will be prescribed. These should be dispensed by licensed heath care professionals.
13. Use a pain rating scale, such as a scale of 1 to 10, to evaluate the effectiveness of the Pain medication and other interventions.
14. Advise the patient to rest and avoid using the strained muscle.
15. Educate the patient on prescribed exercises to follow after healing has begun.
16. Advise the patient to resume activities gradually.

PROCEDURE 21.20 How to Care for a Sprain

BACKGROUND: A sprain occurs when a ligament or the capsule surrounding a joint becomes stretched or torn. A moderate or severe sprain can cause joint instability and loss of function. Sprains are classified into three grades of injury:

- *Grade I* (mild): minor or partial ligament tear with normal joint stability and function
- *Grade II* (moderate): partial ligament tear with mild joint laxity and function loss.
- *Grade III* (severe): complete ligament tear or complete separation of ligament from bone, causing total joint laxity and function loss.

ALERT: Follow Standard Precautions.

PREPROCEDURE

Expect the patient to complain of pain around the affected joint. The patient may also complain of diminished function of the joint. Important points when assessing this patient are:

1. Ask how the injury occurred.
2. Ask about prior joint injuries.
3. Observe the patient as he stands, walks, and sits, noting abnormalities such as change in gait or inability to bear weight on joint.
4. Inspect the injured joint for swelling and bruising.
5. Palpate the joint, noting any tenderness. Palpate nearby pulses to assess the circulatory status.

NOTE: Be sure to compare extremities on both sides of the body when assessing musculoskeletal injuries. The patient needs to be seen by a physician and have x-rays to rule out fracture.

PROCEDURE

6. Consult with the physician for any specific instructions related to the injury.
7. Immobilize the joint, using a splint or aircast.
8. Monitor the patient's neurovascular status by checking for pulses, warmth, color, mobility and sensory function of the region around the injury site. Also note any increased swelling.
9. Elevate the injured extremity to reduce swelling and pain.
10. Apply ice to the injury.
11. Medicate the patient with prescribed pain medication. Remember: Only licensed people can give medication.
12. Use a pain rating scale, such as a scale of 1 to 10, to evaluate the effectiveness of the pain medication and other interventions.
13. Provide education to the patient/family regarding any ongoing care necessary.

PROCEDURE 21.21 Cast Care

BACKGROUND: A cast is a hard mold that encases a body part, usually an extremity, to provide immobilization without discomfort. It can be used to treat injuries such as fractures, correct orthopedic conditions such as deformities, or promote healing after general or plastic surgery, amputation, or nerve and vascular repair.

Casts may be constructed of plaster, fiberglass or other synthetic materials. Typically, a physician applies a cast and a nurse prepares the patient and the equipment and assists during the procedure. The orthopedic technician, after special training, may apply or change a standard cast but the orthopedist must reduce and set the fracture.

ALERT: Follow Standard Precautions.

PREPROCEDURE

Prior to the application of the cast the nurse should establish a baseline assessment of the area to be casted. This would include:

- Palpation of the distal pulses
- Assessment of the color, temperature, and capillary refill of the skin.
- Neurologic function, including sensation and motion in the affected area.

Special Considerations: A fiberglass cast dries immediately after application. A plaster cast dries in approximately 24 to 48 hours. During this drying period, the cast must be properly positioned to prevent a surface depression that could cause pressure areas or dependent anemia

PROCEDURE

1. Assess your patient frequently.
2. Check the casted area for drainage stains.
3. Elevate the extremity above patient's heart level.
4. Place absorptive pads between the moist cast and any bedding to absorb moisture.
5. Periodically check the cast for flat spots or dents. These may cause pressure areas, resulting in skin breakdown.
6. Reposition the patient every 2 hours to ensure even cast drying. Use the palm of the hand, not the fingers for repositioning in order to avoid denting the cast. Make sure bony prominences, such as heels, ankles, and elbows are pressure free.
7. Routinely assess your patient's neurovascular status. Check for swelling, pallor, numbness, tingling, loss of pulses, and cool skin areas around the cast. Notify the doctor immediately for any of these signs.
8. Notify the doctor for:
   - drainage from the wound on the cast
   - malodor from the cast
9. Protect the cast from getting wet.
10. Provide skin care.

PROCEDURE 21.22 Cardiopulmonary Resuscitation—Adult

BACKGROUND: CPR allows you to circulate blood and oxygen to the organs when a patient's heart has stopped. This procedure explains how to perform CPR on an adult victim. NOTE: Your teacher can provide information on the most current American Heart Association CPR guidelines from the *Health Science Fundamentals* Companion Web site

ALERT: Follow Standard Precautions.

PREPROCEDURE

1. Put on disposable gloves.
2. Check for consciousness by shaking victim's shoulder gently and asking if he or she is OK. If there is no response, activate EMS system.

PROCEDURE

3. Check for breathing by placing your ear near victim's mouth and nose. Turn your head so that you can see his or her chest. Look to see if chest is rising or falling. Listen for breathing. Feel for air from victim's mouth or nose on your cheek. If breathing is *not* present:
4. Open airway by placing one hand at victim's chin and the other hand on victim's forehead; gently lift chin by supporting jawbone with fingertips and lifting upward to open mouth. (Do not put pressure on throat; this may block airway.) This is called the *head tilt/chin lift.*
5. Ventilate. Place a pocket mask over mouth and nose. Put apex (point) over bridge of nose and base between lip and chin. Give two breaths (1 1/2 to 2 seconds per breath) through the one-way valve. Allow lungs to empty between each breath. (If dentures obstruct the airway, remove them.) If air does *not* inflate lungs: retilt head to ensure an open airway and repeat the two breaths. Watch for chest to rise, allow for exhalation between breaths.
6. Check carotid pulse for 5–10 seconds.
7. If pulse is absent, begin chest compressions. Kneel on one side of the victim. Draw an imaginary line between the nipples. Place two fingers on the breast bone just below this line. Place the **heel** of one hand at this location. Place the other hand on top and **interlace** fingers. Push straight down on the chest for 30 compressions. The chest should be pushed down about 1 1/2 to 2 inches during each compression. Compressions should be faster than one per second, so that blood is pumped through the body at a rate of 100 pumps per minute.
8. Give two breaths.
9. Continue to deliver 30 **compressions** for every two breaths until help arrives. Recheck pulse every two minutes.

POSTPROCEDURE

10. Ensure that victim has follow-up treatment or assessment by Emergency Medical Technicians or hospital personnel.
11. Discard gloves and wash hands (follow handwashing guidelines).

PROCEDURE 21.23 Performing CPR, Two Person

BACKGROUND: Sudden cardiac arrest is a leading cause of death in the United States. The provision of cardiopulmonary resuscitation can improve a victim's chance of survival.

ALERT: Follow Standard Precautions.

PREPROCEDURE

The provider should understand that the critical concepts of quality CPR include:

- Push hard, push fast: compress at a rate of 100 compressions per minute.
- Allow full chest recoil after each compression.
- Minimize interruptions in chest compressions.
- Avoid hyperventilation

PROCEDURE

When a second rescuer is available to help, that second rescuer should activate the emergency response system and get the AED if available. The first rescuer should remain with the victim to begin CPR immediately.

After the second rescuer returns, the rescuers should take turns doing chest compressions, switching after every 5 cycles of CPR. Follow the procedure for one person cardiopulmonary resuscitation assigning tasks as follows:

Rescuer	Location	Actions
Rescuer 1	At the victim's side	■ Performs chest compressions. ■ Counts out loud. ■ Switches duties with rescuer 2 every 5 cycles, taking less than 5 seconds to switch.
Rescuer 2	At the victim's head	■ Maintains an open airway. ■ Gives breaths, watching for chest rise. ■ Encourages rescuer 1 to perform compressions that are fast and deep enough to allow full chest recoil between compressions. ■ Switches duties with rescuer 1 every 5 cycles taking less than 5 seconds to switch.

PROCEDURE 21.24 Cardiopulmonary Resuscitation—Infant

BACKGROUND: An infant may go into respiratory arrest during a severe asthma attack. CPR can keep oxygen flowing to organs until help arrives. This procedure explains how to perform CPR on an infant.

ALERT: Follow Standard Precautions.

PREPROCEDURE

1. Put on disposable gloves.
2. Check for consciousness. Shake the infant's foot for reflex action gently and speak baby's name. If no response, shout for help.

PROCEDURE

3. Open airway. Use head tilt/chin lift method. Do not overtilt head or neck.
4. Check for breathing. Look, listen, and feel.

If not breathing:

5. Place an infant-sized barrier device on the infant's face.* Ventilate through the one-way valve and give rescue breathing. Give two slow breaths using only air in your cheeks. (Too much air may overinflate an infant's lungs.) Watch for chest to rise and allow chest to fall or deflate between each breath. If air does not inflate lungs:
6. Retilt head to ensure open airway. Repeat the two breaths. If lungs still do not inflate, treat infant for an obstructed airway.

If lungs do inflate:

7. Check pulse. Place three fingers over brachial artery/pulse. The baby's heart may have stopped.
8. If pulse is absent, begin chest compressions. Place two or three fingers near the center of the chest, just below the nipples. Push down gently on the chest for 30 compressions. The chest should be pushed down about 1/3 of its depth during each compression. Compressions should be faster than one per second, so that blood is pumped through the body at a rate of 100 pumps per minute.

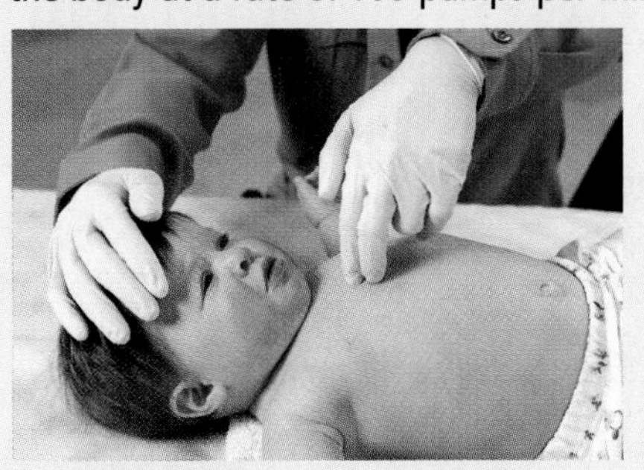

9. Give two breaths and deliver 30 more compressions.
10. After two minutes of breaths and compressions, activate EMS system.
11. Continue cycle of breaths and compressions until help arrives.

POSTPROCEDURE

10. Ensure that victim has follow-up treatment or assessment by Emergency Medical Technicians or hospital personnel.
11. Discard gloves and wash hands (follow handwashing guidelines).

*Adult-sized pocket face masks can be adapted by inverting (reversing) them. See manufacturer's guidelines.

PROCEDURE 21.25 Demonstrating the Use of AED (Automated External Defibrillator)

BACKGROUND: The interval from collapse to defibrillation is one of the most important determinants of survival from cardiac arrest.

AEDS are computerized devices that are attached to a pulseless victim with adhesive pads. They will recommend shock delivery only if the victim's heart rhythm is one that a shock can treat. AEDS give rescuers visual and voice prompts to guide rescuer actions.

AEDs are reliable and simple to operate, allowing laypersons and health care providers to attempt defibrillation safely. More and more often this tool has become available in the community setting and its availability has improved the overall outcomes of cardiopulmonary resuscitation.

Use AEDs only when victims have the following three clinical findings:

- No response
- No breathing
- No pulse

ALERT: Follow Standard Precautions.

PROCEDURE

Once the AED arrives, put it at the victim's side, next to the rescuer who will operate it. This will allow a second rescuer to perform CPR from the opposite side of the victim without interfering with AED operation. The following are four universal steps for operating an AED:

1. Power on the AED:
   - Open the carrying case.
   - Turn the power on.
2. **ATTACH** electrode pads to the victim's bare chest:
   - Choose correct pads for size/age of victim. Child pads will be used for children less than 8 years of age. Adult pads are used for the victim who is over 8 years of age.
   - Peel the backing away from the electrode pads.
   - Quickly wipe the victim's chest dry if covered with sweat or water. If the chest is covered with hair and electrode pads will not stick, pull the pad away from chest. This should take the hair with it. If still will not stick, shave area with razor included in the AED Kit.
   - Attach the adhesive electrode pads to the victim's bare chest.
     - — Place one electrode pad on the upper-right side of the bare chest to the right of the breastbone, directly below the collarbone.
     - — Place the other pad to the left of the nipple, a few inches below the left arm pit.
   - Attach the AED connecting cables to the AED box (some are preconnected).
3. "Clear" the victim and **ANALYZE** the rhythm.
   - Always clear the victim during the analysis. Be sure that no one is touching the victim, not even the person in charge of giving breaths.
   - Some AEDS will tell you to push a button to allow the AED to begin analyzing the heart rhythm; others will do that automatically. The AED may take about 5 to 15 seconds to analyze.
   - The AED then tells you if a shock is needed. Remember if the victim has an unshockable rhythm there will be no advice to shock.

(continued)

PROCEDURE 21.25 Demonstrating the Use of AED (Automated External Defibrillator) (continued)

4. If the AED advises a shock, it will tell you to be sure to clear the victim.
   - Clear the victim before delivering the shock; be sure no one is touching the victim to avoid injury to rescuers.
     - Loudly state a "clear the patient" message, such as "I'm clear, you're clear, everybody's clear."
     - Perform a visual check to ensure that no one is in contact with the victim.
   - Press the **SHOCK** button.
   - The shock will produce a sudden contraction of the victim's muscles.
5. As soon as the AED gives the shock, begin CPR starting with chest compressions.
6. After 2 minutes of CPR, the AED will prompt you to repeat steps 3 and 4.

PROCEDURE 22.1 Bass Toothbrushing Technique

BACKGROUND: Correct brushing is essential for healthy teeth and gums. Explain the importance of correct brushing and show a patient good technique help protect against dental problems.

ALERT: Follow Standard Precautions.

PREPROCEDURE

1. Wash hands.
2. Assemble equipment:
   a. Tooth model (if using a model for teaching)
   b. Protective wear (if brushing patient's teeth or if there is contact with saliva), including gloves, mask, and goggles
   c. Toothbrush

PROCEDURE

3. Explain importance of toothbrushing.
4. Demonstrate correct brushing using model or on patient.

   NOTE: Put on gloves if demonstrating on patient.

   a. Place soft brush on upper right molars (maxillary).
   b. Position brush at 45° angle to teeth.
   c. Gently move bristles into gingival sulcus.
   d. Move brush in short strokes at least 10 to 20 times, keeping brush in place (wiggle-jiggle motion).
   e. Move brush to next two or three teeth and repeat until all buccal/labial surfaces are brushed.

      NOTE: Place brush in vertical or horizontal position for anterior teeth.

   f. Repeat technique beginning at upper right molars until all maxillary teeth are brushed.
   g. Use short, vibrating motion to scrub occlusal surfaces.
   h. Repeat this procedure for lower teeth (mandibular).
5. Ask client if he or she has any questions.

POSTPROCEDURE

6. Remove and clean equipment.
7. Remove protective wear.
8. Wash hands.
9. Chart TBI (toothbrushing instruction).

PROCEDURE 22.2 Dental Flossing

BACKGROUND: Correct dental flossing is essential for healthy teeth and gums. Explaining the importance of correct flossing and showing a patient good technique help protect against dental problems.

ALERT: Follow Standard Precautions.

PREPROCEDURE

1. Wash hands.
2. Assemble equipment:
   a. Tooth model (if using a model for teaching)
   b. Gloves, mask, and goggles (if flossing patient's teeth or if there is contact with saliva)
   c. Dental floss (waxed or unwaxed according to policy)

PROCEDURE

3. Explain importance of flossing.
4. Demonstrate correct flossing technique using model or patient.

   NOTE: Put on protective wear if demonstrating on patient.

   a. Cut floss 18 inches (measure from finger to elbow).
   b. Wrap floss around middle or index finger of both hands, leaving 1 to 2 inches between fingers.
   c. Stretch floss between fingers and gently guide floss in between teeth. Do not snap floss; it can damage gingiva/gums.
   d. Pass floss through contacts (where teeth touch) and wrap it around tooth in a C shape.

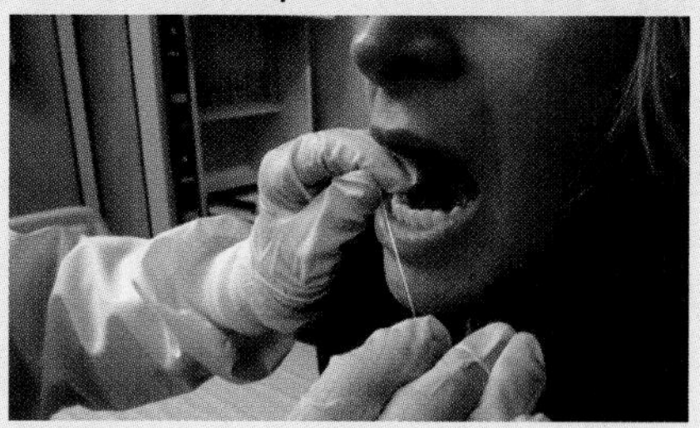

   e. Move floss up and down several times on sides of each tooth.

   NOTE: Make sure that floss goes beneath gingiva/gums into the sulcus.

   f. Unroll new floss from one hand and wrap used floss around middle finger of other hand.
   g. Repeat for each tooth until all teeth in maxilla and mandible are completed.
5. Explain that there may be some bleeding of the gingiva/gums the first few times the patient does this procedure.
6. Ask patient if he or she has any questions.

POSTPROCEDURE

7. Remove protective wear.
8. Remove and clean equipment.
9. Wash hands.
10. Chart DFI (dental flossing instruction).

PROCEDURE 22.3 Mounting Dental Films

BACKGROUND: Correct mounting of dental films helps the dentist assess whether the patient needs treatment.

ALERT: Follow Standard Precautions.

PREPROCEDURE

1. Wash hands.
2. Assemble equipment:
   a. Developed x-rays
   b. X-ray mounts
   c. View box

PROCEDURE

3. Turn on view box.
4. Lay out x-rays. (Make certain that raised dot is facing upward.)
5. Arrange film on view box before placing into mount.
6. Mount the two or four bite-wing films.

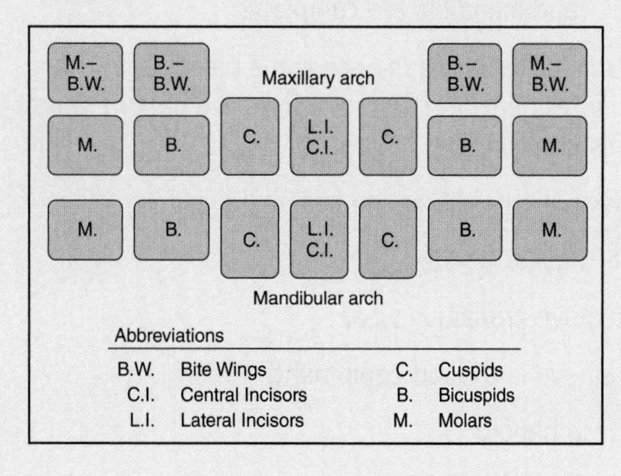

NOTE: Bicuspid views are closest to the center of the mount.

7. Mount two central (CI) and lateral (LI) incisor films. Place mandibular films with roots downward and maxillary films with roots upward.
8. Mount the four cuspid (C) films. The two longest cuspids are maxillary teeth.
9. Mount the four bicuspid (BC) films.
10. Mount the four molars (M) films. The molars with three roots are the maxillary molars.
11. Review the anatomical charts to check mount for accuracy.
12. Turn off view box.

POSTPROCEDURE

13. Clean and replace equipment.
14. Wash hands.
15. Record the following on patient chart and dental x-ray mount:
    a. Patient's name
    b. Date x-rays were taken
    c. Name of person who took x-rays
    d. Dentist's name and address

Health Science Fundamentals

Exploring Career Pathways

Lab Activity Manual

Revised First Edition

Setting the Standard for Today's Health Science Student

The *Lab Activity Manual* helps students apply the Procedures they learn in the Student Edition with 39 real-world Scenarios. The *Lab Activity Manual* lets students make decisions about which Procedure to use, and also tests their knowledge of critical employability skills such as Teamwork, Effective Communication, Professionalism, and Medical Ethics.

The *Lab Activity Manual* contains all the Procedures from the Student Edition, plus critical thinking questions, presenting technical and employability skills in the context of use in health care settings.

ISBN-13: 978-0-558-78161-3
ISBN-10: 0-558-78161-6

9 780558 781613

PEARSON

www.PearsonSchool.com/careertech